Autodesk® Revit® 2016
Architecture Fundamentals

ASCENT – Center for Technical Knowledge®

AUTODESK.
Authorized Author

SDC
Publications

SDC Publications
P.O. Box 1334
Mission KS 66222
913-262-2664
www.SDCpublications.com
Publisher: Stephen Schroff

Contents

Preface ix

In this Guide xi

Practice Files xv

Customizing the Interface xvii

Introduction to BIM and Autodesk Revit

Chapter 1: Introduction to BIM and Autodesk Revit 1-1

  1.1   **BIM and Autodesk Revit** 1-2
      Workflow and BIM 1-3
      Revit Terms 1-4
      Revit and Construction Documents 1-5

  1.2   **Overview of the Interface** 1-6

  1.3   **Starting Projects** 1-18
      Opening Projects 1-19
      Starting New Projects 1-21
      Saving Projects 1-22

  1.4   **Viewing Commands** 1-24
      Zooming and Panning 1-24
      Viewing in 3D 1-26
      Visual Styles 1-30

  Practice 1a Open and Review a Project 1-32

  Chapter Review Questions 1-38

  Command Summary 1-40

Chapter 2: Basic Drawing and Modify Tools..**2-1**

  2.1 **Using General Drawing Tools**.......................................**2-2**
     Draw Tools..2-2
     Drawing Aids..2-5
     Reference Planes...2-8

  2.2 **Editing Elements**...**2-9**
     Selecting Multiple Elements...2-12
     Filtering Selection Sets..2-14

  Practice 2a Draw and Edit Elements.................................**2-16**

  2.3 **Working with Basic Modify Tools**.............................**2-21**
     Moving and Copying Elements.......................................2-21
     Rotating Elements..2-23
     Mirroring Elements...2-25
     Creating Linear and Radial Arrays.................................2-26

  Practice 2b Work with Basic Modify Tools.......................**2-29**

  2.4 **Working with Additional Modify Tools**....................**2-37**
     Aligning Elements..2-37
     Splitting Linear Elements...2-39
     Trimming and Extending...2-40
     Offsetting Elements..2-41

  Practice 2c Work with Additional Modify Tools..............**2-43**

  Chapter Review Questions...**2-47**

  Command Summary...**2-51**

Chapter 3: Setting Up Levels and Grids..............................**3-1**

  3.1 **Setting Up Levels**...**3-2**
     Modifying Levels...3-4
     Creating Plan Views..3-6

  Practice 3a Set Up Levels...**3-7**

  3.2 **Creating Structural Grids**...**3-10**
     Modifying Grid Lines..3-11

  3.3 **Adding Columns**..**3-12**
     Modifying Columns..3-15

  3.4 **Linking and Importing CAD Files**.............................**3-16**

  Practice 3b Add Structural Grids and Columns..............**3-20**

  Chapter Review Questions...**3-25**

  Command Summary...**3-27**

Design Development Phase

Chapter 4: Modeling Walls **4-1**

    4.1 Modeling Walls **4-2**

    4.2 Modifying Walls **4-5**
        Wall Joins 4-6
        Wall Openings 4-7

    Practice 4a Model the Exterior Shell **4-10**

    Practice 4b Add Interior Walls **4-16**

    Chapter Review Questions **4-24**

    Command Summary **4-27**

Chapter 5: Working with Doors and Windows **5-1**

    5.1 Inserting Doors and Windows **5-2**

    Practice 5a Insert Doors and Windows **5-6**

    5.2 Loading Door and Window Types from the Library **5-12**

    5.3 Creating Additional Door and Window Sizes **5-15**

    Practice 5b Load and Create Door Types **5-17**

    Chapter Review Questions **5-21**

    Command Summary **5-23**

Chapter 6: Working with Curtain Walls **6-1**

    6.1 Creating Curtain Walls **6-2**
        Creating Storefronts 6-4

    6.2 Adding Curtain Grids **6-6**
        Modifying Curtain Grids 6-7

    Practice 6a Work with Curtain Walls **6-9**

    6.3 Working with Curtain Wall Panels **6-13**
        Creating a Curtain Wall Panel 6-15

    6.4 Attaching Mullions to Curtain Grids **6-17**
        Modifying Mullions 6-18

    Practice 6b Add Mullions and Panels to Curtain Walls **6-20**

    Chapter Review Questions **6-26**

    Command Summary **6-28**

Chapter 7: Working with Views **7-1**

   7.1 Setting the View Display **7-2**
      Hiding and Overriding Graphics 7-3
      View Properties 7-7
      View Range 7-8

   7.2 Duplicating Views **7-13**
      Duplication Types 7-13

   Practice 7a Duplicate Views and Set the View Display **7-16**

   7.3 Adding Callout Views **7-20**
      Modifying Callouts 7-21

   Practice 7b Add Callout Views **7-23**

   7.4 Elevations and Sections **7-27**
      Elevations 7-28
      Sections 7-29
      Modifying Elevations and Sections 7-30

   Practice 7c Create Elevations and Sections **7-35**

   Chapter Review Questions **7-42**

   Command Summary **7-45**

Chapter 8: Adding Components **8-1**

   8.1 Adding Components **8-2**
      Loading Components 8-3

   8.2 Modifying Components **8-6**
      Working with Host Elements 8-6
      Purging Unused Elements 8-7

   Practice 8a Add Components **8-8**

   Chapter Review Questions **8-14**

   Command Summary **8-16**

Chapter 9: Modeling Floors **9-1**

   9.1 Modeling Floors **9-2**
      Modifying Floors 9-4
      Joining Geometry 9-6

   Practice 9a Model Floors **9-7**

   9.2 Creating Shaft Openings **9-16**

   9.3 Creating Sloped Floors **9-17**
      Creating Multiple Slopes for Drainage 9-18

Practice 9b Add an Elevator Shaft and Slope Floors to Floor Drains 9-20

Chapter Review Questions 9-24

Command Summary 9-25

Chapter 10: Modeling Ceilings 10-1

10.1 Modeling Ceilings 10-2
    Sketching Ceilings 10-4
    Modifying Ceiling Grids 10-5

10.2 Adding Ceiling Fixtures 10-6

Practice 10a Model Ceilings and Add Ceiling Fixtures 10-9

10.3 Creating Ceiling Soffits 10-12

Practice 10b Create Ceiling Soffits 10-14

Chapter Review Questions 10-19

Command Summary 10-21

Chapter 11: Modeling Roofs 11-1

11.1 Modeling Roofs 11-2

11.2 Creating Roofs by Footprint 11-3
    Attaching Walls to Roofs 11-5

Practice 11a Create Roofs by Footprint 11-7

11.3 Establishing Work Planes 11-13

11.4 Creating Roofs by Extrusion 11-16
    Joining Roofs 11-18

Practice 11b Create Roofs by Extrusion 11-20

Chapter Review Questions 11-23

Command Summary 11-25

Chapter 12: Modeling Stairs, Railings, and Ramps 12-1

12.1 Creating Component Stairs 12-2
    Creating Runs 12-3
    Creating Other Types of Runs 12-6
    Creating Landings 12-8
    Adding Supports 12-9

12.2 Modifying Component Stairs 12-10

Practice 12a Create Component Stairs 12-13

12.3 Working with Railings 12-20
    Modifying Railings 12-22

Practice 12b Modify and Add Railings **12-26**

12.4 Sketching Custom Stairs... **12-31**
    Editing Sketched Stairs 12-33

12.5 Creating Ramps.. **12-34**

Practice 12c Sketch Custom Stairs and Ramps........................... **12-36**

Chapter Review Questions.. **12-41**

Command Summary **12-43**

Construction Documents Phase

Chapter 13: Creating Construction Documents **13-1**

13.1 Setting Up Sheets **13-2**
    Sheet (Title Block) Properties 13-4

13.2 Placing and Modifying Views on Sheets............................. **13-5**

Practice 13a Create Construction Documents **13-10**

13.3 Printing Sheets.. **13-16**
    Printing Options.. 13-16

Chapter Review Questions.. **13-20**

Command Summary **13-22**

Chapter 14: Annotating Construction Documents **14-1**

14.1 Working with Dimensions **14-2**
    Modifying Dimensions 14-5

Practice 14a Add Dimensions **14-9**

14.2 Working With Text... **14-13**
    Spell Checking 14-16
    Creating Text Types... 14-17

14.3 Adding Detail Lines and Symbols **14-19**
    Using Symbols 14-20

Practice 14b Annotate Construction Documents........................ **14-22**

14.4 Creating Legends.. **14-27**

Practice 14c Create Legends **14-30**

Chapter Review Questions.. **14-32**

Command Summary **14-34**

Chapter 15: Adding Tags and Schedules **15-1**

15.1 Adding Tags **15-2**
Tagging in 3D Views 15-7

Practice 15a Add Tags **15-10**

15.2 Adding Rooms and Tags **15-14**

Practice 15b Add Rooms and Room Tags **15-18**

15.3 Working with Schedules **15-24**
Modifying Schedules 15-25
Modifying a Schedule on a Sheet 15-26

Practice 15c Work with Schedules **15-28**

Chapter Review Questions **15-32**

Command Summary **15-34**

Chapter 16: Creating Details **16-1**

16.1 Setting Up Detail Views **16-2**
Referencing a Drafting View 16-4
Saving Drafting Views 16-5

16.2 Adding Detail Components **16-8**
Detail Components 16-8
Repeating Details 16-10

16.3 Annotating Details **16-12**
Creating Filled Regions 16-12
Adding Detail Tags 16-15

Practice 16a Create a Detail Based on a Section Callout **16-17**

16.4 Keynoting and Keynote Legends **16-24**
Keynote Legends 16-27

Practice 16b Create Additional Details **16-29**

Practice 16c Create a Detail Based on a CAD File **16-31**

Chapter Review Questions **16-38**

Command Summary **16-40**

Appendix A: Introduction to Worksets **A-1**

A.1 Introduction to Worksets **A-2**
Saving Workset-Related Files A-4

Command Summary **A-6**

Appendix B: Additional Tools **B-1**

 B.1 Reusing Selection Sets **B-2**

 B.2 Wall Sweeps and Reveals **B-5**

 B.3 Creating Curtain Wall Types with Automatic Grids **B-8**

 B.4 Enhancing Views..**B-11**
  Splitting Faces...B-12
  Editing Wall Joins...B-13
  Applying Materials..B-15
  Adjusting Linework B-17
  Editing Plan and Section Profiles B-19

 B.5 Creating Dormers..**B-20**

 B.6 Working with Guide Grids on Sheets.......................**B-23**

 B.7 Revision Tracking **B-25**
  Issuing Revisions B-30

 B.8 Annotating Dependent Views **B-31**
  Annotating Views B-31

 B.9 Importing and Exporting Schedules **B-34**

 B.10 Creating Building Component Schedules **B-36**
  Schedule Properties...B-42

 B.11 Creating a Repeating Detail **B-43**

 Command Summary **B-45**

Appendix C: Autodesk Revit Certification Exam Objectives....................**C-1**

Index **Index-1**

Preface

The Autodesk® Revit® software is a powerful Building Information Modeling (BIM) program that works the way architects think. The program streamlines the design process through the use of a central 3D model, where changes made in one view update across all views and on the printable sheets.

This training guide is designed to teach you the Autodesk Revit functionality as you would work with it throughout the design process. You begin by learning about the user interface and basic drawing, editing, and viewing tools. Then you learn design development tools including how to model walls, doors, windows, floors, ceilings, stairs and more. Finally, you learn the processes that take the model to the construction documentation phase.

Since building projects are extremely complex, the Autodesk Revit software is also complex. The objective of the *Autodesk Revit 2016 Architecture Fundamentals* training guide is to enable students to create full 3D architectural project models and set them up in working drawings. This training guide focuses on basic tools that the majority of users need.

Topics Covered:

- Understanding the purpose of Building Information Management (BIM) and how it is applied in the Autodesk Revit software.

- Navigating the Autodesk Revit workspace and interface.

- Working with the basic drawing and editing tools.

- Creating Levels and Grids as datum elements for the model.

- Creating a 3D building model with walls, curtain walls, windows, and doors.

- Adding floors, ceilings, and roofs to the building model.

- Creating component-based and custom stairs.

- Adding component features, such as furniture and equipment.

- Setting up sheets for plotting with text, dimensions, details, tags, and schedules.

- Creating details.

Note on Software Setup

This training guide assumes a standard installation of the software using the default preferences during installation. Lectures and practices use the standard software templates and default options for the Content Libraries.

Students and Educators can Access Free Autodesk Software and Resources

Autodesk challenges you to get started with free educational licenses for professional software and creativity apps used by millions of architects, engineers, designers, and hobbyists today. Bring Autodesk software into your classroom, studio, or workshop to learn, teach, and explore real-world design challenges the way professionals do.

Get started today - register at the Autodesk Education Community and download one of the many Autodesk software applications available.

Visit www.autodesk.com/joinedu/

Note: Free products are subject to the terms and conditions of the end-user license and services agreement that accompanies the software. The software is for personal use for education purposes and is not intended for classroom or lab use.

In this Guide

The following images highlight some of the features that can be found in this Training Guide.

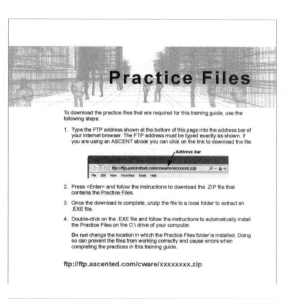

Practice Files

The Practice Files page tells you how to download and install the practice files that are provided with this training guide.

FTP link for practice files

Chapters

Each chapter begins with a brief introduction and a list of the chapter's Learning Objectives.

Learning Objectives for the chapter

Instructional Content

Each chapter is split into a series of sections of instructional content on specific topics. These lectures include the descriptions, step-by-step procedures, figures, hints, and information you need to achieve the chapter's Learning Objectives.

Side notes

Side notes are hints or additional information for the current topic.

Practice Objectives

Practices

Practices enable you to use the software to perform a hands-on review of a topic.

Some practices require you to use prepared practice files, which can be downloaded from the link found on the Practice Files page.

Chapter Review Questions

Chapter review questions, located at the end of each chapter, enable you to review the key concepts and Practice Objectives of the chapter.

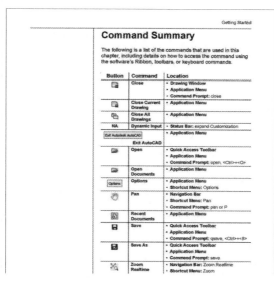

Command Summary

The Command Summary is located at the end of each chapter. It contains a list of the software commands that are used throughout the chapter, and provides information on where the command is found in the software.

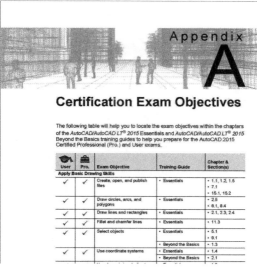

Autodesk Certification Exam Appendix

This appendix includes a list of the topics and objectives for the Autodesk Certification exams, and the chapter and section in which the relevant content can be found.

Icons in this Training Guide

The following icons are used to help you quickly and easily find helpful information.

New in **2016**	Indicates items that are new in the Autodesk Revit 2016 software.
Enhanced in **2016**	Indicates items that have been enhanced in the Autodesk Revit 2016 software.

Practice Files

To download the practice files that are required for this training guide, type the following in the address bar of your web browser:

SDCpublications.com/downloads/978-1-58503-979-1

Customizing the Interface

The Autodesk Revit software has three disciplines: Architecture, Structure, and MEP (Mechanical, Electrical, and Plumbing, which is also know as Systems). When using the Autodesk Building Design Suite, all of the tools for these disciplines are installed in one copy of the software. By default, all of the tools, templates, and sample files are available, as shown in Figure 1. Most users only need access to their specific set of tools and the interface can be customized to suit those needs.

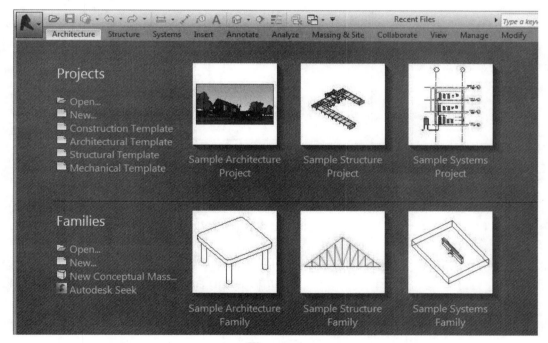

Figure 1

- The following steps describe how to customize the suite-based software with special reference to the layout of the discipline-specific software.

- This training guide uses the all-discipline interface.

How To: Set the User Interface

1. In the upper left corner of the screen, expand (Application Menu) and click **Options**.
2. In the Options dialog box, in the left pane, select **User Interface**.

   In the *Configure* area, under *Tools and analyses* (as shown in Figure 2), clear all of options that you do not want to use.

You are not deleting these tools, just removing them from the current user interface.

Figure 2

- To match the Autodesk Revit Architecture interface, select only the following options:

  - *Architecture* tab and tools
  - *Structure* tab and tools (but not Structural analysis and tools)
  - *Massing and Site* tab and tools
  - Energy analysis and tools

- To match the [icon] Autodesk Revit Structure interface, select only the following options:

    - *Architecture* tab and tools
    - *Structure* tab and tools including Structural analysis and tools
    - *Massing and Site* tab and tools

- To match the [icon] Autodesk Revit MEP interface, clear only the following option:

    - *Structure* tab and tools

How To: Set Template File Locations

1. In the Options dialog box, in the left pane, select **File Locations**.
2. In the right pane (as shown in Figure 3), select and order the templates that you want to display. Typically, these are set up by the company.

All default templates are found in the following location: C:\ProgramData> Autodesk>RVT 2016> Templates>[units].

Name	Path
Construction Tem...	C:\ProgramData\Autodesk\RVT 2016\Tem...
Architectural Temp...	C:\ProgramData\Autodesk\RVT 2016\Tem...
Structural Template	C:\ProgramData\Autodesk\RVT 2016\Tem...
Mechanical Templ...	C:\ProgramData\Autodesk\RVT 2016\Tem...

Figure 3

- To match the [icon] Autodesk Revit Architecture interface, select **Architectural Template** and move it to the top of the list. Remove the **Structural Template** and **Mechanical Template**.

- To match the [icon] Autodesk Revit Structure interface, select **Structural Template** and move it to the top of the list. Remove the **Architectural Template**, **Construction Template**, and **Mechanical Template**.

- To match the [icon] Autodesk Revit MEP interface, remove the **Construction Template, Architectural Template**, and **Structural Template**. Add the **Electrical Template (Electrical-Default.rte)** and **Systems Template (Systems-Default.rte)**.

Setting Tab Locations

You might also want to move the tabs to a different order. To do so, select the tab, hold <Ctrl>, and drag the tab to the new location.

- To match the Autodesk Revit Architecture interface you are not required to modify the tab locations.

- To match the Autodesk Revit Structure interface, select the *Structure* tab and drag it to the front of the tabs.

- To match the Autodesk Revit MEP interface, select the *Systems* tab and drag it to the front of the tabs.

Introduction to BIM and Autodesk Revit

This training guide is divided into three sections: Introduction to BIM and Autodesk Revit, Design Development, and Construction Documents.

The first section provides an overview of using Building Information Modeling (BIM) with the Autodesk® Revit® software, working with the software interface, how to use the basic drawing and modify tools, and incorporating datum elements.

This section includes the following chapters:

- Chapter 1: Introduction to BIM and Autodesk Revit

- Chapter 2: Basic Drawing and Modify Tools

- Chapter 3: Setting Up Levels and Grids

Introduction to BIM and Autodesk Revit

Building Information Modeling (BIM) and the Autodesk® Revit® software work hand in hand to help you create smart, 3D models that are useful at all stages in the building process. Understanding the software interface and terminology enhances your ability to create powerful models and move around in the various views of the model.

Learning Objectives in this Chapter

- Describe the concept and workflow of Building Information Modeling in relation to the Autodesk Revit software.
- Navigate the graphic user interface, including the Ribbon (where most of the tools are found), the Properties palette (where you make modifications to element information), and the Project Browser (where you can open various views of the model).
- Open existing projects and start new projects using templates.
- Use viewing commands to move around the model in 2D and 3D views.

1.1 BIM and Autodesk Revit

Building Information Modeling (BIM) is an approach to the entire building life cycle, including design, construction, and facilities management. The BIM process supports the ability to coordinate, update, and share design data with team members across disciplines.

The Autodesk Revit software is a true BIM product as it enables you to create complete models and the associated views of those models. It is considered a *Parametric Building Modeler:*

- *Parametric:* A relationship is established between building elements; when one element changes other related elements change as well.

- *Building:* The software is designed for working with buildings, as opposed to gears or roads.

- *Modeler:* A project is built in a single file around the 3D building model, as shown on the left in Figure 1–1. All views, such as plans (as shown on the right in Figure 1–1), elevations, sections, details, and reports such as schedules, as well as construction documents, are generated based on the model.

When a change is made anywhere in the model, all of the views update automatically. For example, if you add an element in a plan view, it displays in all of the other views as well.

Figure 1–1

- The Autodesk® Revit® software includes tools for architectural, mechanical, electrical, plumbing, and structural design.

- It is important that everyone works in the same version and build of the software.

Workflow and BIM

BIM has changed the process of how a building is planned, budgeted, designed, constructed, and (in some cases) operated and maintained.

In the traditional design process, plans create the basis for the model, from which you then create sections and elevations, as shown in Figure 1–2. Construction Documents (CDs) can then be created. In this workflow, changes are made at the plan level and then coordinated with other documents in the set.

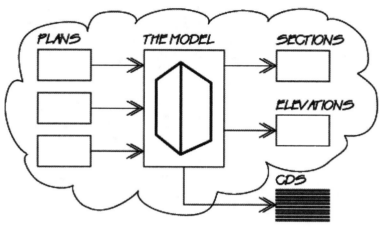

Figure 1–2

In BIM, the design process revolves around the model, as shown in Figure 1–3. Plans, elevations, and sections are simply 2D versions of the 3D model. Changes made in one view automatically update in all views. Even Construction Documents update automatically with callout tags in sync with the sheet numbers. This is called bidirectional associativity.

By creating complete models and associated views of those models, the Autodesk Revit software takes much of the tediousness out of producing a building design.

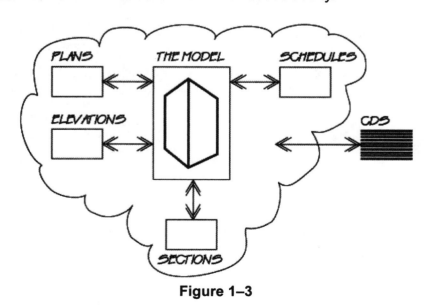

Figure 1–3

Revit Terms

As you start working with the Autodesk Revit software, you should know the typical terms used to describe items. There are several types of elements (as shown in Figure 1–4) as described in the following table.

Figure 1–4

Host	Model elements (such as floors, walls, roofs, ceilings, stairs, and ramps) that can support other elements. They can stand alone in the project.
Components	Elements that need to be attached to host elements (such as doors, windows, and railings), as well as stand-alone items (such as furniture and equipment).
Views	Enables you to display and manipulate the project. For example, you can view and work in floor plans, ceiling plans, elevations, sections, schedules, and 3D views. You can change a design from any view. All views are stored in the project.
Datum	Elements that define the project context. These include levels for the floors, column grids, and reference planes that help you draw.
Annotation	2D elements that are placed in views to define the information drawn in the project. These include dimensions, text, tags, and symbols. The view scale controls their size and they only display in the view in which they are placed.

- The elements that you create in the software are "smart" elements: the software recognizes them as walls, columns, ducts or lighting fixtures. This means that the information stored in their properties automatically updates in schedules, which ensures that views and reports are coordinated across an entire project, generated from a single model.

Revit and Construction Documents

In the traditional workflow, the most time-consuming part of the project is the construction documents. With BIM, the base views of those documents (i.e., plans, elevations, sections, and schedules) are produced automatically and update as the model is updated, saving hours of work. The views are then placed on sheets that form the construction document set.

For example, a floor plan is duplicated to create a Life Safety Plan. In the new view, certain categories of elements are turned off (such as grids and section marks) while furniture elements are set to halftone. Annotation is added as required. The plan is then placed on a sheet, as shown in Figure 1–5.

Figure 1–5

- Work can continue on a view and is automatically updated on the sheet.

- Annotating views in the preliminary design phase is often not required. You might be able to wait until you are further along in the project.

1.2 Overview of the Interface

The Autodesk Revit interface is designed for intuitive and efficient access to commands and views. It includes the Ribbon, Quick Access Toolbar, Application Menu, Navigation Bar, and Status Bar, which are common to most of the Autodesk® software. It also includes tools that are specific to the Autodesk Revit software, including the Properties Palette, Project Browser, and View Control Bar. The interface is shown in Figure 1–6.

Figure 1–6

1. Quick Access Toolbar	6. Properties Palette
2. Status Bar	7. Project Browser
3. Application Menu	8. View Window
4. Ribbon	9. Navigation Bar
5. Options Bar	10. View Control Bar

1. Quick Access Toolbar

The Quick Access Toolbar includes commonly used commands, such as **Open**, **Save**, **Undo** and **Redo**, **Dimension**, and **3D View**, as shown in Figure 1–7.

Figure 1–7

Hint: Customizing the Quick Access Toolbar

Right-click on the Quick Access Toolbar to change the docked location of the toolbar to be above or below the ribbon, or to add, relocate, or remove tools on the toolbar. You can also right-click on a tool in the Ribbon and select **Add to Quick Access Toolbar**, as shown in Figure 1–8.

Figure 1–8

The Quick Access Toolbar also hosts the InfoCenter (as shown in Figure 1–9) which includes a search field to find help on the web as well as access to the Subscription Center, Communication Center, Autodesk A360 sign-in, and other help options.

Click here to collapse the search field to save screen space.

Figure 1–9

2. Status Bar

The Status Bar provides information about the current process, such as the next step for a command, as shown in Figure 1–10.

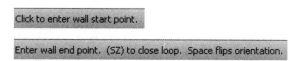

Figure 1–10

- Other options in the Status Bar are related to Worksets and Design Options (advanced tools) as well as selection methods and filters.

Hint: Right-click Menus

Right-click menus help you to work smoothly and efficiently by enabling you to quickly access required commands. These menus provide access to basic viewing commands, recently used commands, and the available Browsers, as shown in Figure 1–11. Additional options vary depending on the element or command that you are using.

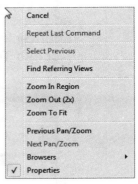

Figure 1–11

---

3. Application Menu

The Application Menu provides access to file commands, settings, and documents, as shown in Figure 1–12. Hover the cursor over a command to display a list of additional tools.

If you click the primary icon, rather than the arrow, it starts the default command.

Figure 1–12

- To display a list of recently used documents, click 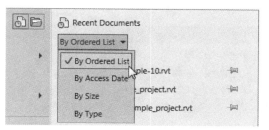 (Recent Documents). The documents can be reordered as shown in Figure 1–13.

Figure 1–13

Click (Pin) next to a document name to keep it available.

- To display a list of open documents and views, click 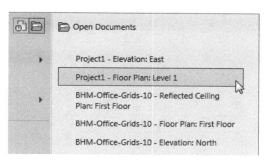 (Open Documents). The list displays the open documents and each view that is open, as shown in Figure 1–14.

Figure 1–14

You can use the Open Documents list to change between views.

- Click (Close) to close the current project.

- At the bottom of the menu, click **Options** to open the Options dialog box or click **Exit Revit** to exit the software.

4. Ribbon

The Ribbon contains tools in a series of tabs and panels as shown in Figure 1–15. Selecting a tab displays a group of related panels. The panels contain a variety of tools, grouped by task.

Figure 1–15

When you start a command that creates new elements or you select an element, the Ribbon displays the *Modify | contextual* tab. This contains general editing commands and command specific tools, as shown in Figure 1–16.

Contextual tab

Figure 1–16

- When you hover over a tool on the Ribbon, tooltips display the tool's name and a short description. If you continue hovering over the tool, a graphic displays (and sometimes a video), as shown in Figure 1–17.

Figure 1–17

- Many commands have shortcut keys. For example, type **AL** for **Align** or **MV** for **Move**. They are listed next to the name of the command in the tooltips. Do not press <Enter> when typing shortcuts.

- To arrange the order in which the Ribbon tabs are displayed, select the tab, hold <Ctrl>, and drag it to a new location. The location is remembered when you restart the software.

- Any panel can be dragged by its title into the drawing area to become a floating panel. Click the **Return Panels to Ribbon** button (as shown in Figure 1–18) to reposition the panel in the ribbon.

Figure 1–18

Hint: You are always in a command when using the Autodesk Revit software.

When you are finished working with a tool, you typically default back to the **Modify** command. To end a command, use one of the following methods:

- In any Ribbon tab, click ⌨ (Modify).
- Press <Esc> once or twice to revert to **Modify**.
- Right-click and select **Cancel...** once or twice.
- Start another command.

---

5. Options Bar

The Options Bar displays options that are related to the selected command or element. For example, when the **Rotate** command is active it displays options for rotating the selected elements, as shown at the top in Figure 1–19. When the **Place Dimensions** command is active it displays dimension related options, as shown at the bottom in Figure 1–19.

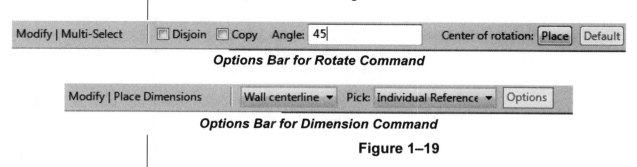

Options Bar for Rotate Command

Options Bar for Dimension Command

Figure 1–19

6. Properties Palette

The Properties palette includes the Type Selector, which enables you to choose the size or style of the element you are adding or modifying. This palette is also where you make changes to information (parameters) about elements or views, as shown in Figure 1–20. There are two types of properties:

- **Instance Properties** are set for the individual element(s) you are creating or modifying.

- **Type Properties** control options for all elements of the same type. If you modify these parameter values, all elements of the selected type change.

The Properties palette is usually kept open while working on a project to easily permit changes at any time. If it does not display, in the Modify tab>Properties panel

click ▣ *(Properties) or type* **PP.**

Some parameters are only available when you are editing an element. They are grayed out when unavailable.

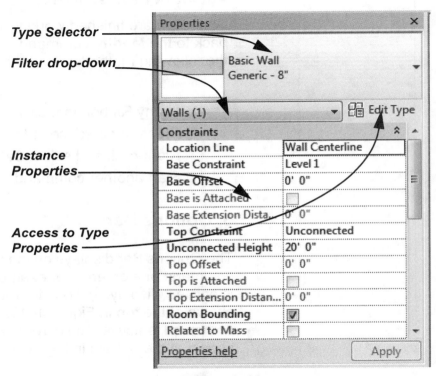

Figure 1–20

- Options for the current view display if the **Modify** command is active, but you have not selected an element.

- If a command or element is selected, the options for the associated element display.

- You can save the changes by either moving the cursor off of the palette, or by pressing <Enter>, or by clicking **Apply**.

- When you start a command or select an element, you can set the element type in the Type Selector, as shown in Figure 1–21.

Search Box ⟶

Figure 1–21

- When multiple elements are selected, you can filter the type of elements that display using the drop-down list, as shown in Figure 1–22.

Figure 1–22

- The Properties palette can be placed on a second monitor, or floated, resized, and docked on top of the Project Browser or other dockable palettes, as shown in Figure 1–23. Click the tab to display its associated panel.

Figure 1–23

7. Project Browser

The Project Browser lists the views that can be opened in the project, as shown in Figure 1–24. This includes all views of the model in which you are working and any additional views that you create, such as floor plans, ceiling plans, 3D views, elevations, sections, etc. It also includes views of schedules, legends, sheets (for plotting), groups, and Autodesk Revit Links.

The Project Browser displays the name of the active project.

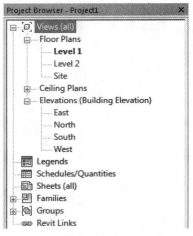

Figure 1–24

- Double-click on an item in the list to open the associated view.

- To display the views associated with a view type, click ⊞ (Expand) next to the section name. To hide the views in the section, click ⊟ (Contract).

- Right-click on a view and select **Rename** or press <F2> to rename a view in the Project Browser.

- If you no longer need a view, you can remove it. Right-click on its name in the Project Browser and select **Delete**.

- The Project Browser can be floated, resized, docked on top of the Properties palette, and customized. If the Properties palette and the Project Browser are docked on top of each other, use the appropriate tab to display the required panel.

How To: Search the Project Browser

1. In the Project Browser, right-click on the top level Views node as shown in Figure 1–25.

Figure 1–25

2. In the Search in Project Browser dialog box, type the words that you want to find (as shown on the left in Figure 1–26), and click **Next**.
3. In the Project Browser, the first instance of that search displays as shown on the right in Figure 1–26.

Figure 1–26

4. Continue using **Next** and **Previous** to move through the list.
5. Click **Close** when you are done.

8. View Window

Each view of a project opens in its own window. Each view displays a Navigation Bar (for quick access to viewing tools) and the View Control Bar, as shown in Figure 1–27.

In 3D views you can also use the ViewCube to rotate the view.

Figure 1–27

- To cycle through multiple views you can use several different methods:

  - Press <Ctrl>+<Tab>
  - Select the view in the Project Browser
  - In the Quick Access Toolbar or *View* tab>Windows panel, expand (Switch Windows) and select the view from the list.

- You can Tile or Cascade views. In the *View* tab> Windows panel click (Cascade Windows) or (Tile Windows). You can also type the shortcuts **WC** to cascade the windows or **WT** to tile the windows.

9. Navigation Bar

The Navigation Bar enables you to access various viewing commands, as shown in Figure 1–28.

Figure 1–28

10. View Control Bar

The View Control Bar (shown in Figure 1–29), displays at the bottom of each view window. It controls aspects of that view, such as the scale and detail level. It also includes tools that display parts of the view and hide or isolate elements in the view.

Figure 1–29

1.3 Starting Projects

File operations to open existing files, create new files from a template, and save files in the Autodesk Revit software are found in the Application Menu, as shown in Figure 1–30.

Figure 1–30

There are three main file types:

- **Project files (.rvt):** These are where you do the majority of your work in the building model by adding elements, creating views, annotating views, and setting up printable sheets. They are initially based on template files.

- **Family files (.rfa):** These are separate components that can be inserted in a project. They include elements that can stand alone (e.g., a table or piece of mechanical equipment) or are items that are hosted in other elements (e.g., a door in a wall or a lighting fixture in a ceiling). Title block and Annotation Symbol files are special types of family files.

- **Template files (.rte):** These are the base files for any new project or family. They are designed to hold standard information and settings for creating new project files. The software includes several templates for various types of projects. You can also create custom templates.

Opening Projects

To open an existing project, in the Quick Access Toolbar or Application Menu click (Open), or press <Ctrl>+<O>. The Open dialog box opens (as shown in Figure 1–31), in which you can navigate to the required folder and select a project file.

Figure 1–31

- When you first open the Autodesk Revit software, the Startup Screen displays, showing lists of recently used projects and family files as shown in Figure 1–32. This screen also displays if you close all projects.

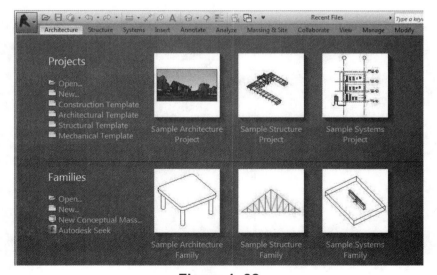

Figure 1–32

- You can select the picture of a recently opened project or use one of the options on the left to open or start a new project using the default templates.

Hint: Opening Workset-Related Files

Worksets are used when the project becomes large enough for multiple people to work on it at the same time. At this point, the project manager creates a central file with multiple worksets (such as element interiors, building shell, and site) that are used by the project team members.

When you open a workset related file it creates a new local file on your computer as shown in Figure 1–33. Do not work in the main central file.

Figure 1–33

New
in **2016**

- It is very important that everyone working on a project uses the same software release. You can open files created in earlier versions of the software in comparison to your own, but you cannot open files created in newer versions of the software.

- When you open a file created in an earlier version, the Model Upgrade dialog box (shown in Figure 1–34) indicates the release of a file and the release to which it will be upgraded. If required, you can cancel the upgrade before it completes.

Figure 1–34

Starting New Projects

New projects are based on a template file. The template file includes preset levels, views, and some families, such as wall styles and text styles. Check with your BIM Manager about which template you need to use for your projects. Your company might have more than one based on the types of building that you are designing.

How To: Start a New Project

1. In the Application Menu, expand (New) and click (Project) (as shown in Figure 1–35), or press <Ctrl>+<N>.

Figure 1–35

2. In the New Project dialog box (shown in Figure 1–36), select the template that you want to use and click **OK**.

The list of Template files is set in the Options dialog box in the File Locations pane. It might vary depending on the installed product and company standards.

Figure 1–36

- You can select from a list of templates if they have been set up by your BIM Manager.

- You can add 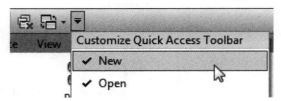 (New) to the Quick Access Toolbar. At the end of the Quick Access Toolbar, click ▼ (Customize Quick Access Toolbar) and select **New**, as shown in Figure 1–37.

Figure 1–37

Saving Projects

Saving your project frequently is a good idea. In the Quick Access Toolbar or Application Menu click 🖫 (Save), or press <Ctrl>+<S> to save your project. If the project has not yet been saved, the Save As dialog box opens, where you can specify a file location and name.

- To save an existing project with a new name, in the Application Menu, expand 🖫 (Save As) and click 🖫 (Project).

- If you have not saved in a set amount of time, the software opens the Project Not Saved Recently alert box, as shown in Figure 1–38. Select **Save the project**. If you want to set reminder intervals or not save at this time, select the other options.

Figure 1–38

- You can set the *Save Reminder interval* to **15** or **30 minutes**, **1**, **2**, or **4 hours**, or to have **No reminders** display. In the Application Menu, click **Options** to open the Options dialog box. In the left pane, select **General** and set the interval as shown in Figure 1–39.

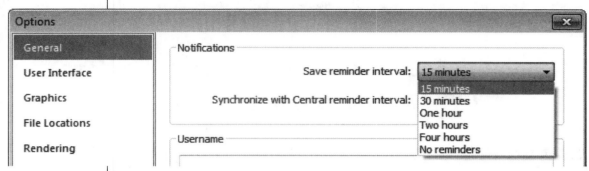

Figure 1–39

Saving Backup Copies

By default, the software saves a backup copy of a project file when you save the project. Backup copies are numbered incrementally (e.g., **My Project.0001.rvt**, **My Project.0002.rvt**, etc.) and are saved in the same folder as the original file. In the Save As dialog box, click **Options...** to control how many backup copies are saved. The default number is three backups. If you exceed this number, the software deletes the oldest backup file.

Hint: Saving Workset-Related Projects

If you use worksets in your project, you need to save the project locally and to the central file. It is recommended to save the local file frequently, just like any other file, and save to the central file every hour or so.

To synchronize your changes with the main file, in the Quick Access Toolbar expand ⬡ (Synchronize and Modify Settings) and click ⬡ (Synchronize Now). After you save to the central file, save the file locally again.

At the end of the day, or when you are finished with the current session, use ⬡ (Synchronize and Modify Settings) to relinquish the files you have been working on to the central file.

1.4 Viewing Commands

Viewing commands are crucial to working efficiently in most drawing and modeling programs and the Autodesk Revit software is no exception. Once in a view, you can use the Zoom controls to navigate within it. You can zoom in and out and pan in any view. There are also special tools for viewing in 3D.

Zooming and Panning

Using The Mouse to Zoom and Pan

Use the mouse wheel (as shown in Figure 1–40) as the main method of moving around the drawing.

Mouse Wheel

Figure 1–40

- Scroll the wheel on the mouse up to zoom in and down to zoom out.
- Hold down the wheel and move the mouse to pan.
- Double-click on the wheel to zoom to the extents of the drawing.
- In a 3D view, hold down <Shift> and the mouse wheel and move the mouse to rotate around the model.

Enhanced in **2016**

- When you save a model and exit the software, the pan and zoom location of each view is remembered. This is especially important for complex models.

Zoom Controls

A number of additional zoom methods enable you to control the screen display. **Zoom** and **Pan** can be performed at any time while using other commands.

*   You can access the **Zoom** commands in the Navigation Bar in the upper right corner of the view (as shown in Figure 1–41). You can also access them from most right-click menus and by typing the shortcut commands.

Figure 1–41

 *(2D Wheel) provides cursor-specific access to **Zoom** and **Pan**.*

Zoom Commands

	Zoom In Region (ZR)	Zooms into a region that you define. Drag the cursor or select two points to define the rectangular area you want to zoom into. This is the default command.
	Zoom Out(2x) (ZO)	Zooms out to half the current magnification around the center of the elements.
	Zoom To Fit (ZF or ZE)	Zooms out so that the entire contents of the project only display on the screen in the current view.
	Zoom All To Fit (ZA)	Zooms out so that the entire contents of the project display on the screen in all open views.
	Zoom Sheet Size (ZS)	Zooms in or out in relation to the sheet size.
N/A	Previous Pan/Zoom (ZP)	Steps back one **Zoom** command.
N/A	Next Pan/Zoom	Steps forward one **Zoom** command if you have done a **Previous Pan/Zoom**.

Viewing in 3D

*There are two types of 3D views: isometric views created by the **3D View** command and perspective views created by the **Camera** command.*

Even if you started a project entirely in plan views, you can quickly create 3D views of the model, as shown in Figure 1–42.

Figure 1–42

Working in 3D views helps you visualize the project and position some of the elements correctly. You can create and modify elements in 3D views just as in plan views.

- Once you have created a 3D view, you can save it and easily return to it.

How To: Create and Save a 3D Isometric View

1. In the Quick Access Toolbar or *View* tab>Create panel, click (Default 3D View). The default 3D Southeast isometric view opens, as shown in Figure 1–43.

Figure 1–43

You can spin the view to a different angle using the mouse wheel or the middle button of a three-button mouse. Hold down <Shift> as you press the wheel or middle button and drag the cursor.

2. Modify the view to display the building from other directions.
3. In the Project Browser, right-click on the {3D} view and select **Rename...**

4. Type a new name in the Rename View dialog box, as shown in Figure 1–44, and click **OK**.

Figure 1–44

• When changes to the default 3D view are saved and you start another default 3D view, it displays the Southeast isometric view once again. If you modified the default 3D view but did not save it to a new name, the **Default 3D View** command opens the view in the last orientation you specified.

How To: Create a Perspective View

1. Switch to a Floor Plan view.
2. In the Quick Access Toolbar or *View* tab>Create panel, expand ⌂ (Default 3D View) and click 📷 (Camera).
3. Place the camera on the view.
4. Point the camera in the direction in which you want it to shoot by placing the target on the view, as shown in Figure 1–45.

Figure 1–45

A new view is displayed, as shown in Figure 1–46.

Figure 1–46

Use the round controls to modify the display size of the view and press <Shift> + the mouse wheel to change the view.

5. In the Properties palette scroll down and adjust the *Eye Elevation* and *Target Elevation* as required. You can also rename perspective views.

New in 2016

- If you move the view around so that it is distorted, you can reset the target so that it is centered in the boundary of the view (called the crop region). In the *Modify | Cameras* tab>Camera panel, click ⌖ (Reset Target).

- You can further modify a view by adding shadows, as shown in Figure 1–47. In the View Control Bar, toggle ☒ (Shadows Off) and ⚊ (Shadows On). Shadows display in any model view, not just in the 3D views.

Figure 1–47

Hint: Using the ViewCube

The ViewCube provides visual clues as to where you are in a 3D view. It helps you move around the model with quick access to specific views (such as top, front, and right), as well as corner and directional views, as shown in Figure 1–48.

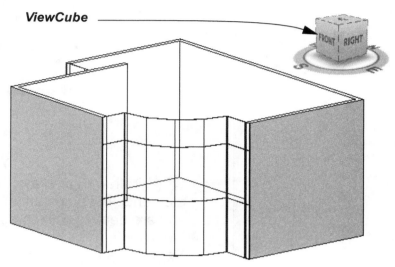

Figure 1–48

Move the cursor over any face of the ViewCube to highlight it. Once a face is highlighted, you can select it to reorient the model. You can also click and drag on the ViewCube to rotate the box, which rotates the model.

- (Home) displays when you roll the cursor over the ViewCube. Click it to return to the view defined as **Home**. To change the Home view, set the view as you want it, right-click on the ViewCube, and select **Set Current View as Home**.

- The ViewCube is available in isometric and perspective views.

- If you are in a camera view, you can switch between Perspective and Isometric mode. Right-click on the View Cube and click **Toggle to Parallel-3D View** or **Toggle to Perspective-3D View**. You can make more changes to the model in a parallel view.

New in 2016

Visual Styles

Any view can have a visual style applied. The **Visual Style** options found in the View Control Bar (as shown in Figure 1–49), specify the shading of the building model. These options apply to plan, elevation, section, and 3D views.

Figure 1–49

- 🗗 (Wireframe) displays the lines and edges that make up elements, but hides the surfaces. This can be useful when you are dealing with complex intersections.

- 🗗 (Hidden Line) displays the lines, edges, and surfaces of the elements, but it does not display any colors. This is the most common visual style to use while working on a design.

- 🗗 (Shaded) and 🗗 (Consistent Colors) give you a sense of the materials, including transparent glass. An example that uses Consistent Colors is shown in Figure 1–50.

Figure 1–50

- (Realistic) displays what is shown when you render the view, including RPC (Rich Photorealistic Content) components and artificial lights. It takes a lot of computer power to execute this visual style. Therefore, it is better to use the other visual styles most of the time as you are working.

- (Ray Trace) is useful if you have created a 3D view that you want to render. It gradually moves from draft resolution to photorealistic. You can stop the process at any time.

Hint: Rendering

Rendering is a powerful tool which enables you to display a photorealistic view of the model you are working on, such as the example shown in Figure 1–51. This can be used to help clients and designers to understand a building's design in better detail.

Figure 1–51

- In the View Control Bar, click (Show Rendering Dialog) to set up the options. **Show Rendering Dialog** is only available in 3D views.

Practice 1a

Open and Review a Project

Practice Objectives

- Navigate the graphic user interface.
- Manipulate 2D and 3D views by zooming and panning.
- Create 3D Isometric and Perspective views.
- Set the Visual Style of a view.

Estimated time for completion: 15 minutes

In this practice you will open a project file and view each of the various areas in the interface. You will investigate elements, commands, and their options. You will also open views through the Project Browser and view the model in 3D, as shown in Figure 1–52.

Figure 1–52

Task 1 - Explore the interface.

1. In the Application Menu, expand (Open) and click (Project).

2. In the Open dialog box, select **Modern-Hotel-Final.rvt**. It is found in your practice folder and is a version of the main project you will work on throughout the training guide.

3. Click **Open**. The 3D view of the modern hotel building opens in the drawing window.

If the Project Browser and Properties palette are docked over each other, use the Project Browser tab at the bottom to display it.

4. In the Project Browser, expand the *Floor Plans* node. Double-click on **Floor 1** to open it. This view is referred to as **Floor Plans: Floor 1**.

5. Take time to review the floor plan to get acquainted with it.

6. Review the various parts of the screen.

7. In the drawing window, hover the cursor over one of the doors. A tooltip displays describing the element, as shown in Figure 1–53.

Figure 1–53

8. Hover the cursor over another element to display its description.

9. Select a door. The Ribbon changes to the *Modify | Doors* tab.

10. Click in an empty space to release the selection.

11. Hold down <Ctrl> and select several elements of different types. The Ribbon changes to the *Modify | Multi-Select* tab.

12. Click in an empty space to release the selection set.

13. In the *Architecture* tab>Build panel, click ⬚ (Wall). The Ribbon changes to the *Modify | Place Wall* tab and at the end of the Ribbon, the Draw panel is displayed. It contains tools that enable you to create walls. The rest of the Ribbon displays the same tools that are found on the *Modify* tab.

14. In the Select panel, click ⬚ (Modify) to return to the main Ribbon.

15. In the *Architecture* tab>Build panel, click ☐ (Door). The Ribbon changes to the *Modify | Place Door* tab and displays the options and tools you can use to create doors.

16. In the Select panel, click ⬚ (Modify) to return to the main Ribbon.

Task 2 - Look at views.

You might need to widen the Project Browser to display the full names of the views.

1. In the Project Browser, verify that the *Floor Plans* node is open. Double-click on the **Floor 1 - Furniture Plan** view.

2. The basic floor plan displays with the furniture, but without the annotations that were displayed in the **Floor 1** view. Open the **1st Floor Life Safety Plan** view by double-clicking on it.

3. The walls and furniture display, but the furniture is grayed out and red lines describing important life safety information display.

*This view is referred to as **Elevations (Building Elevation): East** view.*

4. In the Project Browser, scroll down and expand *Elevations (Building Elevation)*. Double-click on the **East** elevation to open the view.

5. Expand *Sections (Building Section)* and double-click on the **East-West Section** to open it.

6. At the bottom of the drawing window, in the View Control Bar, click ▱ (Visual Style) and select **Shaded**. The elements in the section are now easier to read.

7. In the Project Browser, scroll down to the *Sheets (all)* node and expand the node.

8. View several of the sheets. Some have views already applied, (e.g., **A2.3 - 2nd-8th Floor Plan (Typical)** as shown in Figure 1–54).

Figure 1–54

9. Which sheet displays the view that you just set to **Shaded**?

***

Task 3 - Practice viewing tools.

***

1. Return to the **Floor Plans: Floor 1** view.

2. In the Navigation Bar, click [icon] and select **Zoom In Region** or type **ZR**. Zoom in on one of the stairs.

3. Pan to another part of the building by holding and dragging the middle mouse button or wheel. Alternatively, you can use the 2D Wheel in the Navigation Bar.

4. Double-click on the mouse wheel to zoom out to fit the extents of the view.

5. In the Quick Access Toolbar, click (Default 3D View) to open the default 3D view, as shown in Figure 1–55.

Figure 1–55

6. Hold down <Shift> and use the middle mouse button or wheel to rotate the model in the 3D view.

7. In the View Control Bar, change the *Visual Style* to (Shaded). Then try (Consistent Colors). Which one works best when you view the back of the building?

8. Use the ViewCube to find a view that you want to use.

9. In the Project Browser, expand *3D Views* and right-click on the {3D} view and select **Rename....** In the Rename View dialog box type in a useful name.

10. Review the other 3D views that have already been created.

11. Press <Ctrl>+<Tab> to cycle through the open views.

12. In the Quick Access Toolbar, expand (Switch Windows) and select the **Modern-Hotel-Final.rvt - Floor Plan: Floor 1** view.

13. In the Quick Access Toolbar, click (Close Hidden Windows). This closes all of the other windows except the one in which you are working.

14. In the Quick Access Toolbar, expand (Default 3D View) and click (Camera).

15. Click the first point near the Lobby room name and click the second point (target) outside the building, as shown in Figure 1–56.

1st Point   **2nd Point**

Figure 1–56

16. The furniture and planters display even though they did not display in the floor plan view.

17. In the View Control Bar, set the *Visual Style* to (Realistic).

18. In the Project Browser, right-click on the new camera view and select **Rename...** In the Rename View dialog box, type **Lobby Seating Area** and click **OK**.

19. In the Quick Access Toolbar, click (Save) to save the project.

20. In the Application Menu, click (Close). This closes the entire project.

This file is not set up to work with Raytrace.

Chapter Review Questions

1. When you create a project in the Autodesk Revit software, do you draw in 3D (as shown on the left in Figure 1–57) or 2D (as shown on the right in Figure 1–57)?

Figure 1–57

   a. You draw in 2D in plan views and in 3D in non-plan views.

   b. You model in 3D almost all of the time, even when you are using what looks like a flat view.

   c. You draw in 2D or 3D depending on how you toggle the 2D/3D control.

   d. You draw in 2D in plan and section views and model in 3D in isometric views.

2. What is the purpose of the Project Browser?

   a. It enables you to browse through the building project, similar to a walk through.

   b. It is the interface for managing all of the files that are needed to create the complete architectural model of the building.

   c. It manages multiple Autodesk Revit projects as an alternative to using Windows Explorer.

   d. It is used to access and manage the views of the project.

3. Which part(s) of the interface changes according to the command you are using?

   a. Ribbon

   b. View Control Bar

   c. Options Bar

   d. Properties Palette

4. The difference between Type Properties and Properties (the Ribbon location is shown in Figure 1–58) is...

Figure 1–58

   a. Properties stores parameters that apply to the selected individual element(s). Type Properties stores parameters that impact every element of the same type in the project.

   b. Properties stores the location parameters of an element. Type Properties stores the size and identity parameters of an element.

   c. Properties only stores parameters of the view. Type Properties stores parameters of model components.

5. When you start a new project, how do you specify the base information in the new file?

   a. Transfer the base information from an existing project.

   b. Select the right template for the task.

   c. The Autodesk Revit software automatically extracts the base information from imported or linked file(s).

6. What is the main difference between a view made using

   ![] (Default 3D View) and a view made using ![] (Camera)?

   a. Use Default **3D View** for exterior views and **Camera** for interiors.

   b. **Default 3D View** creates a static image and a **Camera** view is live and always updated.

   c. **Default 3D View** is isometric and a **Camera** view is perspective.

   d. **Default 3D View** is used for the overall building and a **Camera** view is used for looking in tight spaces.

Command Summary

Button	Command	Location
General Tools		
	Modify	• **Ribbon:** All tabs>Select panel • **Shortcut:** MD
	New	• **Quick Access Toolbar** (Optional) • **Application Menu** • **Shortcut:** <Ctrl>+<N>
	Open	• **Quick Access Toolbar** • **Application Menu** • **Shortcut:** <Ctrl>+<O>
	Open Documents	• **Application Menu**
	Properties	• **Ribbon:** *Modify* tab>Properties panel • **Shortcut:** PP
	Recent Documents	• **Application Menu**
	Save	• **Quick Access Toolbar** • **Application Menu** • **Shortcut:** <Ctrl>+<S>
	Synchronize and Modify Settings	• **Quick Access Toolbar**
	Synchronize Now/	• **Quick Access Toolbar**>expand Synchronize and Modify Settings
	Type Properties	• **Ribbon:** *Modify* tab>Properties panel • **Properties palette**
Viewing Tools		
	Camera	• **Quick Access Toolbar**> Expand Default 3D View • **Ribbon:** *View* tab>Create panel> expand Default 3D View
	Default 3D View	• **Quick Access Toolbar** • **Ribbon:** *View* tab>Create panel
	Home	• **ViewCube**
N/A	**Next Pan/Zoom**	• **Navigation Bar** • **Right-click Menu**
N/A	**Previous Pan/Zoom**	• **Navigation Bar** • **Right-click Menu** • **Shortcut:** ZP
	Shadows On/Off	• **View Control Bar**

Icon	Name	Access
	Show Rendering Dialog/ Render	• **View Control Bar** • **Ribbon:** *View* tab>Graphics panel • **Shortcut:** RR
	Zoom All to Fit	• **Navigation Bar** • **Shortcut:** ZA
	Zoom in Region	• **Navigation Bar** • **Right-click Menu** • **Shortcut:** ZR
	Zoom Out (2x)	• **Navigation Bar** • **Right-click Menu** • **Shortcut:** ZO
	Zoom Sheet Size	• **Navigation Bar** • **Shortcut:** ZS
	Zoom to Fit	• **Navigation Bar** • **Right-click Menu** • **Shortcut:** ZF, ZE

Visual Styles

Icon	Name	Access
	Consistent Colors	• **View Control Bar:**
	Hidden Line	• **View Control Bar** • **Shortcut:** HL
	Ray Trace	• **View Control Bar:**
	Realistic	• **View Control Bar**
	Shaded	• **View Control Bar** • **Shortcut:** SD
	Wireframe	• **View Control Bar** • **Shortcut:** WF

Basic Drawing and Modify Tools

Basic drawing, selecting, and modifying tools are the foundation of working with all types of elements in the Autodesk® Revit® software. Using these tools with drawing aids helps you to place and modify elements to create accurate building models.

Learning Objectives in this Chapter

- Draw linear elements such as walls, beams, and pipes.
- Ease the placement of elements by incorporating drawing aids, such as alignment lines, temporary dimensions, and snaps.
- Place Reference Planes as temporary guide lines.
- Use techniques to select and filter groups of elements.
- Modify elements using the contextual Ribbon tab, Properties pane, temporary dimensions, and controls.
- Move, copy, rotate, and mirror elements and create array copies in linear and radial patterns.
- Align, trim, and extend elements with the edges of other elements.
- Split linear elements anywhere along their length.
- Offset elements to create duplicates a specific distance away from the original.

2.1 Using General Drawing Tools

When you start a command, the contextual Ribbon tab, Options Bar, and Properties palette enable you to set up features for each new element you are placing in the project. As you are drawing, several features called *drawing aids* display, as shown in Figure 2–1. They help you to create designs quickly and accurately.

Figure 2–1

Draw Tools

Many linear elements (such as walls, beams, ducts, pipes, and conduits) are drawn using the tools on the contextual tab on the *Draw* panel, as shown for Walls in Figure 2–1. Other elements (such as floors, ceilings, roofs, and slabs) are sketched using many of the same tools. Draw tools are also used when you create details or schematic drawings.

Two methods are available:

- *Draw* the element using a geometric form
- Pick an existing element (such as a line, face, or wall) as the basis for the new element's geometry and position.

The exact tools vary according to the element being drawn.

How To: Draw Linear Elements

1. Start the command you want to use.
2. In the contextual tab>Draw panel, as shown in Figure 2–2, select a drawing tool.
3. Select points to define the elements.

Figure 2–2

4. Finish the command. (Remember: You can click

    (Modify), press <Esc> twice, or right-click and select **Cancel** twice.)

Draw Options

When you are in Drawing mode, several options display in the Options Bar, as shown in Figure 2–3.

Figure 2–3

- **Chain** controls how many segments are drawn in one process. If this option is not selected, the **Line** and **Arc** tools only draw one segment at a time. If it is selected, you can continue drawing segments until you select the command again.

- **Offset** enables you to enter values to draw the linear elements at a specified distance from the selected points.

- **Radius** enables you to enter values when using a radial draw tool.

You can change from one Draw tool shape to another in the middle of a command.

Different options display according to the type of element that is selected or the command that is active.

Draw Tools

⟋	**Line**	Draws a straight line defined by the first and last points. If Chain is enabled, you can continue selecting end points for multiple segments.
▱	**Rectangle**	Draws a rectangle defined by two opposing corner points. You can adjust the dimensions after selecting both points.
⬠	**Inscribed Polygon**	Draws a polygon inscribed in a hypothetical circle with the number of sides specified in the Options Bar.
⬠	**Circumscribed Polygon**	Draws a polygon circumscribed around a hypothetical circle with the number of sides specified in the Options Bar.
◎	**Circle**	Draws a circle defined by a center point and radius.
⌒	**Start-End-Radius Arc**	Draws a curve defined by a start, end, and radius of the arc. The outside dimension shown is the included angle of the arc. The inside dimension is the radius.
⌒	**Center-ends Arc**	Draws a curve defined by a center, radius, and included angle. The selected point of the radius also defines the start point of the arc.
⌒	**Tangent End Arc**	Draws a curve tangent to another element. Select an end point for the first point, but do not select the intersection of two or more elements. Then select a second point based on the included angle of the arc.
⌐	**Fillet Arc**	Draws a curve defined by two other elements and a radius. Because it is difficult to select the correct radius by clicking, this command automatically moves to edit mode. Select the dimension and then modify the radius of the fillet.
⋏	**Spline**	Draws a spline curve based on selected points. The curve does not actually touch the points (Model and Detail Lines only).
⬭	**Ellipse**	Draws an ellipse from a primary and secondary axis (Model and Detail Lines only).
⊃	**Partial Ellipse**	Draws only one side of the ellipse, like an arc. A partial ellipse also has a primary and secondary axis (Model and Detail Lines only).

Pick Tools

Pick Lines	Pick Lines	Use this option to select existing linear elements in the project. This is useful when you start the project from an imported 2D drawing.
	Pick Face	Use this option to select the face of a 3D massing element (walls and 3D views only).
	Pick Walls	Use this option to select an existing wall in the project to be the basis for a new sketch line (floors, ceilings, etc.).

Drawing Aids

As soon as you start sketching or placing elements, three drawing aids display, as shown in Figure 2–4:

- Alignment lines

- Temporary dimensions

- Snaps

These aids are available with most drawing and many modification commands.

Figure 2–4

Alignment lines display as soon as you select your first point. They help keep lines horizontal, vertical, or at a specified angle. They also line up with the implied intersections of walls and other elements.

- Hold down <Shift> to force the alignments to be orthogonal (90 degree angles only).

Temporary dimensions display to help place elements at the correct length, angle and location.

- You can type in the dimension and then move the cursor until you see the dimension you want, or you can place the element and then modify the dimension as required.
- The length and angle increments shown vary depending on how far in or out the view is zoomed.
- For Imperial measurements (feet and inches), the software uses a default of feet. For example, when you type **4** and press <Enter>, it assumes 4'-0". For a distance such as 4'-6", you can type any of the following: **4'-6"**, **4'6**, **4-6**, or **4 6** (the numbers separated by a space). To indicate distances less than one foot, type the inch mark (") after the distance, or enter **0**, a space, and then the distance.

> **Hint: Temporary Dimensions and Permanent Dimensions**
>
> Temporary dimensions disappear as soon as you finish adding elements. If you want to make them permanent, select the control shown in Figure 2–5.
>
>
>
> **Figure 2–5**

Snaps are key points that help you reference existing elements to exact points when drawing, as shown in Figure 2–6.

Figure 2–6

- When you move the cursor over an element, the snap symbol displays. Each snap location type displays with a different symbol.

Hint: Snap Settings and Overrides

In the *Manage* tab>Settings panel, click 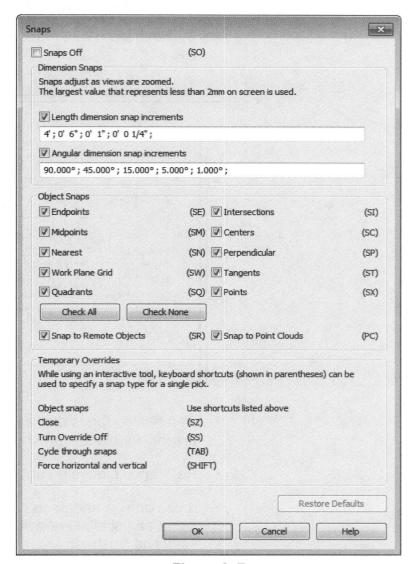 (Snaps) to open
the Snaps dialog box, which is shown in Figure 2–7. The Snaps
dialog box enables you to set which snap points are active, and
set the dimension increments displayed for temporary
dimensions (both linear and angular).

Figure 2–7

- Keyboard shortcuts for each snap can be used to override
  the automatic snapping.Temporary overrides only affect a
  single pick, but can be very helpful when there are snaps
  nearby other than the one you want to use.

Reference Planes

As you develop designs in the Autodesk Revit software, there are times when you need lines to help you define certain locations. You can draw *reference planes* (displayed as dashed green lines) and snap to them whenever you need to line up elements. For the example shown in Figure 2–8, the lighting fixtures in the reflected ceiling plan are placed using reference planes.

- To insert a reference plane, in the *Architecture, Structure,* or *Systems* tab>Work Plane panel, click (Ref Plane) or type **RP**.

Figure 2–8

- Reference planes display in associated views because they are infinite planes, and not just lines.

- Reference planes do not display in 3D views.

- If you draw a reference pane within Sketch Mode (used with floors and similar elements) they do not display once the sketch is finished.

2.2 Editing Elements

Building design projects typically involve extensive changes to the model. The Autodesk Revit software was designed to make such changes quickly and efficiently. You can change an element using the following methods, as shown in Figure 2–9:

- Type Selector enables you to specify a different type. This is frequently used to change the size and/or style of the elements.

- Properties enables you to modify the information (parameters) associated with the selected elements.

- Temporary dimensions enable you to change the element's dimensions or position.

- The contextual tab in the Ribbon contains the Modify commands and element-specific tools.

- Controls enable you to drag, flip, lock, and rotate the element.

- Shape handles (not shown) enable you to drag elements to modify their height or length.

Figure 2–9

- To delete an element, select it and press <Delete>, right-click and select **Delete**, or in the Modify panel, click ✖ (Delete).

Working with Controls and Shape Handles

When you select an element, various controls and shape handles display depending on the element and view. For example, in plan view you can use controls to drag the ends of a wall and change its orientation. You can also drag the wall ends in a 3D view, and you can also use the arrow shape handles to change the height of the wall, as shown in Figure 2–10

Figure 2–10

- If you hover the cursor over the control or shape handle, a tool tip displays showing its function.

Hint: Editing Temporary Dimensions

Temporary dimensions automatically link to the closest wall. To change this, drag the *Witness Line* control (as shown in Figure 2–11) to connect to a new reference. You can also click on the control to toggle between justifications within the wall.

Figure 2–11

- The new location of a temporary dimension for an element is remembered as long as you are in the same session of the software.

Selecting Multiple Elements

- Once you have selected at least one element, to add another element to a selection set, hold down <Ctrl> and select another item.

- To remove an element from a selection set, hold <Shift> and select the element.

- If you click and drag the cursor to *window* around elements, you have two selection options, as shown in Figure 2–12. If you drag from left to right, you only select the elements completely inside the window. If you drag from right to left, you select elements both inside and crossing the window.

Window: Left to Right   **Crossing: Right to Left**

Figure 2–12

- If several elements are on or near each other, press <Tab> to cycle through them before you click. If there are elements that might be linked to each other, such as walls that are connected, pressing <Tab> selects the chain of elements.

- Press <Ctrl>+<Left Arrow> to reselect the previous selection set. You can also right-click in the drawing window with nothing selected and select **Select Previous**.

- To select all elements of a specific type, right-click on an element and select **Select All Instances>Visible in View** or **In Entire Project**, as shown in Figure 2–13.

Figure 2–13

Hint: Selection Options

You can control how the software selects specific elements in a project by toggling Selection Options on and off on the Status Bar, as shown in Figure 2–14. Alternatively, in any Ribbon tab expand the Select panel's title and select the option.

Figure 2–14

- **Select links:** When toggled on, you can selected linked drawings or Autodesk Revit models. When it is toggled off you cannot select them when using **Modify** or **Move**.

- **Select underlay elements:** When toggled on, you can select underlay elements. When toggled off, you cannot select them when using **Modify** or **Move**.

- **Select pinned elements:** When toggled on, you can selected pinned elements. When toggled off, you cannot select them when using **Modify** or **Move**.

- **Select elements by face:** When toggled on you can select elements (such as the floors or walls in an elevation) by selecting the interior face or selecting an edge. When toggled off, you can only select elements by selecting an edge.

- **Drag elements on selection:** When toggled on, you can hover over an element, select it, and drag it to a new location. When toggled off, the Crossing or Box select mode starts when you press and drag, even if you are on top of an element. Once elements have been selected they can still be dragged to a new location.

Filtering Selection Sets

When multiple element categories are selected, the *Multi-Select* contextual tab opens in the Ribbon. This gives you access to all of the Modify tools, and the **Filter** command. The **Filter** command enables you to specify the types of elements to select. For example, you might only want to select columns, as shown in Figure 2–15.

Figure 2–15

How To: Filter a Selection Set

1. Select everything in the required area.
2. in the *Modify | Multi-Select* tab>Selection panel, or in the Status Bar, click (Filter). The Filter dialog box opens, as shown in Figure 2–16.

The Filter dialog box displays all types of elements in the original selection.

Figure 2–16

3. Click **Check None** to clear all of the options or **Check All** to select all of the options. You can also select or clear individual categories as required.

4. Click **OK**. The selection set is now limited to the elements you specified.

• In the Status Bar, the number of elements selected displays beside the Filter icon, as shown in Figure 2–17. You can also see the number of selected elements in the Properties palette.

Figure 2–17

• Clicking the Filter icon in the Status Bar also opens the Filter dialog box.

Practice 2a

Estimated time for completion: 10 minutes

Draw and Edit Elements

Practice Objective

- Use draw tools and drawing aids.

In this practice you will use the **Wall** command along with Draw tools and drawing aids, such as temporary dimensions and snaps. You will use the **Modify** command and modify the walls using grips, temporary dimensions, the Type Selector, and Properties. You will add a door and modify it using temporary dimensions and controls. The completed drawing is shown in Figure 2–18.

Figure 2–18

Task 1 - Draw and modify walls.

1. In the Application Menu, click ⬜ (New)> 🗋 (Project).

2. In the New Project dialog box, select **Architectural Template** in the Template file drop-down list, and click **OK**.

3. In the Quick Access Toolbar, click 🖫 (Save). When prompted, name the project **Simple Building.rvt**.

4. In the *Architecture* tab>Build panel, click 🗋 (Wall).

5. In the *Modify | Place Wall* tab>Draw panel, click

    (Rectangle) and draw a rectangle approximately
    100' x 70'. You do not have to be precise because you can
    change the dimensions later.

6. Note that the dimensions are temporary. Select the vertical
    dimension text and type **70' 0"**, as shown in Figure 2–19.
    Press <Enter>.

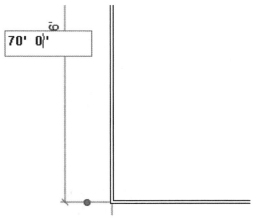

Figure 2–19

7. The dimensions are still displayed as temporary. Click the
    dimension controls of both the dimensions to make them
    permanent, as shown in Figure 2–20.

Figure 2–20

    • You will change the horizontal wall dimension using the
      permanent dimension.

8. In the Select panel, click ⌖ (Modify). You can also use one
    of the other methods to switch to **Modify:**

    • Type the shortcut **MD**
    • Press <Esc> once or twice
    • Right-click and select **Cancel**

9. Select either vertical wall. The horizontal dimension becomes active (changes to blue). Click the dimension text and type **100' 0"**, as shown in Figure 2–21.

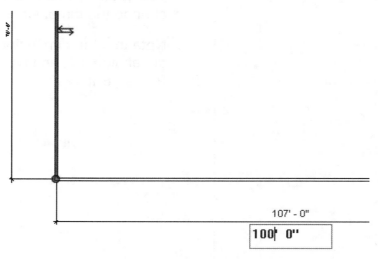

107' - 0"

100 0"

Figure 2–21

10. Click in an empty space to end the selection. You are still in the **Modify** command.

11. In the *Architecture* tab>Build panel, click (Wall). In the Draw panel, verify that (Line) is selected. Draw a wall horizontally from midpoint to midpoint of the vertical walls.

12. Draw another horizontal wall **8'-0"** above the middle horizontal wall. You can use temporary dimensions or the *Offset* field to do this.

13. Draw a vertical wall exactly **16'-0"** from the left wall, as shown in Figure 2–22.

16' - 0"

Figure 2–22

14. In the Draw panel, click (Circle) and draw a **14'-0"** radius circular wall at the midpoint of the lower interior horizontal wall, as shown in Figure 2–23.

Figure 2–23

15. Click (Modify) to finish the command.

16. Hover the cursor over one of the outside walls, press <Tab> to highlight the chain of outside walls, and click to select the walls.

17. In the Type Selector, select **Basic Wall: Generic-12"**, as shown in Figure 2–24. The thickness of the outside walls change.

Figure 2–24

18. Click in empty space to release the selection.

19. Select the vertical interior wall. In the Type Selector, change the wall to one of the small interior partition styles.

20. Click in an empty space to release the selection.

Task 2 - Add and modify a door.

1. Zoom in on the room in the upper left corner.

2. In the *Architecture* tab>Build panel, click (Door).

3. In the *Modify | Place Door* tab>Tag panel, click (Tag on Placement) if it is not already selected.

4. Place a door anywhere along the wall in the hallway.

5. Click (Modify) to finish the command.

6. Select the door. Use temporary dimensions to move it so that it is **2'-6"** from the right interior vertical wall. If required, use controls to flip the door so that it swings into the room, as shown in Figure 2–25.

Figure 2–25

7. Type **ZE** to zoom out to the full view.

8. Save the project.

2.3 Working with Basic Modify Tools

The Autodesk Revit software contains controls and temporary dimensions that enable you to edit elements. Additional modifying tools can be used with individual elements or any selection of elements. They are found in the *Modify* tab>Modify panel, as shown in Figure 2–26, and in contextual tabs.

Figure 2–26

- The **Move**, **Copy**, **Rotate**, **Mirror**, and **Array** commands are covered in this topic. Other tools are covered later.

- For most modify commands, you can either select the elements and start the command, or start the command, select the elements, and press <Enter> to finish the selection and move to the next step in the command.

Moving and Copying Elements

The **Move** and **Copy** commands enable you to select the element(s) and move or copy them from one place to another. You can use alignment lines, temporary dimensions, and snaps to help place the elements, as shown in Figure 2–27.

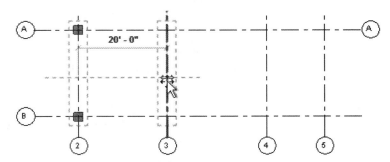

Figure 2–27

Hint: Nudge

Nudge enables you to move an element in short increments. When an element is selected, you can press one of the four arrow keys to move the element in that direction. The distance the element moves depends on how far in or out you are zoomed.

---

*You can also use the shortcut for **Move, MV** or for **Copy, CO**.*

How To: Move or Copy Elements

1. Select the elements you want to move or copy.
2. In the Modify panel, click ✥ (Move) or ⟳ (Copy). A boundary box displays around the selected elements.
3. Select a move start point on or near the element.
4. Select a second point. Use alignment lines and temporary dimensions to help place the elements.
5. When you are finished, you can start another modify command using the elements that remain selected, or switch back to **Modify** to end the command.

- If you start the **Move** command and hold down <Ctrl>, the elements are copied.

Move/Copy Elements Options

The **Move** and **Copy** commands have several options that display in the Options Bar, as shown in Figure 2–28.

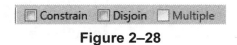

Figure 2–28

Constrain	Restricts the movement of the cursor to horizontal or vertical, or along the axis of an item that is at an angle. This keeps you from selecting a point at an angle by mistake. **Constrain** is off by default.
Disjoin (Move only)	Breaks any connections between the elements being moved and other elements. If **Disjoin** is on, the elements move separately. If it is off, the connected elements also move or stretch. **Disjoin** is off by default.
Multiple (Copy only)	Enables you to make multiple copies of one selection. **Multiple** is off by default.

- These commands only work within the current view, not between views or projects. To copy between views or projects, use ▣ (Copy to Clipboard) and ▣ (Paste).

Hint: Pinning Elements

If you do not want elements to be moved, you can pin them in place, as shown in Figure 2–29. Select the elements and in the

Modify tab, in the Modify panel, click (Pin). Pinned elements can be copied, but not moved. If you try to delete a pinned element, a warning dialog displays reminding you that you must unpin the element before the command can be started.

Figure 2–29

Select the element and click ⁻ᶰₓ (Unpin) or type the shortcut **UP** to free it.

Rotating Elements

The **Rotate** command enables you to rotate selected elements around a center point or origin, as shown in Figure 2–30. You can use alignment lines, temporary dimensions, and snaps to help specify the center of rotation and the angle. You can also create copies of the element as it is being rotated.

Figure 2–30

How To: Rotate Elements

1. Select the element(s) you want to rotate.

2. In the Modify panel, click ↻ (Rotate) or type the shortcut **RO**.

3. The center of rotation is automatically set to the center of the element or group of elements, as shown on the left in Figure 2–31. To change the center of rotation, as shown on the right in Figure 2–31, use the following:

- Drag the ⟳ (Center of Rotation) control to a new point.
- In the Options Bar, next to **Center of rotation**, click **Place** and use snaps to move it to a new location.
- Press <Spacebar> to select the center of rotation and click to move it to a new location.

*To start the **Rotate** command with a prompt to select the center of rotation, select the elements first and type **R3**.*

Figure 2–31

4. In the Options Bar, specify if you want to make a Copy (select **Copy** option), type an angle in the *Angle* field (as shown in Figure 2–32), and press <Enter>. You can also specify the angle on screen using temporary dimensions.

Figure 2–32

5. The rotated element(s) remain highlighted, enabling you to start another command using the same selection, or click

   ⌖ (Modify) to finish.

- The **Disjoin** option breaks any connections between the elements being rotated and other elements. If **Disjoin** is on (selected), the elements rotate separately. If it is off (cleared), the connected elements also move or stretch, as shown in Figure 2–33. **Disjoin** is toggled off by default.

Disjoin off   *Disjoin on*

Figure 2–33

Mirroring Elements

The **Mirror** command enables you to mirror elements about an axis defined by a selected element, as shown in Figure 2–34, or by selected points.

Figure 2–34

How To: Mirror Elements

1. Select the element(s) to mirror.
2. In the Modify panel, select the method you want to use:

   - Click ▨ (Mirror - Pick Axis) or type the shortcut **MM**. This prompts you to select an element as the **Axis of Reflection** (mirror line).

   - Click ▨ (Mirror - Draw Axis) or type the shortcut **DM**. This prompts you to select two points to define the axis about which the elements mirror.

3. The new mirrored element(s) remain highlighted, enabling you to start another command, or return to **Modify** to finish.

- By default, the original elements that were mirrored remain. To delete the original elements, clear the **Copy** option in the Options Bar.

> **Hint: Scale**
>
> The Autodesk Revit software is designed with full-size elements. Therefore, not much can be scaled. However, you can use ▢ (Scale) in reference planes, images, and imported files from other programs.

Creating Linear and Radial Arrays

The **Array** command creates multiple copies of selected elements in a linear or radial pattern, as shown in Figure 2–35. For example, you can array a row of columns to create a row of evenly spaced columns on a grid, or array a row of parking spaces. The arrayed elements can be grouped or placed as separate elements.

A linear array creates a straight line pattern of elements, while a radial array creates a circular pattern around a center point.

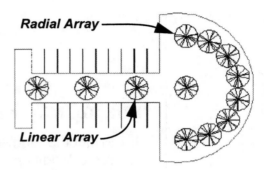

Figure 2–35

How To: Create a Linear Array

1. Select the element(s) to array.
2. In the Modify panel, click ⊞ (Array) or type the shortcut **AR**.
3. In the Options Bar, click ⬚ (Linear).
4. Specify the other options as required.
5. Select a start point and an end point to set the spacing and direction of the array. The array is displayed.
6. If the **Group and Associate** option is selected, you are prompted again for the number of items, as shown in Figure 2–36. Type a new number or click on the screen to finish the command.

Figure 2–36

- To make a linear array in two directions, you need to array one direction first, select the arrayed elements, and then array them again in the other direction.

Array Options

In the Options Bar, set up the **Array** options for **Linear Array** (top of Figure 2–37) or **Radial Array** (bottom of Figure 2–37).

Figure 2–37

Group and Associate	Creates an array group element out of all arrayed elements. Groups can be selected by selecting any elements in the group.
Number	Specifies how many instances you want in the array.
Move To:	**2nd** specifies the distance or angle between the center points of the two elements. **Last** specifies the overall distance or angle of the entire array.
Constrain	Restricts the direction of the array to only vertical or horizontal (Linear only).
Angle	Specifies the angle (Radial only).
Center of rotation	Specifies a location for the origin about which the elements rotate (Radial only).

How To: Create a Radial Array

1. Select the element(s) to array.

2. In the Modify panel, click ⊞ (Array).

3. In the Options Bar, click 🔄 (Radial).

4. Drag ↻ (Center of Rotation) or use Place to the move the center of rotation to the appropriate location, as shown in Figure 2–38.

*Remember to set the **Center of Rotation** control first, because it is easy to forget to move it before specifying the angle.*

Figure 2–38

5. Specify the other options as required.
6. In the Options Bar, type an angle and press <Enter>, or specify the rotation angle by selecting points on the screen.

Modifying Array Groups

When you select an element in an array that has been grouped, you can change the number of instances in the array, as shown in Figure 2–39. For radial arrays you can also modify the distance to the center.

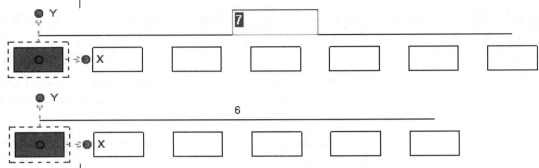

Figure 2–39

- Dashed lines surround the element(s) in a group, and the XY control lets you move the origin point of the group

If you move one of the elements within the array group, the other elements move in response based on the distance and/or angle, as shown in Figure 2–40.

Figure 2–40

- To remove the array constraint on the group, select all of the elements in the array group and, in the *Modify* contextual tab>Group panel, click ⧉ (Ungroup).

- If you select an individual element in an array and click ⧉ (Ungroup), the element you selected is removed from the array, while the rest of the elements remain in the array group.

- You can use ▽ (Filter) to ensure that you are selecting only **Model Groups**.

Practice 2b

Work with Basic Modify Tools

Estimated time for completion: 15 minutes

Practice Objective

• Use basic modify tools, including Move, Copy, Mirror, and Array

In this practice you will create a series of offices using the Copy and Mirror commands. You will then array desks around a circular wall, and add, rotate, and array a pair of columns across the front of a simple building, as shown in Figure 2–41.

Figure 2–41

Task 1 - Modify walls and doors.

1. Open the project **Simple-Building-1.rvt** from your practice folder.

2. Select the top arc of the circular wall.

*Remember that you can also press <Delete>, or right-click and select **Delete**.*

3. In the Modify panel, click ✖ (Delete). The walls that the circular wall crossed are automatically cleaned up.

4. Select the vertical interior wall, door, and door tag. Hold down <Ctrl> to select more than one element, or use a selection window.

5. In the Modify panel, click ⟳ (Copy).

6. In the Options Bar, select the **Constrain** and **Multiple** options. The **Constrain** option forces the cursor to move only horizontally or vertically.

7. Select the start point and the end point, as shown in Figure 2–42. The wall, door, and door tag are copied to the right and the door tag displays *2*.

Figure 2–42

8. The new elements are still selected and you can continue to copy them. Use similar start and end points for the additional copies, or type **16** (16'-0") and press <Enter> to set the distance between each copy. The final layout is shown in Figure 2–43.

Figure 2–43

9. Click (Modify) to finish the command.

10. Zoom in on the room to the far right.

11. Select door #5 and the associated door tag.

12. In the Modify panel, click (Mirror - Pick Axis). In the Options Bar, ensure that **Copy** is selected.

13. Select the vertical wall between the rooms as the mirror axis. An alignment line displays along the center of the wall. Place the new door, as shown in Figure 2–44.

Figure 2–44

14. Click in empty space to release the selection.

Task 2 - Add reference planes and use them to place a component.

1. In the *Architecture* tab>Work plane panel, click (Ref Plane).

2. Draw two reference planes, as shown in Figure 2–45. The vertical one starts at the midpoint of the wall. You can place the horizontal plane anywhere, and then use temporary dimensions to place it more exactly.)

Figure 2–45

3. In the *Architecture* tab>Build panel, click (Component).

4. In the Properties palette, in the Type Selector, verify that **Desk: 60" x 30"** is selected, as shown in Figure 2–46.

Figure 2–46

5. As you move the cursor you can see that the desk is horizontal. Press <Spacebar> to rotate the desk 90 degrees.

6. Place the desk at the intersection of the two reference planes, as shown in Figure 2–47. Zoom in as required to ensure that you are connected to the reference planes, and not to any other alignment lines.

Figure 2–47

7. Click ⬞ (Modify) and select the desk you just placed.

8. In the Modify panel, click ✥ (Move). Select the start point of the move as the vertical alignment line of the desk, and the end point as the vertical reference plane.

9. Save the project.

Task 3 - Create a Radial Array.

1. Select the desk.

2. In the Modify panel, click ⊞ (Array).

3. In the Options Bar, click (Radial). Clear the **Group and associate** option, set the *Number* field to 15, and set the *Move to:* field to **2nd.**

4. Drag the center of rotation from the center of the desk to the midpoint of the wall, as shown in Figure 2–48.

Drag or click to move center of rotation to new position.

Figure 2–48

5. Return to the Options Bar and set the *Angle* to **360**. Press <Enter>. The array displays as shown in Figure 2–49.

Sometimes it is easier to create more elements then you need, and then delete the ones that are not required, as is done in this example.

Figure 2–49

6. Delete all of the desks that are outside of the room that has the original desk.

7. Delete the reference planes. These are no longer needed, and deleting them ensures they do not display in other views.

8. Zoom out to display the entire view.

Task 4 - Add columns.

1. In the *Architecture* tab>Build panel, expand ▯ (Column), and click ▯ (Column: Architectural).

2. In the Type Selector, verify that **Rectangular Column:24" x 24"** is selected.

3. Using alignment lines and temporary dimensions, place the column on the front left of the building, as shown in Figure 2–50.

Figure 2–50

4. In the *Architecture* tab>Build panel, expand ▯ (Column), and click ▯ (Structural Column).

5. In the Type Selector, verify that **W-Wide Flange - Column: W10x49** is selected.

6. In the Options Bar, set the **Height** to **Level 2**, as shown in Figure 2–51.

Figure 2–51

7. Place the structural column at the center of the architectural column using the **Midpoint and Extension** snaps, as shown in Figure 2–52.

Figure 2–52

8. Save the project.

Task 5 - Rotate and Array the columns.

1. Click ▷ (Modify) and select the two columns.

2. In the *Modify | Multi-Select* tab>Modify panel, click
   ↻ (Rotate).

3. For the start ray, click horizontally, as shown on the left in Figure 2–53.

4. Move the ray line until you see the temporary dimension 45.000, as shown on the right in Figure 2–53.

Figure 2–53

5. With the two columns still selected, in the *Modify |*

   Multi-Select tab>Modify panel, click ▦ (Array).

6. In the Options Bar, click ▥ (Linear), clear **Group and Associate**, set the *Number* to **10**, and set *Move To:* to **Last**.

7. For the start point, click the midpoint of the columns. For the endpoint of the array, select the **Horizontal and Extension** of the center of the far right wall as shown in Figure 2–54.

Figure 2–54

8. Zoom out to display the entire building.

9. The columns are arrayed evenly across the front of the building as shown in Figure 2–55.

Figure 2–55

10. Save the project.

2.4 Working with Additional Modify Tools

As you work on a project, some additional tools on the *Modify* tab>Modify panel, as shown in Figure 2–56, can help you with placing, modifying, and constraining elements. **Align** can be used with a variety of elements, while **Split Element**, **Trim/Extend**, and **Offset** can only be used with linear elements.

Figure 2–56

Aligning Elements

The **Align** command enables you to line up one element with another, as shown in Figure 2–57. Most Autodesk Revit elements can be aligned. For example, you can line up the tops of windows with the top of a door, or line up furniture with a wall.

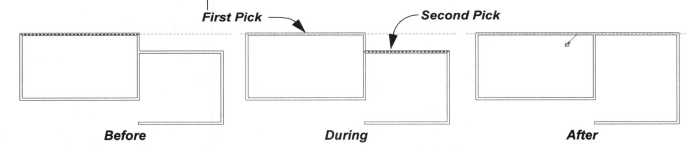

First Pick *Second Pick*

Before *During* *After*

Figure 2–57

How To: Align Elements

1. In the *Modify* tab>Modify panel, click 🔲 (Align).
2. Select a line or point on the element that is going to remain stationary. For walls, press <Tab> to select the correct wall face.
3. Select a line or point on the element to be aligned. The second element moves into alignment with the first one.

• The **Align** command works in all model views, including parallel and perspective 3D views.

Enhanced in **2016**

- You can lock alignments so that the elements move together if either one is moved. Once you have created the alignment, a padlock is displayed. Click on the padlock to lock it, as shown in Figure 2–58.

Figure 2–58

Locking elements enlarges the size of the project file, so use this option carefully.

- Select the **Multiple Alignment** option to select multiple elements to align with the first element. You can also hold <Ctrl> to make multiple alignments.

- For walls, you can specify if you want the command to prefer **Wall centerlines**, **Wall faces**, **Center of core**, or **Faces of core**, as shown in Figure 2–59. The core refers to the structural members of a wall as opposed to facing materials, such as sheet rock.

Figure 2–59

New in **2016**

Hint: Toggle between Parallel and Perspective Views

You can align, move and pin or unpin elements in perspective views. If you want to use other editing commands, right-click on the ViewCube and select **Toggle to Parallel-3D View**. Make the modifications, right-click on the ViewCube again, and select **Toggle to Perspective-3D View** to return to the perspective.

Splitting Linear Elements

You can split walls in plan, elevation or 3D views.

The **Split** Element command enables you to break a linear element at a specific point. You can use alignment lines, snaps, and temporary dimensions to help place the split point. After you have split the linear element, you can use other editing commands to modify the two parts, or change the type of one part, as shown with walls in Figure 2–60.

Figure 2–60

How To: Split Linear Elements

1. In the *Modify* tab>Modify panel, click ⊕ (Split Element) or type the shortcut **SL**.
2. In the Options Bar, select or clear the **Delete Inner Segment** option.
3. Move the cursor to the point you want to split and select the point.
4. Repeat for any additional split locations.
5. Modify the elements that were split, as required.

- The **Delete Inner Segment** option is used when you select two split points along a linear element. When the option is selected, the segment between the two split points is automatically removed.

- An additional option, ⊕ (Split with Gap), splits the linear element at the point you select (as shown in Figure 2–61), but also creates a *Joint Gap* specified in the Options Bar.

This command is typically used with structural precast slabs.

Figure 2–61

Trimming and Extending

There are three trim/extend methods that you can use with linear elements: **Trim/Extend to Corner**, **Trim/Extend Single Element**, and **Trim/Extend Multiple Elements**.

- When selecting elements to trim, click the part of the element that you want to keep. The opposite part of the line is then trimmed.

How To: Trim/Extend to Corner

1. In the *Modify* tab>Modify panel, click ![icon] (Trim/Extend to Corner) or type the shortcut **TR**.
2. Select the first linear element on the side you want to keep.
3. Select the second linear element on the side you want to keep, as shown in Figure 2–62.

Figure 2–62

How To: Trim/Extend a Single Element

1. In the *Modify* tab>Modify panel, click ![icon] (Trim/Extend Single Element).
2. Select the cutting or boundary edge.
3. Select the linear element to be trimmed or extended, as shown in Figure 2–63.

Figure 2–63

How To: Trim/Extend Multiple Elements

1. In the *Modify* tab>Modify panel, click 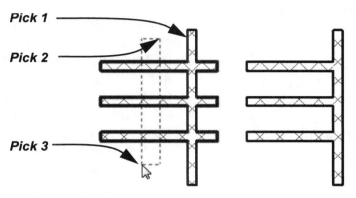 (Trim/Extend Multiple Elements).
2. Select the cutting or boundary edge.
3. Select the linear elements that you want to trim or extend by selecting one at a time, or by using a crossing window, as shown in Figure 2–64. For trimming, select the side you want to keep.

Pick 1

Pick 2

Pick 3

Figure 2–64

- You can click in an empty space to clear the selection and select another cutting edge or boundary.

Offsetting Elements

The **Offset** command is an easy way of creating parallel copies of linear elements at a specified distance, as shown in Figure 2–65. Walls, beams, braces, and lines are among the elements that can be offset.

Figure 2–65

- If you offset a wall that has a door or window embedded in it, the elements are copied with the offset wall.

The offset distance can be set by typing the distance (**Numerical** method shown in Figure 2–66) or by selecting points on the screen (**Graphical** method).

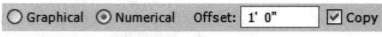

Figure 2–66

How To: Offset using the Numerical Method

1. In the *Modify* tab>Modify panel, click (Offset) or type the shortcut **OF**.
2. In the Options Bar, select the **Numerical** option.
3. In the Options Bar, type the desired distance in the *Offset* field.
4. Move the cursor over the element you want to offset. A dashed line previews the offset location. Move the cursor to flip the sides, as required.
5. Click to create the offset.
6. Repeat Steps 4 and 5 to offset other elements by the same distance, or to change the distance for another offset.

- With the **Numerical** option, you can select multiple connected linear elements for offsetting. Hover the cursor over an element and press <Tab> until the other related elements are highlighted. Select the element to offset all of the elements at the same time.

How To: Offset using the Graphical Method

1. Start the **Offset** command.
2. In the Options Bar, select the **Graphical** option.
3. Select the linear element to offset.
4. Select two points that define the distance of the offset and which side to apply it. You can type an override in the temporary dimension for the second point.

- Most linear elements connected at a corner automatically trim or extend to meet at the offset distance, as shown in Figure 2–67.

Figure 2–67

*The **Copy** option (which is on by default) makes a copy of the element being offset. If this option is not selected, the **Offset** command moves the element the set offset distance.*

Practice 2c

Work with Additional Modify Tools

Estimated time for completion: 10 minutes

Practice Objective

- Align, Split, Trim/Extend, and Offset elements.

In this practice you will split a wall into three parts and delete the middle portion. You will offset walls and then trim or extend them to form new rooms. You will then align the new walls to match existing walls.as shown in Figure 2–68.

Figure 2–68

Task 1 - Split and Remove Walls

1. Open the project **Simple-Building-2.rvt,** found in your practice folder.

2. In the *Modify* tab>Modify panel click ⊕ (Split Element).

3. In the Options Bar, select **Delete Inner Segment**.

4. Click on the horizontal wall where it intersects with the curved wall at both ends. The wall segment between these points is removed, as shown in Figure 2–69.

Figure 2–69

5. Click 👆 (Modify) to finish.

Task 2 - Offset and Trim Walls

1. In the *Modify* tab> Modify panel click 🔩 (Offset).

2. In the Options Bar set the *Offset* to **14'-0"** and ensure that **Copy** is selected.

3. Select the top horizontal wall while ensuring that the dashed alignment line displays inside the building, as shown in Figure 2–70.

Figure 2–70

4. With **Offset** still active, change the *Offset* to **10'-0"** and offset the last vertical interior wall to the right, as shown in Figure 2–71.

Figure 2–71

5. Click ⬧ (Modify) and select the new horizontal wall that was created from the exterior wall. Change the wall to **Basic Wall: Interior - 3 1/8" Partition (1-hr).** The layout of the new walls should display as shown in Figure 2–72.

The vertical wall does not need to be changed because it was offset from an interior wall.

Figure 2–72

6. In the *Modify* tab>Modify panel, click ⬧ (Trim/Extend Multiple Elements).

7. Select the new horizontal wall as the element to trim against.

8. Select every other wall BELOW the new wall. (Remember, you select the elements that you want to keep.) The walls should display as shown in Figure 2–73.

Figure 2–73

9. In the *Modify* tab>Modify panel click (Trim/Extend to corner) and select the two walls to trim as shown in Figure 2–74.

Figure 2–74

10. Add doors into the new rooms.

11. Save the project.

Task 3 - Align Walls.

1. In the *Architecture* tab>Work Plane panel click (Ref Plane).

2. Draw a reference plane vertically up from the midpoint of the curved wall, as shown in Figure 2–75.

Figure 2–75

3. In the *Modify* tab>Modify panel, click (Align).

4. Select the reference plane, and then the wall to the left. The wall should line up with the reference plane.

5. Save and close the project.

Chapter Review Questions

1. What is the purpose of an alignment line?

    a. Displays when the new element you are placing or drawing is aligned with the grid system.

    b. Indicates that the new element you are placing or drawing is aligned with an existing object.

    c. Displays when the new element you are placing or drawing is aligned with a selected tracking point.

    d. Indicates that the new element is aligned with true north rather than project north.

2. When you are drawing (not editing) a linear element, how do you edit the temporary dimension, as that shown in Figure 2–76?

Figure 2–76

    a. Select the temporary dimension and enter a new value.

    b. Type a new value and press <Enter>.

    c. Type a new value in the Distance/Length box in the Options Bar and press <Enter>.

3. How do you select all door types, but no other elements in a view?

    a. In the Project Browser, select the *Door* category.

    b. Select one door, right-click and select **Select All Instances>Visible in View**.

    c. Select all of the objects in the view and use ![filter icon] (Filter) to clear the other categories.

    d. Select one door, and click ![select multiple icon] (Select Multiple) in the Ribbon.

4. What are the two methods for starting (Move) or

    (Copy)?

   a. Start the command first and then select the objects, or select the objects and then start the command.

   b. Start the command from the *Modify* tab, or select the object and then select **Move** or **Copy** from the right-click menu.

   c. Start the command from the *Modify* tab, or select the objects and select **Auto-Move**.

   d. Use the **Move/Copy** command or **Cut/Copy** and **Paste** using the Clipboard.

5. Where do you change the wall type for a selected wall, as shown in Figure 2–77?

Figure 2–77

   a. In the *Modify | Walls* tab> Properties panel, click

      (Type Properties) and select a new wall type in the dialog box.

   b. In the Options Bar, click **Change Element Type**.

   c. Select the dynamic control next to the selected wall and select a new type in the drop-down list.

   d. In Properties, select a new type in the Type Selector drop-down list.

6. Both ⟳ (Rotate) and ▦ (Array) with 🔁 (Radial) have a center of rotation that defaults to the center of the element or group of elements you have selected. How do you move the center of rotation to another point as shown in Figure 2–78? (Select all that apply.)

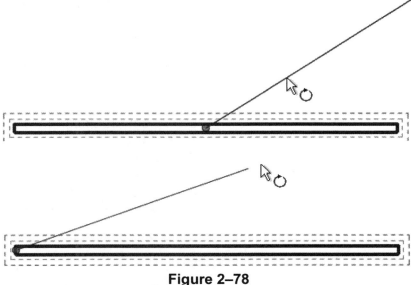

Figure 2–78

   a. Select the center of rotation and drag it to a new location.

   b. In the Options Bar, click **Place** and select the new point.

   c. In the *Modify* tab> Placement panel, click ⊚ (Center) and select the new point.

   d. Right-click and select **Snap Overrides>Centers** and select the new point.

7. Which command would you use to remove part of a wall?

   a. ⸬ (Split Element)

   b. 📐 (Wall Joins)

   c. 🗗 (Cut Geometry)

   d. 🔨 (Demolish)

8. Which of the following are ways in which you can create additional parallel walls, as shown in Figure 2–79? (Select all that apply.)

Figure 2–79

a. Select an existing wall, right-click and select **Create Offset**.

b. Use the **Offset** tool in the *Modify* tab.

c. Select an existing wall, hold down <Ctrl> and drag the wall to a new location.

d. Use the **Wall** tool and set an offset in the Options Bar.

9. Which command do you use if you want two walls that are not touching to come together, as shown in Figure 2–80?

Figure 2–80

a. ![icon] (Edit Wall Joins)

b. ![icon] (Trim/Extend to Corner)

c. ![icon] (Join Geometry)

d. ![icon] (Edit Profile)

Command Summary

Button	Command	Location
Draw Tools		
	Center-ends Arc	• **Ribbon:** *Modify | (various linear elements)* tab>Draw panel
	Circle	• **Ribbon:** *Modify | (various linear elements)* tab>Draw panel
	Circumscribed Polygon	• **Ribbon:** *Modify | (various linear elements)* tab>Draw panel
	Ellipse	• **Ribbon:** *Modify | Place Lines, Place Detail Lines, and various boundary sketches*>Draw panel
	Ellipse Arc	• **Ribbon:** *Modify | Place Lines, Place Detail Lines, and various boundary sketches*>Draw panel
	Fillet Arc	• **Ribbon:** *Modify | (various linear elements)* tab>Draw panel
	Inscribed Polygon	• **Ribbon:** *Modify | (various linear elements)* tab>Draw panel
	Line	• **Ribbon:** *Modify | (various linear elements)* tab>Draw panel
	Pick Faces	• **Ribbon:** *Modify | Place Wall*> Draw panel
	Pick Lines	• **Ribbon:** *Modify | (various linear elements)* tab>Draw panel
	Pick Walls	• **Ribbon:** *Modify | (various boundary sketches)*>Draw panel
	Rectangle	• **Ribbon:** *Modify | (various linear elements)* tab>Draw panel
	Spline	• **Ribbon:** *Modify | Place Lines, Place Detail Lines, and various boundary sketches*>Draw panel
	Start-End-Radius Arc	• **Ribbon:** *Modify | (various linear elements)* tab>Draw panel
	Tangent End Arc	• **Ribbon:** *Modify | (various linear elements)* tab>Draw panel
Modify Tools		
	Align	• **Ribbon:** *Modify* tab>Modify panel • **Shortcut:** AL
	Array	• **Ribbon:** *Modify* tab>Modify panel • **Shortcut:** AR
	Copy	• **Ribbon:** *Modify* tab>Modify panel • **Shortcut:** CO

⎕	**Copy to Clipboard**	• **Ribbon:** *Modify* tab>Clipboard panel • **Shortcut:** <Ctrl>+<C>
✕	**Delete**	• **Ribbon:** *Modify* tab>Modify panel • **Shortcut:** DE
⬚	**Mirror - Draw Axis**	• **Ribbon:** *Modify* tab>Modify panel • **Shortcut:** DM
⬚	**Mirror - Pick Axis**	• **Ribbon:** *Modify* tab>Modify panel • **Shortcut:** MM
✛	**Move**	• **Ribbon:** *Modify* tab>Modify panel • **Shortcut:** MV
⬚	**Offset**	• **Ribbon:** *Modify* tab>Modify panel • **Shortcut:** OF
⬚	**Paste**	• **Ribbon:** *Modify* tab>Clipboard panel • **Shortcut:** <Ctrl>+<V>
⬚	**Pin**	• **Ribbon:** *Modify* tab>Modify panel • **Shortcut:** PN
↻	**Rotate**	• **Ribbon:** *Modify* tab>Modify panel • **Shortcut:** RO
⬚	**Scale**	• **Ribbon:** *Modify* tab>Modify panel • **Shortcut:** RE
⬚	**Split Element**	• **Ribbon:** *Modify* tab>Modify panel • **Shortcut:** SL
⬚	**Split with Gap**	• **Ribbon:** *Modify* tab>Modify panel
⬚	**Trim/Extend Multiple Elements**	• **Ribbon:** *Modify* tab>Modify panel
⬚	**Trim/Extend Single Element**	• **Ribbon:** *Modify* tab>Modify panel
⬚	**Trim/Extend to Corner**	• **Ribbon:** *Modify* tab>Modify panel • **Shortcut:** TR
⬚	**Unpin**	• **Ribbon:** *Modify* tab>Modify panel • **Shortcut:** UP

Select Tools

⬚	**Drag elements on selection**	• **Ribbon:** All tabs>Expanded Select panel • **Status Bar**
▼	**Filter**	• **Ribbon:** *Modify	Multi-Select* tab>Filter panel • **Status Bar**
⬚	**Select Elements By Face**	• **Ribbon:** All tabs>Expanded Select panel • **Status Bar**

	Select Links	• **Ribbon:** All tabs>Expanded Select panel	
		• **Status Bar**	
	Select Pinned Elements	• **Ribbon:** All tabs>Expanded Select panel	
		• **Status Bar**	
	Select Underlay Elements	• **Ribbon:** All tabs>Expanded Select panel	
		• **Status Bar**	
	Selection Sets: Add to Selection	• **Ribbon:** *Edit Selection Set* tab>Edit Selection panel	
	Selection Sets: Edit	• **Ribbon:** *Modify	Multi-Select* tab> Selection panel or *Manage* tab> Selection panel	
	Selection Sets: Load	• **Ribbon:** *Modify	Multi-Select* tab> Selection panel or *Manage* tab> Selection panel	
	Selection Sets: Remove from Selection	• **Ribbon:** *Edit Selection Set* tab>Edit Selection panel	
	Selection Sets: Save	• **Ribbon:** *Modify	Multi-Select* tab> Selection panel or *Manage* tab> Selection panel	

Setting Up Levels and Grids

Datum elements provide the framework for a building and include levels, which define vertical heights, and grids, which define the structural layout for architectural and structural columns. Imported or linked CAD files can also be used as a basis for developing a project.

Learning Objectives in this Chapter

- Add and modify levels to define floor to floor heights and other vertical references.
- Add and modify structural grids that provide locations for architecture and structural columns.
- Add architectural (decorative) and structural (load-bearing) columns.
- Link and import .CAD files to be used as a basis for developing a design.

3.1 Setting Up Levels

Levels define stories and other vertical heights (such as a parapet or other reference heights), as shown in Figure 3–1. The default template includes two levels, but you can define as many levels in a project as required. They can go down (for basements) as well as up.

Figure 3–1

- You must be in an elevation or section view to define levels.

- Once you constrain an element to a level it moves with the level when the level is changed.

How To: Create Levels

1. Open an elevation or section view.

2. In the *Architecture* tab>Datum panel, click (Level), or type **LL**.

3. In the Type Selector, set the Level Head type if needed.

4. In the Options Bar, select or clear **Make Plan View** as required. You can also click **Plan View Types...** to select the types of views to create when you place the level.

5. In the *Modify | Place Level* tab>Draw panel, click either

   (Pick Lines) to select an element or (Line) to draw a level.

6. Continue adding levels as required.

- Level names are automatically incremented as you place them. This automatic numbering is most effective when you use names such as Floor 1, Floor 2, etc. (as opposed to First Floor, Second Floor, etc.). In addition, this makes it easier to find the view in the Project Browser.

- A fast way to create multiple levels is to use the (Pick Lines) option. In the Options Bar specify an *Offset,* select an existing level, and then pick above or below to place the new level, as shown in Figure 3–2.

Figure 3–2

You can draw the level lines from left to right or right to left depending on where you want the bubble. However, ensure they are all drawn in the same direction.

- When using the ✏ (Line) option, alignments and temporary dimensions help you place the line correctly, as shown in Figure 3–3.

Figure 3–3

- You can also use (Copy) to duplicate level lines. The level names are incremented but a plan view is not created.

Modifying Levels

You can change levels using standard controls and temporary dimensions, as shown in Figure 3–4. You can also make changes in the Properties palette.

Figure 3–4

- ☑ ☐ (Hide / Show Bubble) displays on either end of the level line and toggles the level head symbol and level information on or off.

- 2D 3D (Switch to 3d / 2d extents) controls whether any movement or adjustment to the level line is reflected in other views (3D) or only affects the current view (2D).

- ⊕ (Modify the level by dragging its model end) at each end of the line enables you to drag the level head to a new location.

- 🔒 🔓 (Create or remove a length or alignment constraint) controls whether the level is locked in alignment with the other levels. If it is locked and the level line is stretched, all of the other level lines stretch as well. If it is unlocked, the level line stretches independent of the other levels.

- Click 〰 (Add Elbow) to add a jog to the level line as shown in Figure 3–5. Drag the shape handles to new locations as required. This is a view-specific change.

Figure 3–5

- To change the level name or elevation, double-click on the information next to the level head, or select the level and modify the *Name* or *Elevation* fields in Properties, as shown in Figure 3–6.

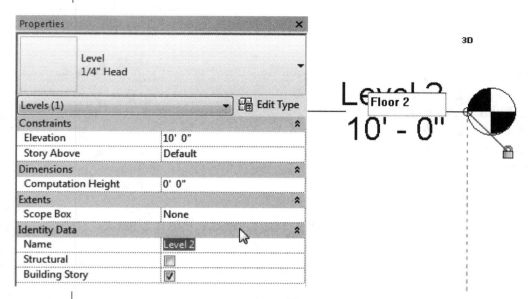

Figure 3–6

- When you rename a Level, an alert box opens, prompting you to rename the corresponding views as shown in Figure 3–7.

Figure 3–7

- The view is also renamed in the Project Browser.

Hint: Copying Levels and Grids from other projects

Levels and grid lines can be added by drawing over existing levels or grids in an imported or linked CAD file. It can also be copied and monitored from a linked Autodesk® Revit® file. Some projects might require both methods.

Creating Plan Views

Typically, you do not need to create plan views for levels that specify data, such as the top of a storefront window or the top of a parapet.

By default, when you place a level, plan views for that level are automatically created. If **Make Plan View** was toggled off when adding the level, or if the level was copied, you can create plan views to match the levels.

- Level heads with views are blue and level heads without views are black, as shown in Figure 3–8.

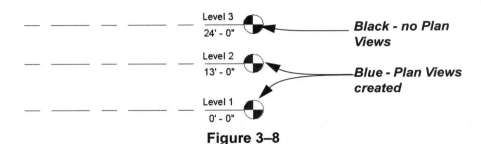

Figure 3–8

How To: Create Plan Views

1. In the *View* tab>Create panel, expand (Plan Views) and select the type of plan view you want to create, as shown on the left in Figure 3–9.
2. In the New Plan dialog box (shown on the right in Figure 3–9), select the levels for which you want to create plan views.

Hold down <Ctrl> to select more than one level.

Figure 3–9

3. Click **OK**.

Practice 3a

Set Up Levels

Practice Objective

- Add and modify levels.

Estimated time for completion: 10 minutes

In this practice you will set up the levels needed in the Modern Hotel project, including the floors, the top of the footing, and the parapet, as shown in Figure 3–10.

Figure 3–10

Task 1 - Add and Modify Levels.

1. Open the project **Modern-Hotel-Start.rvt** from your practice folder.

2. Open the **Elevations (Building Elevation): North** view.

3. The project has two existing levels named **Level 1** and **Level 2**. These were defined in the template.

4. Zoom in on the level names.

5. Double-click on the name Level 1 and rename it as **Floor 1** as shown in Figure 3–11. Press <Enter>.

Figure 3–11

6. Click **Yes** (press <Enter> or type **Y**) when prompted to rename the corresponding views.

7. Repeat the process and rename *Level 2* as **Floor 2**. Double-click on the height of Floor 2 (10'-0") and change it to **18'- 0"**.

8. In the *Architecture* tab>Datum panel, click ⬦ (Level).

9. In the *Modify | Place Level* tab>Draw panel, click

   ⚲ (Pick Lines). In the Options Bar, set the *Offset* to **12' - 0"**.

10. Hover the cursor over the level line of **Floor 2** and move the cursor slightly upward so that the offset level line is displayed above the **Floor 2** level. Click to create the new level **Floor 3**.

11. Create additional levels until there are a total of eight levels above Floor 1 (up to Floor 9).

12. Rename *Floor 9* as **Roof**. (Rename the corresponding views.)

13. In the Options Bar, clear the **Make Plan View** option and set the *Offset* to **5' 0"**. Create one additional level above the highest level, **Roof**. This level does not need a plan view.

14. Rename the top level as **Parapet**, as shown in Figure 3–12.

Figure 3–12

15. Add two levels below **Floor 1**. Name them **Basement** and **T.O. Footing** and set the heights as shown in Figure 3–13. You can modify the levels for clarity using controls such as **Add Elbow**.

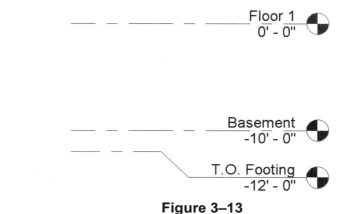

Figure 3–13

16. Zoom out to display the entire project.

17. Save the project.

3.2 Creating Structural Grids

The structural grid indicates how to space the bays of a building and where to place columns, as shown in Figure 3–14. Any changes to the grid influences the elements that are referenced to them.

Figure 3–14

Each line or arc in a grid is a separate entity and can be placed, moved, and modified individually.

How To: Create a Structural Grid

1. In the *Architecture* tab>Datum panel, click ⊞ (Grid) or type **GR**.
2. In the Type Selector, select the Grid type which controls the size of the bubble and the linestyle.
3. In the *Modify | Place Grid* tab>Draw panel (shown in Figure 3–15) select the method you want to use.

Figure 3–15

4. In the Options Bar, set the *Offset* if required.
5. Continue adding grid lines as required.

• Grids can be drawn at any angle, but you should ensure that all parallel grids are drawn in the same direction (i.e., from left to right, or from bottom to top).

- When using the Multi-Segment tool (shown in Figure 3–16), sketch the line and click ✓ (Finish Edit Mode) to complete the command.

Figure 3–16

Modifying Grid Lines

Grid lines are very similar to Level lines. You can modify grid lines using controls, alignments, and temporary dimensions (as shown in Figure 3–17), as well as in the Properties palette and Type Selector.

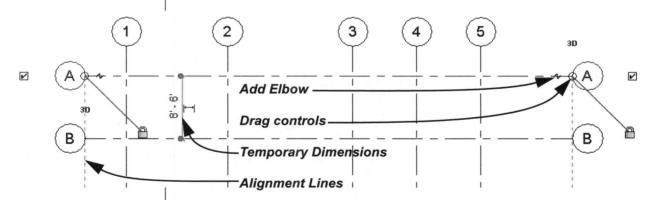

Figure 3–17

- To modify a grid number, double-click on the number in the bubble and type the new number. Grid numbers can be numbers, letters, or a combination of the two.

3.3 Adding Columns

The Autodesk Revit software includes two types of columns: architectural and structural, as shown in Figure 3–18. Architectural columns are placeholders or decorative elements, while structural columns include more precise information relative to strength and load-bearing parameters.

Architectural Column   *Structural Columns*

Figure 3–18

How To: Add Columns

Structural Column is the default.

1. In the *Architecture* tab>Build panel, expand 🯅 (Column) and click either 🯅 (Column: Architectural) or 🯅 (Structural Column).
2. In the Type Selector, select the column you want to use, as shown in Figure 3–19.

Figure 3–19

3. In the Options Bar, set the *Height* (or *Depth*) for the column. You can select a level (as shown in Figure 3–20), or select **Unconnected** to specify a height.

Architectural columns are typically placed from the level that you are on up to a specific height. Structural columns are typically placed from the level you are on down to a specific depth.

Figure 3–20

4. Place the column as required. It snaps to grid lines and walls. You can also place a column as a free instance unconnected to any grid lines.

   • If you select the **Rotate after placement** option, you are prompted for a rotation angle after you select the insertion point for the column.

5. Continue placing columns as required.

• If you are working with structural columns, you have two additional options in the *Modify | Place Structural Column* tab>Multiple panel:

   • To place columns at the intersection of grid lines, click

      (At Grids) and select the grid lines. Columns will only be placed at the intersections of the selected grid lines.

   • To place structural columns wherever you have an

      architectural column, click   (At Columns) and select the columns. The structural columns are placed at the center of the architectural columns, as shown in Figure 3–21.

Figure 3–21

- An architectural column placed in a wall is automatically cleaned up if the material of the column and wall match. Structural columns remain separate even if they are the same material as the surrounding walls. as shown in Figure 3–22.

Figure 3–22

- To access additional architectural column styles, in the *Modify | Place Column* tab>Mode panel, click (Load Family). In the Load Family dialog box, navigate to the *Columns* folder in the software's Library, as shown in Figure 3–23.

Figure 3–23

- Structural columns are divided into folders by material type in the *Structural Columns* folder. They include *Concrete, Light Gauge Steel, Precast Concrete, Steel,* and *Wood*.

Modifying Columns

Structural columns have additional parameters.

- By default, columns move with nearby grids. This connects the column to the grid without absolutely locking it. However, you can still move it independently. When you select a column to modify, you can turn this option off by clearing the **Move With Grids** option in the Options Bar or in the Properties of selected columns.

- In Properties, you can change the *Base Level* and *Top Level*, as well as the offsets from these levels and several other options, as shown in Figure 3–24.

Figure 3–24

- Deleting a grid line or wall does not delete the columns placed on them.

- In the *Modify | Column* tab>Modify Column panel (shown in Figure 3–25), you can attach or detach a column's top and base to floors, ceilings, roofs, reference planes, and structural framing.

Figure 3–25

3.4 Linking and Importing CAD Files

While not specifically a datum element, linked or imported files can help you to establish information. For example, the designer might lay out a floor plan using the standard 2D AutoCAD® software, and you need to incorporate that information into your building model. In addition, many renovation projects start with existing 2D drawings. Instead of redrawing from scratch, link or import the CAD file (as shown in Figure 3–26) and trace over it in the Autodesk Revit software.

Service-A.dwg : Import Symbol : location <Not Shared>

Figure 3–26

- CAD files that can be linked or imported include AutoCAD .DWG and .DXF, Microstation .DGN, ACIS .SAT, and Sketchup .SKP files.

Linking vs. Importing

- **Linked files:** Become part of the project, but are still connected to the original file. Use them if you expect the original drawing to change. The link is automatically updated when you open the project.

- **Imported files:** Become part of the project and are not connected to the original file. Use them if you know that the original drawing is not going to change.

How To: Link or Import a CAD File

1. Open the view into which you want to link or import the file.
   - For a 2D file, this should be a 2D view. For a 3D file, open a 3D view.

2. In the *Insert* tab>Link panel, click (Link CAD), or in the *Insert* tab>Import panel, click (Import CAD).

3. In the Link CAD Formats or Import CAD Formats dialog box (shown in Figure 3–27), select the file that you want to import.

The dialog boxes for Link CAD Formats and Import CAD Formats are the same.

Figure 3–27

- Select a file type in the **Files of Type** drop-down list to limit the files that are displayed.

4. Set the other options as shown in Figure 3–28.

Figure 3–28

5. Click **Open**.

Link and Import Options

Current view only	Determine whether the CAD file is placed in every view, or only in the current view. This is especially useful if you are working with a 2D floor plan that you only need to have in one view.
Colors	Specify the color settings. Typical Autodesk Revit projects are mainly black and white. However, other software frequently uses color. You can **Invert** the original colors, **Preserve** them, or change everything to **Black and White**.
Layers	Indicates which CAD layers are going to be brought into the model. Select how you want layers to be imported: **All**, **Visible**, or **Specify...**.
Import units	Select the units of the original file, as required. **Auto-Detect** works in most cases.
Correct Lines...	If lines in a CAD file are off axis by less than 0.1 degree selecting this option straightens them. It is selected by default.
Positioning	Specify how you want the imported file to be positioned in the current project: **Auto-Center to Center**, **Auto-Origin to Origin**, **Manual-Origin**, **Manual-Base Point**, or **Manual-Center**. The default position is **Auto-Origin to Origin**. If linking the file, **Auto-By Shared Coordinates** is also available.
Place at	Select a level in which to place the imported file. If you selected **Current view only**, this option is grayed out.

Enhanced in **2016**

- When a file is positioned **Auto-Origin to Origin**, it is pinned in place and cannot be moved. To move the file, click on the pin to unpin it, as shown in Figure 3–29.

Prevent or allow change of element position

Figure 3–29

Setting an Imported or Linked File to Halftone

To see the difference between new elements and the linked or imported file, you can set the file to Halftone, as shown in Figure 3–30.

Linked/Imported file

Revit elements

Figure 3–30

How To: Set an Element Halftone

1. Select the imported file.
2. Right-click and select **Override Graphics in View>By Element...**.
3. In the View Specific Element Graphics dialog box, select **Halftone**, as shown in Figure 3–31.

Figure 3–31

4. Click **OK**.

Practice 3b

Add Structural Grids and Columns

Practice Objectives

- Link a CAD file.
- Add and modify structural grid lines.
- Add structural columns.

Estimated time for completion: 15 minutes

In this practice you will import floor plans from the AutoCAD software and use them as a base layout for the first floor lobby and for a typical guest floor. You will then add grid lines using information in the imported file and add structural columns to the grid, as shown in Figure 3–32.

Figure 3–32

Task 1 - Import a CAD file.

1. Open the project **Modern-Hotel-Grids.rvt** from your practice folder.

2. Open the **Floor Plans: Floor 1** view.

3. In the *Insert* tab>Link panel, click ⬚ (Link CAD).

4. In the Link CAD Formats dialog box, select the file **Hotel-Lobby-Floor-Plan.dwg**.

5. Set the following options:

   - Current view only: Select this option
   - Colors: **Black and White**
   - Layers: **All**
   - Import Units: **Auto-Detect**
   - Positioning: **Auto-Origin to Origin**

6. Click **Open**. The linked file is placed in the project on the **Floor Plans: Floor 1** view.

7. Select the linked file. It is all in one element and pinned in place because it was imported origin to origin.

8. Right-click and select **Override Graphics in View>By Element...**.

9. In the View-Specific Element Graphics dialog box, select **Halftone**.

10. Click **OK**.

11. Click in empty space to release the selection. The linked file displays in halftone with columns and grids, as shown in Figure 3–33.

Figure 3–33

12. Open the **Floor Plans: Floor 2** view.

13. Link the CAD file **Hotel-Typical-Guest-Floor-Plan.dwg** using the options that were used for **Floor 1**.

14. Override the graphics and set the imported file to halftone.

15. Save the project.

Task 2 - Create structural grids.

1. Open the **Floor Plans: Floor 1** view.

2. In the *Architecture* tab>Datum panel, click ▦ (Grid).

3. In the *Modify | Place Grid* tab>Draw panel, click ✐ (Pick Lines).

4. Select the first vertical grid line on the left of the linked file. Click inside the bubble, type **A**, and press <Enter>.

5. Continue selecting the vertical grid lines displayed in the imported file. The letters automatically increment.

6. Click the first horizontal grid line and change the letter in the bubble to **1**.

7. Continue selecting the horizontal grid lines. The numbers automatically increment.

8. Click ▯ (Modify).

9. Check the lengths of all grid lines. Modify the length by dragging the ends if required. The final drawing is shown in Figure 3–34.

Figure 3–34

10. Save the project.

Task 3 - Add columns.

1. In the *Architecture* tab>Build panel, click (Structural Column).

2. In the Type Selector, select **Precast-Square Column: 12" x 12"**.

Verify that Height (not Depth) is selected in the Options Bar.

3. In the Options Bar, set the *Height* to **Floor 2**.

4. In the *Modify | Place Structural Column* tab>Multiple panel, click (At Grids).

You can use a crossing window drawn from right to left to select the grids. All other elements are automatically filtered out.

5. Select all of the horizontal and vertical grid lines in the project.

6. In the *Modify | Place Structural Column>At Grid Intersection* tab>Multiple panel, click (Finish).

7. Return to the **Modify** command.

8. Delete the columns at locations **A1**, **A2**, **A4**, **B1**, and **B4**. The project displays as shown in Figure 3–35.

Delete the columns at these intersections.

Figure 3–35

The linked file does not display in the 3D view because it was only linked to the plan view.

9. In the Quick Access Toolbar, click (Default 3D View). The columns are only set to the height of the 2nd floor (Floor 2), as shown in Figure 3–36.

Figure 3–36

10. Select all of the columns. You can select one column, then right-click and select **Select All Instances>Visible in View**.

11. In Properties, in the *Constraints* area, change the *Base Level* to **T.O. Footing** and the *Top Level* to **Roof**. The columns now extend from the top of the footing to the roof.

12. Click in space to release the selection.

*Type **ZA** to zoom out in the view if needed.*

13. View several different floor plan views to verify the columns display.

14. Return to the **Floor Plans: Floor 1** view.

15. Save the project.

Chapter Review Questions

1. What type of view do you need to be in to add a level to your project?

    a. Any non-plan view.

    b. As this is done using a dialog box, the view does not matter.

    c. Any view except for 3D.

    d. Any section or elevation view.

2. How do you line up grid lines that might be different lengths, as shown in Figure 3–37?

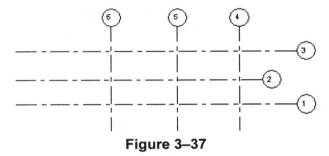

Figure 3–37

    a. Use ⇛ (Trim/Extend Multiple Elements) to line them up with a common reference line.

    b. Select the grid line and drag its model end to line up with the other grid lines.

    c. Select the grid line, right-click and select **Auto-Align**.

    d. In Properties, change the *Length* and then use ✛ (Move) to get them into position.

3. Where can columns (whose command access is shown in Figure 3–38) be placed?

Figure 3–38

a. Columns can only be placed on grids.

b. Architectural columns can be placed anywhere, but structural columns can only be placed on grids.

c. Both types of columns can be placed wherever you want.

d. Grid-based column types must be placed on the grid, but free-standing column types can be placed anywhere.

4. Which of the following types of CAD formats can you import into the Autodesk Revit software? (Select all that apply.)

a. .DWG

b. .XLS

c. .SAT

d. .DGN

Command Summary

Button	Command	Location
	At Columns	• **Ribbon:** *Modify	Place Structural Column* tab>Multiple panel
	At Grids	• **Ribbon:** *Modify	Place Structural Column* tab>Multiple panel
	Column	• **Ribbon:** *Architecture* tab>Build panel
	Column> Column: Architectural	• **Ribbon:** *Architecture* tab>Build panel>expand Column
	Column> Structural Column	• **Ribbon:** *Architecture* tab>Build panel>expand Column
	Grid	• **Ribbon:** *Architecture* tab>Datum panel • Shortcut: GR
	Import CAD	• **Ribbon:** *Insert* tab>Import panel
	Level	• **Ribbon:** *Architecture* tab>Datum panel • Shortcut: LL
	Link CAD	• **Ribbon:** *Insert* tab>Link panel
	Multi-Segment (Grid)	• **Ribbon:** *Modify	Place Grid* tab>Draw panel

Design Development Phase

The second section of this training guide focuses on teaching you how to use the tools available in the Autodesk® Revit® software to create the building model. It also describes the viewing tools needed to produce the model.

This section includes the following chapters:

- Chapter 4: Modeling Walls

- Chapter 5: Working with Doors and Windows

- Chapter 6: Working with Curtain Walls

- Chapter 7: Working with Views

- Chapter 8: Adding Components

- Chapter 9: Modeling Floors

- Chapter 10: Modeling Ceilings

- Chapter 11: Modeling Roofs

- Chapter 12: Modeling Stairs, Railings, and Ramps

Modeling Walls

Walls are the primary elements that define spaces in buildings. The Autodesk® Revit® software contains a variety of wall types that are available in different widths and materials. You can change the height, length, and type as required.

Learning Objectives in this Chapter

- Model walls using specific wall types to show the design intent.
- Modify walls by changing the wall type, height, and length.
- Define how walls join at intersections.
- Add wall openings that are not cased or filled with a door or window.

4.1 Modeling Walls

Walls in the Autodesk® Revit® software are more than just two lines on a plan. They are full 3D elements that store detailed information, including height, thickness, and materials. This means they are useful in 2D and 3D views, and also impact material takeoff schedules, as shown in Figure 4–1.

<Stucco - Material Takeoff>			
A	B	C	D
Material: Description	Material: Area	Material: Cost	Total Cost
EIFS	3786 SF	0.00	0
EIFS: 21	3786 SF		0

Walls : Basic Wall : Exterior - Stucco

Figure 4–1

- Basic curtain walls are added using the **Wall** command.

- To display the hatching in the walls in plan views, in the View Control Bar, set the *Detail Level* to **Medium** or **Fine**, as shown in Figure 4–2.

Figure 4–2

How To: Model a Wall

1. In the *Architecture* tab>Build panel, click ⬜ (Wall) or type the shortcut **WA**.
2. In the Type Selector, select a wall type as shown in Figure 4–3.

Figure 4–3

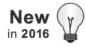

You can use the Search box to quickly find specific types of walls.

3. In the Options Bar (shown in Figure 4–4), specify the following information about the wall before you start drawing:

Figure 4–4

- **Height:** Set the height of a wall to either Unconnected (with a specified height) or to a level.
- **Location Line:** Set the justification of the wall using the options shown in Figure 4–4.
- **Chain:** Enables you to draw multiple connected walls.
- **Offset:** Enables you to enter the distance at which a new wall is created from an existing element.
- **Radius:** Adds a curve of a specified radius to connected walls as you draw.

4. In the *Modify | Place Wall* tab>Draw panel (shown in Figure 4–5), select one of the options to create the wall.

Figure 4–5

Compound walls are a wall type that contain multiple layers (e.g., blocks, air space, bricks, etc.).

- Use alignment lines, temporary dimensions, and snaps to place the walls.
- As you are sketching you can press <Spacebar> to flip the orientation of compound walls.
- When using the *Chain* option, press <Esc> to finish the string of walls and remain in the Wall command.

Hint: Underlays

Sometimes it helps to display a different level as an underlay in the current view, as shown in Figure 4–6. You can trace or copy elements in an underlay into the current level of a view.

Figure 4–6

- In the Properties, in the *Graphics* area, set *Underlay* to the desired level. Underlays are only available in plan views.

- To prevent moving elements in the underlay by mistake, in the Status Bar, toggle off ⬛ (Select Underlay Elements).

4.2 Modifying Walls

There are several methods of modifying walls. You can change the type of wall using the Type Selector, use controls and shape handles to modify the length and wall orientation, and use temporary and permanent dimensions to change the location or length of a wall in 2D and 3D, as shown in Figure 4–7. Additional tools enable you to modify wall joins and add wall openings.

Type Selector

Temporary dimensions

Figure 4–7

Hint: Using Dimensions to Model

When modeling, adding permanent dimensions to elements as you are working help to provide you with additional temporary dimensions. The most basic dimension method is (Aligned Dimension), which is found on the Quick Access Toolbar.

To add the dimensions, select the elements in order and then pick a final point not on an element at the location where you want to place dimension string, as shown in Figure 4–8.

7' - 0"   3' - 6"   2' - 4"   3' - 7"   5' - 5"

First Point   Last Point

Figure 4–8

- For more information on dimensioning see the chapter on annotating construction documents.

Wall Joins

The software automatically joins walls with common materials when they come together at an intersection, as shown on the left in Figure 4–9. However, there are times when you do not want the walls to clean up, such as when one fire-rated wall butts into another, or when a wall touches a column surround, as shown on the right in Figure 4–9.

Wall joined   *Wall not joined*

Figure 4–9

- To change how a wall joins to another wall, right-click on the control at the end of the wall and select **Disallow Join**, as shown on the left in Figure 4–10. Once the end is not joined, you can drag it to the appropriate location, as shown on the right in Figure 4–10.

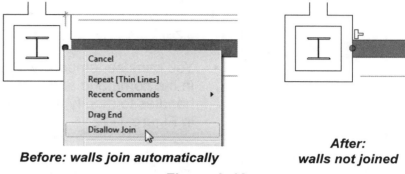

Before: walls join automatically   *After:*
                                             walls not joined

Figure 4–10

- To rejoin the walls, click ⌐ (Allow Join) or right-click on the end control and select **Allow Join**. Manually drag the wall back to where you want it to touch the target wall.

Wall Openings

You can add openings in walls that are not windows or doors by using the **Wall Opening** tool. This creates rectangular openings for both straight and curved walls, as shown in Figure 4–11.

Figure 4–11

How To: Add Wall Openings

1. Open an elevation, section, or 3D view.

2. In the *Architecture* tab>Openings panel click ⊞ (Wall Opening).
3. Select the wall.
4. Pick two points on the diagonal to determine the opening size.

- You can use temporary dimensions to size the opening while in the command and both temporary dimensions and shape handles to modify the opening when it is selected, as shown in Figure 4–12.

Figure 4–12

Hint: Matching Properties

You can select an existing wall and use it to assign the wall type and instance properties to other walls by using the **Match Type** command. This command also works with all elements that have types.

1. In the *Modify* tab>Clipboard panel, click 🖌 (Match Type) or type **MA**. The cursor changes to an arrow with a clean paintbrush.
2. Select the source element that you want all of the others to match. The paintbrush changes to look as if it has been dipped in black paint as shown in Figure 4–13.

Figure 4–13

3. To select more than one element, in the *Modify | Match Type* tab>Multiple panel, click 🔲 (Select Multiple). You can then use windows, crossings, <Ctrl>, and <Shift> to create a selection set of elements to change.
4. Select the elements that you want to change. For multiple selections, press <Enter> or click ✔ (Finish) to apply the type to the selection.

• Click in an empty space in the project to empty the brush so that you can repeat the command with a different element.

• Elements to be matched must be of the same type (e.g., all walls, all doors, etc.).

Practice 4a

Model the Exterior Shell

Estimated time for completion: 20 minutes

Practice Objectives

- Trace over walls in an imported DWG file.
- Add curtain walls.
- Modify wall joins.

In this practice you will add exterior walls, including a curtain wall, to create the exterior shell of the project. You will use an imported file to help establish the location of the walls. You will then add a parapet wall over the curtain wall. The completed model is shown in Figure 4–14.

Figure 4–14

Task 1 - Add walls by picking lines.

1. Open the project **Modern-Hotel-Walls.rvt** from your practice folder.

2. Verify that you are in the **Floor Plans: Floor 1** view.

3. In the View Control Bar, set the *Detail Level* to ▩ (Medium). Doing so enables the multiple layers of the wall that is going to be added to be displayed.

4. In the *Architecture* tab>Build panel, click ⬳ (Wall).

5. In the Type Selector, select **Basic Wall: Exterior - Brick and CMU on MTL. Stud**.

6. In the Options Bar, set the *Height* to **Parapet** and the *Location Line* to **Finish Face: Exterior**. Verify that the **Chain** option is selected. In Properties, verify that both *Base Offset* and *Top Offset* are set to **0' 0"**.

7. In the Draw panel, click (Pick Lines).

8. Select one of the exterior walls in the imported file, as shown in Figure 4–15. Ensure the dashed line displays inside the wall. This wall is a compound wall and you want the brick to display on the outside.

Do not place a wall on this small segment.

Figure 4–15

9. Continue selecting lines around the exterior of the building. Do not select the curved curtain wall lines.

   • Use (Flip) to change the wall's orientation if the stucco side of the wall is not on the outside.

10. Click (Modify).

11. At the door openings on either end of the building, do not add walls on either side of the door. Instead, use the **Drag Wall End** control, as shown in Figure 4–16, to lengthen the wall across the opening. The intersections should clean up automatically.

Figure 4–16

12. Save the project.

Task 2 - Add basic curtain walls.

---

1. Click ⬭ (Wall).

2. In the Type Selector, select **Curtain Wall: Exterior Glazing** and set the following properties:

   - Base Constraint: **Level 1**
   - Base Offset: (negative) **0**
   - Top Constraint: **Up to level: Roof**
   - Top Offset: **-6'-0"**

This places the top of the curtain wall below the roof level.

3. Use ⟋ (Pick Lines) and select the three curved lines.

4. In the Quick Access Toolbar, click 🏠 (3D View).

The columns are hidden to make this graphic more readable.

5. In the View Control Bar, set the *Visual Style* to
   (Consistent Colors). The curtain wall does not extend to the top of the parapet, as shown in Figure 4–17.

Figure 4–17

Task 3 - Add a parapet.

1. Open the **Floor Plans: Roof** view.

2. In the View Control Bar, set the *Detail Level* to (Medium) to display the layers of the walls.

3. Select the small curved piece of wall at the northeast corner of the building on Column Line J. Right-click on the right end point grip and select **Disallow Join,** as shown in Figure 4–18.

Some walls, when they try to automatically clean up, cause problems. Disallowing a join can resolve the issue.

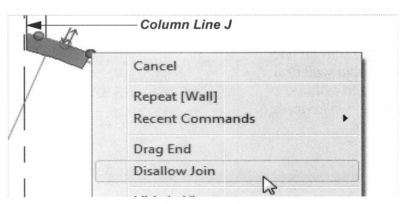

Figure 4–18

4. Repeat the process again on the other wall that connects to the curtain wall near the intersection of Grid D5.

5. Start the **Wall** command.

6. In the Type Selector, select **Basic Wall: Exterior - Brick on MTL. Stud - parapet**. The alert, shown in Figure 4–19, displays because the software remembered the last settings of the properties.

Figure 4–19

7. Click **Reset constraints**. All of the properties are reset.

8. Select the **Basic Wall: Exterior - Brick on MTL. Stud - parapet** again and set the following properties:

- Base Constraint: **Roof**
- Base Offset: (negative) **-6' 0"**
- Top Constraint: **Up to level: Parapet**
- Top Offset: **0' 0"**

9. In the Draw panel, click ⚞ (Pick Lines). Move the cursor over the middle curved curtain wall and press <Tab> until the curtain wall reference displays as shown in Figure 4–20 and then click to place the wall.

Ensure that you are selecting the main line of the curtain wall or a grid line and not one of the curtain wall panels.

Walls : Curtain Wall : Exterior Glazing : Reference

Figure 4–20

10. In the *Modify | Place Wall* tab>Draw panel, click ⌒ (Start-End-Radius Arc).

11. Select the points in the order shown in Figure 4–21. Ensure that you select the endpoints before selecting the tangent point on the arc.

Figure 4–21

- Creating the wall this way solves some issues because the center line of the curtain wall is at a slight offset from the main wall.
- If a warning displays about a wall sweep you can ignore it.

12. Repeat the process in a similar manner for the other part of the arc, starting with the endpoint of the small wall, and then the endpoint of the curved wall, and finally the tangent point.

13. Click ⌖ (Modify).

14. Type **ZA** to display the full floor plan.

15. Return to the 3D view. The new parapet wall over the curtain wall displays as shown in Figure 4–22.

The columns are hidden to clarify the image.

Figure 4–22

16. Save the project.

Practice 4b

Add Interior Walls

Practice Objectives

Estimated time for completion: 20-30 minutes

- Model and modify walls.
- Use modify tools including **Align**, **Offset**, **Trim/Extend**, **Copy**, and **Mirror**.

In this practice you will add interior walls to the first floor plan, as shown in Figure 4–23, and use **Offset**, **Split Element**, **Trim**, and **Align** to help create them. As optional tasks, you can add walls to the second floor, basement, and foundation.

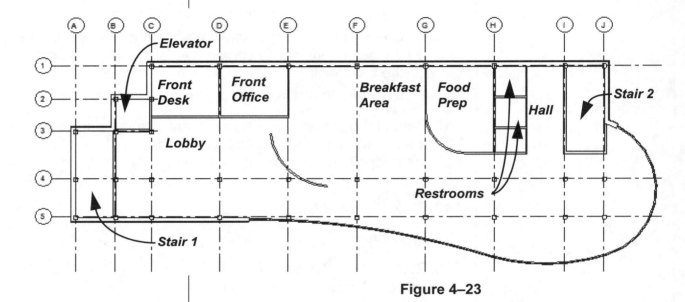

Figure 4–23

Task 1 - Add and align the stair and elevator walls.

1. Open the project **Modern-Hotel-Interior-Walls.rvt** from your practice folder.

2. Open the **Floor Plans: Floor 1** view.

3. Zoom in on the stair and elevator area on the left side of the building.

4. Start the **Wall** command.

5. In the Options Bar and Properties, set the following options:

   - Wall Type: **Basic Wall: Generic 8" Masonry**
   - Height: **Roof**
   - Base Offset: **0'-0"**
   - Top Offset: **0' 0"**

6. Draw the stair and elevator walls from column to column, as shown in Figure 4–24.

Figure 4–24

7. Click ⌖ (Modify).

8. Zoom in on the elevator walls and ensure you can also display some of the related grid lines.

9. In the *Modify* tab>Modify panel, click ⬛ (Align) and select the vertical **Grid C**.

10. Hover the cursor over the vertical elevator wall to display its center line (as shown in Figure 4–25), and then select it. Press <Tab> to display the center line if it is not displayed.

Figure 4–25

11. Align the horizontal elevator wall to Grid 3 and the vertical stairs wall to the Grid B.

12. Click ⌖ (Modify) and use the drag controls on the ends of the walls to connect any of the places where the walls do not touch other walls.

13. Repeat the process of creating walls on the other stairwell. Align the center line of the left concrete block wall to the grid line and the right concrete wall to the inside face of the exterior wall, as shown in Figure 4–26.

If required, before aligning, disallow the join between the interior and exterior walls. After everything is in place, you can enable the join again.

Figure 4–26

14. Zoom out to display the entire building floor plan.

15. Save the project.

Task 2 - Add the front desk and office walls.

1. Select the linked file. Right-click and select **Hide in View>Elements**.

2. Click [] (Wall) and set the following properties:

   - Wall type: **Basic Wall: Interior - 4 7/8" Partition (1-hr)**
   - Height: **Floor 2**
   - Location Line: **Wall Centerline**
   - Top Offset: (negative) **-1' 0"**

Setting the Top Offset to a negative number leaves room for the floor above.

3. Draw the walls shown in Figure 4–27.

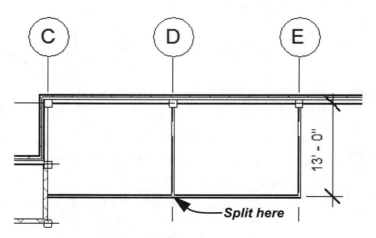

Figure 4–27

4. In the *Modify I Place Wall* tab>Modify panel, click ⊹ (Split Element).

5. Click the horizontal wall at the point shown in Figure 4–27.

6. Click ↳ (Modify) and select the wall on the left. Change the *Top Constraint* to **Unconnected** and the *Unconnected Height* to **4'-0"**. This becomes the base for the Front Desk shelf.

7. Modify the lower wall to butt up against the taller walls, as shown in Figure 4–28.

In the Quick Access Toolbar, click ☰ (Thin Lines) to make the close-up easier to see.

Figure 4–28

Task 3 - Add the support room walls.

1. Pan over to the other stairwell and add the walls shown in Figure 4–29. Use the same wall type and properties as the other main interior walls.

Figure 4–29

- Use ⌐ (Offset) to locate the 8'-0" distance walls after you have drawn some of the others.

- Use ⊟ (Align) to match up the front face of the lower wall with the front face of the stairwell wall.

- To create the arc wall, add two straight walls first. Click

  ⌐ (Fillet Arc), set the *Fillet radius* to **10' 0"**, and select the two walls to create the arc at the corner.

The exact size and location does not matter, but ensure there is enough room for people to get by on both sides.

The linked drawing has been hidden in the view for clarity.

- Use (Trim/Extend to Corner), (Trim/Extend Single), and (Trim/Extend Multiple) as required to get the walls in place.

2. Zoom out and add a **8'-0"** high curved wall using the same interior wall type to separate the Lobby from the Breakfast area, as shown in Figure 4–30.

Figure 4–30

3. Zoom out and save the project.

Task 4 - (Optional) Add typical guest floor walls .

1. Open the **Floor Plans: Floor 2** view. The view displays the walls created in the project and the linked drawing of the second floor.

2. Add walls for the guest rooms, as shown in Figure 4–31, using the wall type **Interior - 4 7/8" Partition (1-hr)** with a *Height* of **Floor 3** and a *Top Offset* of (negative) **-1' 0"**.

   - Align the center of the vertical walls to the grids.
   - Ignore all of the door openings.
   - You can use (Copy) and (Mirror) to duplicate the walls once you have drawn one guest room layout.
   - Be aware that the distance between grids C and D is slightly shorter than the distance between the rest of the room grids. This impacts copying the rooms.

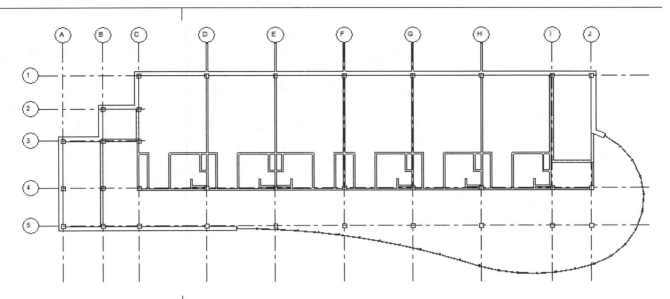

Figure 4–31

3. Return to **Floor Plans: Floor 1** view.

Task 5 - (Optional) Add basement walls.

The following tasks use the standard **Wall** command to draw foundations and wall footings. Additional structural foundation tools are also available.

1. Open the **Floor Plans: T.O. Footing** view.

2. Hide the column grids.

3. In Properties, in the *Graphics* area, set the *Underlay* to **Floor 1** so that the existing walls are displayed.

4. In the *Architecture* tab>Build panel, click 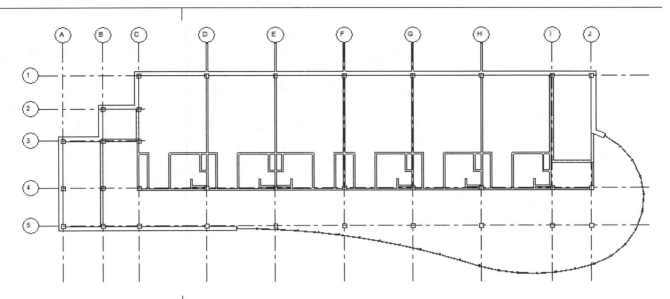 (Wall).

5. In Properties set the following options: (Reset the constraints if needed.)

    *   Wall type: **Basic Wall: Generic - 12" Masonry**
    *   Location Line: **Core Centerline**
    *   Base Constraint: **T.O. Footing**
    *   Base Offset: **0' 0"**
    *   Top Constraint: **Up to Level: Floor 1**
    *   Top Offset: **0' 0"**

Hover the cursor over a wall and then press <Tab> until the center line displays.

6. In the *Modify | Place Wall* tab>Draw panel, click ☝ (Pick Lines). In the main building underlay, select the core center line of the exterior walls and curtain walls, and around the stairs and elevator to create the walls, as shown in Figure 4–32. (Hint: For the stairwell on the right side, create the inner vertical and horizontal wall and then drag the endpoint of the right exterior wall down so that it intersects with the inner horizontal wall).

Extend the exterior wall to intersect with the stairwell wall

Figure 4–32

7. Click ☝ (Modify).

8. In Properties, change the *Underlay* back to **None**.

Task 6 - (Optional) Add footings to the walls.

---

1. Click ⬜ (Wall).

2. In Properties or the Options Bar, set the following options:

   - Wall type: **Basic Wall: Generic - 24" Concrete**
   - Location Line: **Core Centerline**
   - Base Constraint: **T.O. Footing**
   - Base Offset: (negative) **-1' 6"**
   - Top Constraint: **Up to Level:T.O.Footing**
   - Top Offset: **0' 0"**

You might need to zoom in to highlight the core center line.

3. Click 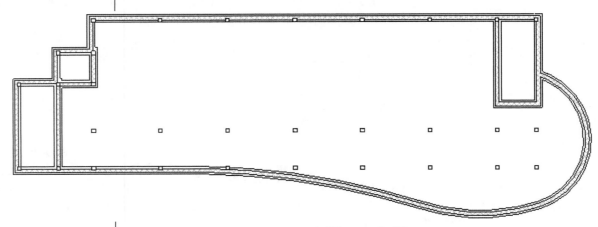 (Pick Line) and select the core center line of all the foundation walls. The wall footings display as shown in Figure 4–33. You add column footings later.

Figure 4–33

4. Save the project.

Chapter Review Questions

1. Where do you specify the height of a wall before you start drawing it? (Select all that apply.)

   a. In the *Modify | Place Wall* tab.

   b. In the Options Bar.

   c. In Properties Palette.

   d. In the Quick Access Toolbar.

2. Some walls are made from multiple layers of materials, such as brick, block, and drywall, as shown on the bottom in Figure 4–34. If the hatching for these materials is not displayed (as shown at the top in Figure 4–34), how do you change this?

Figure 4–34

   a. Set the *Visual Style* to **Realistic**.

   b. Set the *Detail Level* to **Medium**.

   c. Set the *View Scale* to be higher.

   d. Set the *Phase* to **New**.

3. Which of the following tools allows you to change a wall from one made out of studs and brick, to one made out of concrete?

   a. Properties

   b. Change Wall

   c. Type Selector

   d. Edit Wall

4. Match the names for the following controls with the numbers shown in Figure 4–35.

24' - 0'

45' - 0"

1
2
3
4

Figure 4–35

Control	Number
Drag wall end	4
Flip	3
Move witness line	1
Make this temporary dimension permanent	2

5. What is the difference between the column surround and the associated walls to the left and right shown in Figure 4–36? (Select all that apply.)

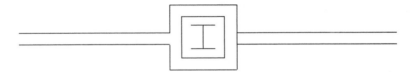

Figure 4–36

(a.) The column surround and wall on the left are made with the same wall type, while the wall type on the right is different.

(b.) The wall on the left has been joined together with the column surround, while the wall on the right was set to **Disallow Join**.

c. The wall on the left was trimmed against the column surround.

d. The wall on the right was extended to the column surround.

6. Which of the following would be true if you changed the top constraint of a wall from an unconnected height to a level? (Select all that apply.)

    a. All walls of that type would also change height.

    b. Only that wall would change height.

    c. If you changed the height of the level, the wall height would change as well.

Command Summary

Button	Command	Location
	Detail Level: Coarse	• **View Control Bar**
	Detail Level: Fine	• **View Control Bar**
	Detail Level: Medium	• **View Control Bar**
	Edit Type/ Type Properties	• **Ribbon:** *Modify* tab>Properties panel • **Properties palette:** Edit Type
	Match Type	• **Ribbon:** *Modify* tab>Clipboard panel • **Shortcut:** MA
	Properties	• **Ribbon:** *Modify* tab>Properties panel • **Shortcut:** PP
N/A	Type Selector	• **Properties palette** • **Ribbon:** *Modify* tab (*optional*) • **Quick Access Toolbar** (*optional*)
	Wall	• **Ribbon:** *Architecture* tab>Build panel
	Wall Opening	• **Ribbon:** *Architecture* tab>Opening panel

Chapter 5

Working with Doors and Windows

Doors and windows are host elements that are placed in walls. There are many different types of doors and windows available in the Autodesk® Revit® libraries, and you can easily create additional sizes of the types that come with the software to meet your design requirements.

Learning Objectives in this Chapter

- Insert doors and windows in walls.
- Modify door and window locations and properties that can be referenced in schedules.
- Load additional door and window types from the library.
- Create additional door and window sizes of a selected type.

5.1 Inserting Doors and Windows

Doors and windows in the Autodesk Revit software are designed to be hosted by walls. You can use temporary dimensions (as shown in Figure 5–1) as well as alignment lines and snaps to help place the openings exactly where you need them in the walls.

Figure 5–1

How To: Add a Door or Window

1. In the *Architecture* tab>Build panel, click ⬜ (Door) or

    ⬜ (Window). The keyboard shortcuts are **DR** for doors and **WN** for windows.

2. To insert a tag with each door or window, verify that ⬡ (Tag on Placement) is toggled on. You can specify the tag options using the Options Bar, as shown in Figure 5–2.

Figure 5–2

3. In the Type Selector, select the type of door or window, as shown in Figure 5–3.

Figure 5–3

4. Select the wall to place the door or window.
   - To force the opening to snap to the midpoint of the wall, type **SM**.

5. Continue adding other doors or windows as required.

- While placing or modifying doors or windows, you can adjust the element using temporary dimensions and the **Flip the instance facing** and **Flip the instance hand** controls to change the swing and hinge locations, as shown in Figure 5–4. With windows, you can flip the interior and exterior using the same technique.

Figure 5–4

- If you are including window tags, select a point close to the outside of the wall when inserting the window so that the tag is placed on the outside.

- To move a door or window tag, select the tag. A control displays, as shown in Figure 5–5, enabling you to drag the tag to a new location.

Figure 5–5

Modifying Door and Window Properties

The door or window types control most of their properties. To change the property information, you change the type in the Type Selector. You can also change Instance Parameters (as shown in Figure 5–6) that impact the specific door or window in the associated schedule. Instance Parameters include things such as the *Swing Angle, Masonry* or *Drywall Frame*, etc.

Enhanced in **2016**

Figure 5–6

Hint: Copying Elements to Levels

The standard Windows commands ✂ (Cut or <Ctrl>+<X>),

🗐 (Copy To Clipboard or <Ctrl>+<C>), and 🗐 (Paste From Clipboard or <Ctrl>+<V>) work in the Autodesk Revit software just as they do in other Windows-compatible software. They are available in the *Modify* tab>Clipboard panel, but not in the right-click menu.

In the software, you can also paste elements aligned to various views or levels, as shown in Figure 5–7.

Figure 5–7

Aligned to Selected Levels: Opens a dialog box where you can select the level to which you want to copy. This enables you to copy items on one level and paste them to the same location on another level (e.g., windows in a high-rise building).

Aligned to Selected Views: Copies view-specific elements (such as text or dimensions) into a view that you select in a dialog box. Only the Floor Plan or Reflected Ceiling Plan views are available.

Aligned to Current View: Pastes elements copied in one view to the same location in another view.

Aligned to Same Place: Pastes elements to the same location in the same view.

Aligned to Picked Level: Pastes elements to the level you select in an elevation or section view.

Practice 5a

Insert Doors and Windows

Practice Objectives

- Add doors and windows.
- Copy elements to multiple levels.

Estimated time for completion: 15 minutes

In this practice you will add doors and windows to a model, as shown for Floor 1 in Figure 5–8. You will use controls, temporary dimensions, and dimensions set to Equal to help you place the doors and windows. You will also copy windows to multiple levels.

Figure 5–8

Task 1 - Add doors.

1. Open the project **Modern-Hotel-Doors.rvt** from your class folder.

2. Working in the **Floor Plans: Floor 1** view, select one of the grid lines. Right-click and select **Hide in view>Category** to turn off all of the grid lines.

3. In the *Architecture* tab>Build panel, click (Door).

4. In the Type Selector, select **Single-Flush: 36" x 80"**.

5. In the *Modify | Place Door* tab>Tag panel, verify that (Tag on Placement) is on.

6. Place the door near the lower left corner of the building, as shown in Figure 5–9. Use the flip arrows to make it swing in the right direction and use temporary dimensions to place it to the correct location on the wall. Click on the tag and change the number to **101**.

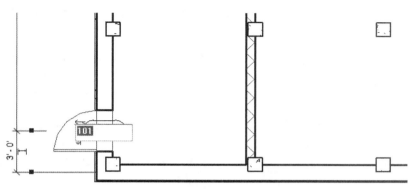

Figure 5–9

7. Continue adding single flush doors in the project, similar to the locations shown in Figure 5–10. Use the same door type. The tag number automatically increments.

Figure 5–10

8. Click ⬉ (Modify) and select the two sets of stairwell doors (two doors on the left side and two doors on the right side of the building).

    *   If you select multiple categories, use ▼ (Filter) to help select only the doors.

9. In the Type Selector, select **Single-Flush Vision: 36" x 84"**.

10. Zoom in on the upper right corner of the building, in the area of the stairwell and hallway.

11. Click (Door) and in the Type Selector, select **Double-Glass 1: 72" x 84"**.

12. Place the door at the end of the hall. At this point the location does not need to be exact as you are going to modify the placement in the following steps.

13. In the Quick Access Toolbar, click (Aligned Dimension). Note that by starting another command, you automatically end the previous command.)

Press <Tab> to cycle through the reference points.

14. For the dimension locations select the inside of the left wall, the center of the door, and in the inside of the right wall, as shown on the left in Figure 5–11. Click to place the dimension.

15. Click the **EQ** control. The door is centered evenly between the two walls, as shown on the right in Figure 5–11.

Figure 5–11

16. Delete the dimension. An alert displays, as shown in Figure 5–12. In this case, you want the dimensions constrained to be equal. Click **OK**.

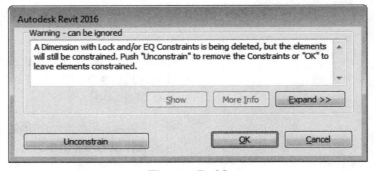

Figure 5–12

17. Zoom out to see the full floor plan.

18. Save the project.

Task 2 - Add windows and space them equally apart.

1. Open the **Floor Plans: Floor 2** view.

2. The linked CAD file is still displayed in this view. Select it and in the Status Bar click ✎ (Temporary Hide/Isolate)>**Hide Element**. Leave the grids displayed, as they enable you to place the windows correctly.

3. In the *Architecture* tab>Build panel, click ▦ (Window).

4. In the *Modify | Place Window* tab>Tag panel, verify that ⌐① (Tag on Placement) is turned on.

5. In the Type Selector, select **Casement 3x3 with Trim: 48" x 48"**.

6. Add four windows along the lower exterior wall, as shown in Figure 5–13. The exact location is not important right now.

Figure 5–13

7. Click ⌖ (Modify) and select the window closest to the stair and use temporary dimensions to move it so it is 4'-0" from the grid line, as shown in Figure 5–14. You might need to move the witness line so that it references the grid, rather than a wall.

Figure 5–14

8. In the Quick Access Toolbar or in the *Annotate* tab> Dimension panel, click (Aligned Dimension). Dimension from the grid to the center of the window and lock the dimension in place, as shown in Figure 5–15.

Figure 5–15

9. With the (Aligned Dimension) still active, dimension from center to center of the windows. Click the **EQ** control and lock the padlocks, as shown in Figure 5–16.

Figure 5–16

10. Delete the dimensions, but keep the constraints.

Task 3 - Copy windows to multiple levels.

---

1. Open the 3D view and verify that the front of the building where the windows are located is displayed.

2. Select all four windows by holding <Ctrl> and selecting each one.

3. In the *Modify | Windows* tab>Clipboard panel, click (Copy to Clipboard).

4. In the Clipboard panel, expand (Paste) and click (Aligned to Selected Levels).

5. In the Select Levels dialog box, select the floors between and including **Floor 3** and **Floor 8**, as shown in Figure 5–17.

Figure 5–17

6. Click **OK**. The windows are copied up the side of the building, as shown in Figure 5–18.

Additional doors and windows will be placed using storefront curtain walls.

Figure 5–18

7. Save the project.

5.2 Loading Door and Window Types from the Library

A variety of door and window styles are available in the Autodesk Revit Library, as shown in Figure 5–19. They are grouped in *Family* files with the extension .RFA. For example, when you load the family **Door-Double-Glass.rfa** you can then select various sizes of this door you want to use in the project.

- The process is similar for loading all types of families.

Figure 5–19

How To: Load a Family

1. Start the **Door** or **Window** command and, in the *Modify |
   contextual* tab>Mode panel or the *Insert* tab>Load from
   Library panel, click ⬇ (Load Family).
2. In the Load Family dialog box, navigate to the folder that
   contains the family you want to load and select the family.
3. Click **Open**.

New
in **2016**

4. For some door families the Specify Types dialog box displays, as shown in Figure 5–20. Select the types you want to include in your project and click **OK**.

Figure 5–20

- To select more than one type, hold <Ctrl> as you select.
- You can use the drop-down lists under the columns to filter the sizes.

5. Once the family is loaded, in the Type Selector, select the type you want to use.

- When you are working within a command such as **Door** or **Window**, you can only load families that are from that category of elements. For example, you cannot load window families while working in the **Door** command.

- There are several families used for openings. In the *Doors* folder: **Door-Opening.rfa** and in the *Windows* folder: **Window-Round Opening.rfa** and **Window-Square Opening.rfa**.

Hint: Transferring Project Standards

Some elements (such as wall types) are not accessible from a specific library. However, you can copy them from other projects.

1. Open the project from which you want to copy information.
2. Open the project to which you want to copy the information.
3. In the *Manage* tab>Settings panel, click (Transfer Project Standards).
4. In the Select Items To Copy dialog box, select an option in the *Copy from* drop-down list and then select the settings you want to copy into the current file, as shown in Figure 5–21. Click **OK**.

Figure 5–21

5. In the Duplicate Types dialog box, click either **Overwrite** or **New Only** to apply the settings to the current project.

5.3 Creating Additional Door and Window Sizes

You can easily add additional sizes to existing families of doors or windows that have been loaded into a project. To do this, you create a new type of the required size based on an existing type, as shown in Figure 5–22.

You can specify materials for door and window sub-elements in the Type Properties.

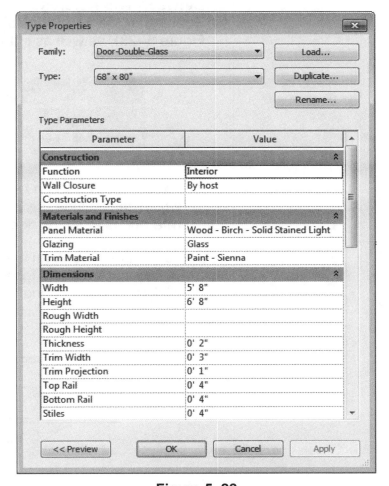

Figure 5–22

How To: Create Additional Door and Window Sizes

1. Start the **Door** or **Window** command.
2. In the Type Selector, select the type you want to modify. In Properties, click ⊞ (Edit Type) or in the *Modify* tab> Properties panel, click ⊞ (Type Properties).
3. In the Type Properties dialog box, click **Duplicate**.
4. Type a new name for the element and click **OK**.

5. In the Type Properties dialog box, change the *Height* and *Width* parameters to match the size.

6. Click **OK** to close the dialog box. The new window or door type is now available for use.

Hint: Measuring Distances

As you are working in a project, you might need to know some existing distances. Two methods can be used: **Measure Between Two References** and **Measure Along An Element**. Both are available in the Quick Access Toolbar (as shown in Figure 5–23), as well as in the *Modify* tab>Measure panel.

Figure 5–23

- To measure between two references, select the references, which can include any snap point, wall lines, or other references (such as door center lines).

- To measure along an element, select the element you want to measure or use <Tab> to select other elements and then click to measure along all of them, as shown in Figure 5–24.

Figure 5–24

Practice 5b

Load and Create Door Types

Estimated time for completion: 15 minutes

Practice Objectives

- Load door types.
- Duplicate and modify a door type.

In this practice you will load specialty door types used in the guest rooms, create a new door size, and add doors to the second floor, as shown in Figure 5–25.

Figure 5–25

Task 1 - Load door types.

1. Open the project **Modern-Hotel-Load.rvt** from the class folder.

2. Open the **Floor Plans: Floor 1** view and zoom in on the kitchen area.

3. In the *Architecture* tab>Build panel, click (Door).

4. In the *Modify | Place Door* tab>Mode panel, click (Load Family).

5. In the Load Family dialog box, navigate to the *Doors* folder and select **Door-Double-Flush_Panel-Double-Acting.rfa**. Click **Open.**

6. In the Specify Types dialog box, select the *Type* **72"x 80"** as shown in Figure 5–26 and click **OK**.

Figure 5–26

7. Start the Load Family command again. (Hint: Press <Enter> to repeat the last command.)

8. In the Load Family dialog box, navigate to the *Residential* folder and select **Door-Interior-Single-6_Panel-Wood.rfa.** Click **Open**.

9. In the Specify Types dialog box, scroll down the *Type* list and select **36" x 80"** and click **OK**.

10. In the Type Selector, select **Door-Double-Flush_Panel-Double-Acting: 72" x 80"**, and place an instance of it in the wall between the kitchen and dining area, as shown in Figure 5–27.

Figure 5–27

11. Zoom to the extents of the view and save the project.

Task 2 - Add doors to Floor 2.

1. Open the **Floor Plans: Floor 2** view.

2. To make the view easier to read, temporarily hide the grids. Leave the linked CAD file displayed to help place the doors.

3. In the *Architecture* tab>Build panel, click ▯ (Door).

4. In the Type Selector, select **Single-Flush-Vision: 36" x 80".**

5. Place the first door in the lower left stairwell as shown in the linked file and change the tag number to **201**.

6. Add another door of the same type to the other stairwell at the opposite end of the building.

7. Change the door type to **Door-Interior-Single-6_Panel-Wood. 36" x 80"** and place a door at the entrance of each of the rooms, using the CAD file as a guideline.

8. Use the same type to add doors to the bathrooms.

9. Change the door type to **Single Flush: 30" x 80"**.

10. In Properties, click ▦ (Edit Type) or in the *Modify | Place Door* tab>Properties panel, click ▦ (Type Properties).

11. In the Type Properties dialog box, click **Duplicate**.

12. Enter **24" x 80"** for the name and click **OK**.

13. In the Type Properties dialog box, change the **Width** parameter to **2'-0"**. You can type either **2' 0"** or **24"** but you must add the " symbol to the value if you are using inches.

14. Click **OK** to close the dialog box. The new door type is available for use. Add it to the small closets.

The door to the small closet in the guest bathroom is smaller than the existing door sizes. Therefore, you need to find out what size it is and create a new size.

15. Continue adding other doors using different door styles (i.e., Bifold and Double-Glass). The rooms should look similar to the layout shown in Figure 5–28, though your numbering might be different.

Figure 5–28

16. Select and hide the CAD file.

17. Save the project.

Chapter Review Questions

1. How do you change the swing direction of a door, as shown in Figure 5–29? (Select all that apply.)

Before   *After*

Figure 5–29

   a. When placing the door, press <Spacebar>.

   b. When placing the door, right-click and select **Change Swing**.

   c. Select an existing door and select the flip arrows.

   d. Select an existing door, right-click and select **Change Swing**.

2. How do you add additional window or door families to a project?

   a. Find the window or door family using Windows Explorer, right-click and select **Import into Revit Project**.

   b. Import them from the Window or Door Catalog.

   c. Load them from the Library.

   d. Use the Window/Door Wizard to create new families.

3. How do you include a tag with a door or window, as shown in Figure 5–30?

Figure 5–30

   a. Select a door or window family that includes a tag.

   b. Select the Tag box in the Options Bar before placing the door or window.

   c. Tags can only be used after placing the door or window.

   d. Select **Tag on Placement** in the contextual tab.

4. Where are the door and window sizes stored?

   a. In Properties.

   b. In Type Properties.

   c. In Door/ Window Settings.

   d. In the template file.

5. How do you create additional door or window sizes, as shown in Figure 5–31?

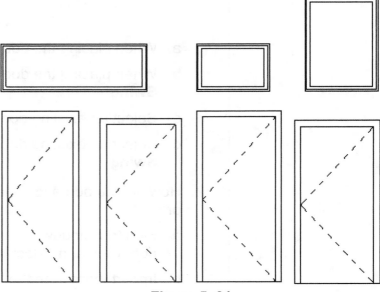

Figure 5–31

   a. Select the required door or window and use the Size Wizard to specify a new size.

   b. Select the required door or window and in Type Properties, Duplicate an existing door and modify it.

   c. Find the existing door or window family in the Project Browser, right-click and select **New Size**.

   d. Select the door or window in the view, and edit it using size controls to the required size.

Command Summary

Button	Command	Location
Clipboard		
	Copy to Clipboard	• **Ribbon:** *Modify* tab>Clipboard panel • **Shortcut:** <Ctrl>+<C>
	Cut to the Clipboard	• **Ribbon:** *Modify* tab>Clipboard panel • **Shortcut:** <Ctrl>+<X>
	Paste - Aligned to Current View	• **Ribbon:** *Modify* tab>Clipboard panel> expand Paste
	Paste - Aligned to Same Place	• **Ribbon:** *Modify* tab>Clipboard panel> expand Paste
	Paste - Aligned to Selected Levels	• **Ribbon:** *Modify* tab>Clipboard panel> expand Paste
	Paste - Aligned to Selected Views	• **Ribbon:** *Modify* tab>Clipboard panel> expand Paste
	Paste - Aligned to Picked Level	• **Ribbon:** *Modify* tab>Clipboard panel> expand Paste
	Paste from Clipboard	• **Ribbon:** *Modify* tab>Clipboard panel • **Shortcut:** <Ctrl>+<V>
Doors and Windows		
	Door	• **Ribbon:** *Architecture* tab>Build panel • **Shortcut:** DR
	Edit Type/ Type Properties	• **Properties palette:** Edit Type • **Ribbon:** *Modify* tab>Properties panel
	Measure	• **Quick Access Toolbar** • **Ribbon:** *Modify* tab>Measure panel
	Window	• **Ribbon:** *Architecture* tab>Build panel • **Shortcut:** WN

Working with Curtain Walls

Curtain walls are the "skin" of a building, and are often used to create complex windows and storefronts. Curtain walls are created based on a selected wall type to which additional grids and mullions can be added and individual panels swapped out to create the required pattern.

Learning Objectives in this Chapter

- Create basic curtain walls and storefronts using curtain wall types.
- Modify the curtain grid pattern.
- Switch out curtain wall panels with other types, doors, or windows.
- Add mullions to curtain wall grids.

6.1 Creating Curtain Walls

Curtain walls are non-bearing walls consisting of panels laid out in a grid pattern. They can encase an entire building like a membrane or, as shown in Figure 6–1, fill a cutout in a standard wall, often called a storefront.

Figure 6–1

How To: Create a Curtain Wall.

1. In a plan view, draw a wall using a curtain wall type.
2. In an elevation or 3D view, add grids to the curtain wall.
3. Modify the panels of the curtain wall. Panels can be a specific material (such as glass or stone) or can incorporate doors, windows, or other wall types.
4. Add mullions to separate the panels.

The components of a curtain wall are shown in Figure 6–2.

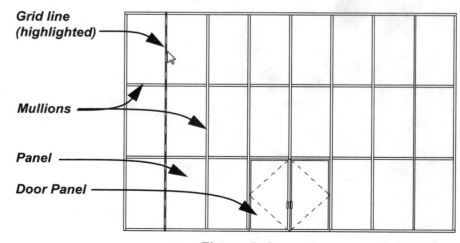

Figure 6–2

- The simplest way to create a curtain wall is to use a curtain wall type with a preset uniform grid already applied to it, such as **Curtain Wall:Exterior Glazing** or **Curtain Wall: Storefront**, which come with the software, as shown in Figure 6–3.

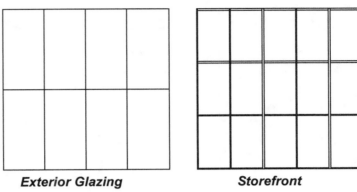

Exterior Glazing   *Storefront*

Figure 6–3

- The Autodesk® Revit® software also comes with a standard curtain wall type, **Curtain Wall 1**, that creates a single glass panel to which you can apply a grid in any pattern.

- Many curtain walls do not have a uniform pattern of exact distances between grids, as shown in Figure 6–4. Therefore, you need to create these designs directly on the curtain wall. You can start with a curtain wall type that has a basic uniform grid, if applicable.

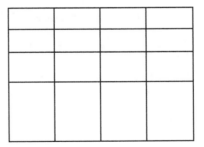

Figure 6–4

Creating Storefronts

Storefronts are a special type of curtain wall that can be embedded into other walls, as shown in Figure 6–5. They can also be used to create what looks like a complex set of windows. Some curtain wall types, such as the **Storefront** wall type, are designed to be embedded in another wall.

Window   *Storefront*

Figure 6–5

How To: Add a Storefront Wall in an Existing Wall

1. In the *Architecture* tab>Build panel, click 🗍 (Wall).
2. In the Type Selector, select the curtain wall type you want to use. In Properties, set the *Base Constraint, Top Constraint*, and *Offsets* as required.The height can be less than the height of the wall in which you are embedding.
3. Select a point on the existing wall, as shown in Figure 6–6.

Figure 6–6

4. Select the second point along the wall. (Hint: Press <Tab> to cycle from the default Horizontal and Nearest snap to the dynamic dimension and then type the distance for the embedded curtain wall.) The wall displays as shown in Figure 6–7.

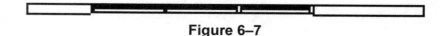

Figure 6–7

5. Open the appropriate elevation view. Select the outside edge of the curtain wall and use the shape handles and dynamic dimensions, as shown in Figure 6–8, to place the storefront in the wall as required.

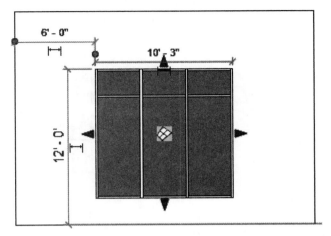

Figure 6–8

6.2 Adding Curtain Grids

Once you have a curtain wall in place with at least one panel, you need to separate it into multiple panels for the design. Each grid line divides a panel into two or more smaller panels, as shown in Figure 6–9.

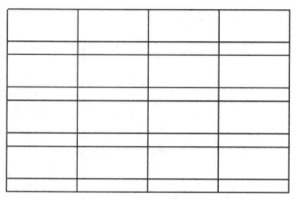

Figure 6–9

How To: Create a Curtain Grid

1. After you have drawn the base curtain wall in a plan view, switch to an elevation or 3D view.

2. In the *Architecture* tab>Build panel, click ⊞ (Curtain Grid).
3. In the *Modify | Place Curtain Grid* tab>Placement panel, select an insertion method, as described below.

‡ **(All Segments)**	Creates a grid line through the entire curtain wall height or width.
‡ **(One Segment)**	Creates a grid line between only the selection point and the next line. The entire grid line is established, but only one segment displays. You can add other segments later.
‡ **(All Except Picked)**	Creates a grid line through the entire grid and permits you to go back and remove segments of the grid line. The removed segment displays as a dashed line until you draw another grid line or start another command.

4. Move the cursor over an edge of the curtain wall or an existing grid line. Dynamic dimensions are displayed, as shown in Figure 6–10. The new grid line is perpendicular to the edge at the point you select. Click at the required location.

Figure 6–10

- Curtain grids automatically snap to the midpoint or 1/3 point of the panel. They also snap to levels, column grids, and reference planes.

- You can use (Copy) and (Array) on the curtain grid lines. This method can be the fastest way of creating grids across the length of a wall.

- You can add additional grids to curtain wall types that include grids when they are created.

Modifying Curtain Grids

Once you have placed the grid lines, they might not be exactly where you want them or overlap other lines where you do not want them to overlap. You can modify the location of lines in the grid and add or remove segments from the lines, as shown in Figure 6–11.

Figure 6–11

- To modify the grid, you must select a grid line, not a wall or the mullion. Press <Tab> to cycle through elements.

- To move a grid line, select it and use dynamic dimensions or 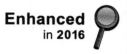 (Move).

- If you select a grid line that was created using a curtain wall type, (Prevent or allow change of element position) is displayed, indicating that the element is constrained to a host element. Click on the icon to enable you to move the line.

Enhanced in **2016**

How To: Add or Remove Segments of Curtain Grids

1. Select a grid line to modify.
2. In the *Modify|Curtain Wall Grids* tab>Curtain Grid panel, click (Add/Remove Segments).
3. Click on the part of the grid that you want to add or remove. The line displays as dashed when you click to remove a segment, as shown in Figure 6–12. You must select grid lines one at a time with this command.

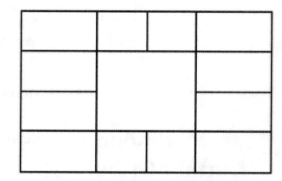

Figure 6–12

4. Click in empty space to finish the command.

- You can create non-rectangular panels by removing individual grid segments.

Hint: Aligning and Locking

When you use the **Align** command, you can also lock the lines together so if one moves, the other does as well. However, locking also causes the software to slow down. Therefore, be careful how much you use the **Lock** option and apply it only when you expect to make a lot of modifications.

Practice 6a

Estimated time for completion: 10 minutes

Work with Curtain Walls

Practice Objectives

- Modify curtain wall properties.
- Add curtain wall grid lines.

In this practice you will modify a curtain wall using Properties to ensure that the lines match up with other elements. You will also add grid lines that follow the pattern of a nearby wall. The finished elevation is shown in Figure 6–13.

Figure 6–13

Task 1 - Modify the curtain wall.

1. Open the project **Modern-Hotel-Curtain-Walls.rvt**.

2. Open the **Elevations (Building Elevation):South** view.

3. To make the view easier to understand, select one grid line, one column, and one level line. (Hold <Ctrl> to select more than one element.) Then, right-click and select **Hide in View>Category**.

The curtain wall grid does not match up with any of the other features, as shown in Figure 6–14.

Parapet walls

Figure 6–14

4. Select the three parapet walls. In Properties, change the *Base Offset* to (negative) **-2' 0"** and click **Apply**. This shortens the parapet.

5. Select the three curtain walls. In Properties, change the *Top Offset* to (negative) **-2' 0"** and click **Apply**. This extends the curtain wall up to the parapet.

6. With the curtain walls still selected, change *the Horizontal Grid Offset* to **4' 0"** (*Offset* field in the *Horizontal Grid* area), as shown in Figure 6–15.

Figure 6–15

The grid now fits better, as shown in Figure 6–16.

Figure 6–16

Task 2 - Add grid lines.

In this task you will add grid lines to match up with multiple lines at the bottom of the building.

1. Zoom in to the bottom edge of the building and ensure that the brick/CMU and the curtain wall is displayed. Select the grid line and unpin it, as shown in Figure 6–17.

Figure 6–17

2. Use ⬒ (Align) to move the curtain grid line so it matches with the top of the CMU sill, as shown in Figure 6–18.

Figure 6–18

3. In the *Architecture* tab>Build panel, click 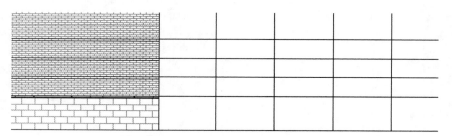 (Curtain Grid).

4. Add three grid lines aligned with the top of the reveals in the brick, as shown in Figure 6–19.

Zoom in until the heavier lines of the brick reveals are displayed.

Figure 6–19

5. Select these four curtain grid lines (hold <Ctrl> and select each line individually) and move them down **1 1/4"**. Ensure you drag the cursor down before entering the move value. This places them correctly for the mullions, that are added later.

6. Pan over and align and add curtain grid lines to the other two parts of the curtain wall, as shown in Figure 6–20. Ensure you unpin the existing horizontal curtain grid lines before aligning them.

Figure 6–20

7. Zoom out until the entire front of the building is displayed.

8. Save the project.

6.3 Working with Curtain Wall Panels

The default panel for a curtain wall is typically a glazed panel. As you create the curtain grid and refine the wall design, you might want to use other materials for some of the panels, as shown in Figure 6–21. You can select the existing panels and in the Type Selector, select a panel type with the material you want to use. The panel type also controls the thickness and can define a door or window for the panel.

*To select all of the panels, select the edge of the curtain wall, right-click, and select **Select Panels on Host**.*

Figure 6–21

- To select a panel, move the cursor over its edge, press <Tab> until it highlights, and then click to select it. If 🔍 (Prevent or allow change of element position) displays (as shown in Figure 6–22), it indicates that the panel is locked and that changes to the element are not permitted. Click the icon to turn off the lock and modify the panel.

- To unpin multiple panels, select them and type **UP** (for **Unpin**).

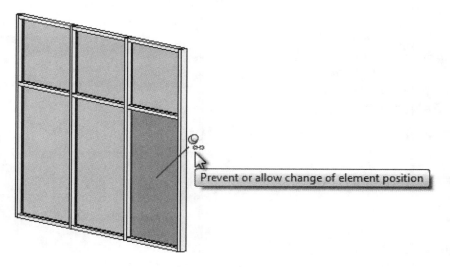

Figure 6–22

Default Panel Types

Three panel types come with the default project template:

Empty Panel	You cannot delete a panel in a curtain wall, but you can change the panel type to an empty panel.
Glazed Panel	A typical panel type with glass as its material.
Solid Panel	A panel type using a solid material. You can create variations of this type with other materials.

- You can use any other wall type (including other curtain wall types) to fill in a panel.

- Door and window panels are available through the Library. Similar to other panel types, door and window panels fill the size of the panel to which they are applied. Adjust the curtain grid for the correct sizes.

Hint: Placing Doors in Curtain Walls

You can place doors in curtain wall panels, as shown in Figure 6–23. You first need to have a door type that can be used as a curtain wall panel (the software comes with several). Then, ensure the size of the opening in the curtain wall matches the size of the door you want to use. The door type expands to fill the grid opening.

Figure 6–23

• When you tag a curtain wall panel door, you need to add the number to the tag. It does not automatically increment.

• You can also use a standard wall type as a panel. Then you can add a door into the panel using the standard **Door** command.

Creating a Curtain Wall Panel

While you can create curtain wall panels in many complex ways, a basic technique is to specify a material for a flat system panel, as shown in Figure 6–24.

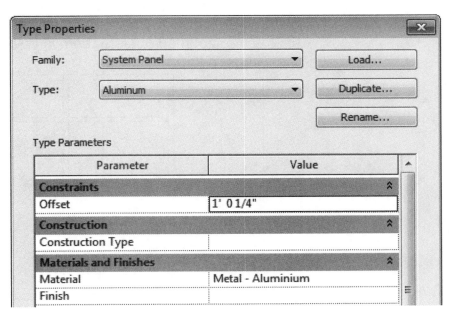

Figure 6–24

How To: Create a Curtain Wall Panel

1. Select a panel similar to the one you want to create (e.g., select a solid panel to create a new solid panel type). If it is locked, unlock it by clicking 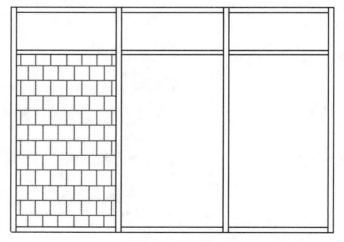 (Prevent or allow change of element position).

2. In Properties, click (Edit Type), or, in the *Modify | Curtain Panels* tab>Properties panel, click (Type Properties).

3. In the Type Properties dialog box, click **Duplicate** to create a copy of the existing family type.

4. Give the panel a new name that describes its purpose (e.g., **Brick** or **Aluminum**). The new name automatically includes the family name, such as **System Panel**.

5. Set the *Thickness*, *Offset*, and *Material* and any other parameters as required. Many materials are available in the Materials dialog box that opens when you click (Browse) in the Materials list.

6. Click **OK** to close the dialog box and finish the panel. It is automatically applied to the panel you selected for modification.

- The *Thickness* of the material is centered on the grid if you did not specify an *Offset*. If you want the panel to be recessed in the wall, use a negative offset. If you want the panel to stand out from the wall, use a positive offset.

- Materials with patterns, such as the glass block shown in Figure 6–25, do not display the pattern when the view is zoomed out far. Zoom in to view the material.

Figure 6–25

6.4 Attaching Mullions to Curtain Grids

Mullions are the frameworks for curtain wall panels, as shown in Figure 6–26. They can be many sizes, shapes, and materials. Add them as the final step in your curtain wall design after you have placed the grid lines.

Figure 6–26

How To: Add Mullions

1. In the *Architecture* tab>Build panel, click ⊞ (Mullion).
2. In the Type Selector, select the mullion style. There are no modifiable properties when you insert a mullion.
3. In the *Modify | Place Mullion* tab>Placement panel, select a

   Create Mullion on method: ⊞ (Grid Line), ⊞ (Grid Line

   Segment), or ⊞ (All Grid Lines), as shown in Figure 6–27.

Mullions must be placed individually; they cannot be copied or arrayed.

Figure 6–27

4. Select the grid line on which you want to place the mullion. If the grid line is inside a grid, the mullion is placed on the grid's center line. If it is on the edge of the wall, the mullion is placed so that its exterior is flush with the outside of the wall.

   • Hold <Shift> to place a mullion only on the selected segment.

   • Hold <Ctrl> to place the mullion on all empty grid segments (i.e., all without mullions).

   • Corner mullion types are designed for the intersection of two curtain walls. They adjust to fit the angle of the intersection.

Modifying Mullions

To quickly select mullions, right-click on the edge of the curtain wall and select **Select Mullions**. The mullion options include **On Vertical Grid** or **On Horizontal Grid**, **Inner Mullions**, **Border Mullions**, or **Mullions on Host**, as shown in Figure 6–28.

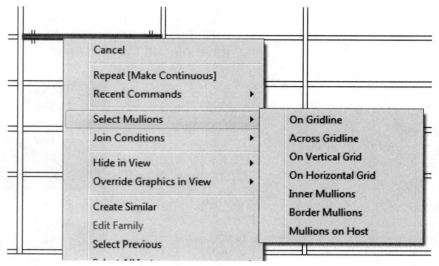

Figure 6–28

- Modify mullion styles by changing their type in the Type Selector.

- If you move a grid line, the mullion moves with it.

- If you delete a grid line, the mullion is also deleted. However, if you delete a mullion, the grid line is not deleted.

- You can change the way mullions intersect. Select the mullion to display the *Modify | Curtain Wall Mullions* tab. In the Mullion panel, click ⊞ (Make Continuous) or ⊪ (Break at Join), You can also do this directly on the mullion, as shown in Figure 6–29.

Before   *After*

Figure 6–29

Hint: Temporary Hide/Isolate

You might want to temporarily remove elements from a view, modify the project, and then restore the elements. Instead of completely turning the elements off, you can temporarily hide them.

Select the elements you want to hide (make invisible) or isolate (keep displayed while all other elements are hidden) and click

 (Temporary Hide/Isolate). Select the method you want to use, as shown in Figure 6–30.

Figure 6–30

The elements or category are hidden or isolated. A cyan border displays around the view with a note in the upper left corner, as shown in Figure 6–31. It indicates that the view contains temporarily hidden or isolated elements.

Figure 6–31

- Click (Temporary Hide/Isolate) again and select **Reset Temporary Hide/Isolate** to restore the elements to the view.

- If you want to permanently hide the elements in the view, select **Apply Hide/Isolate to View**.

- Elements that are temporarily hidden in a view are not hidden when the view is printed.

Practice 6b

Estimated time for completion: 15 minutes

Add Mullions and Panels to Curtain Walls

Practice Objectives

- Add and modify mullions.
- Add a storefront entrance and door panel.

In this practice you will add and modify mullions along the curtain walls. You will also create a storefront that includes a door panel as the front entrance of the building. The finished elevation is shown in Figure 6–32.

Figure 6–32

Task 1 - Add and modify mullions.

1. Open the project **Modern-Hotel-Mullions.rvt**.

2. Open the **Elevations (Building Elevations): South** view, or work in the 3D view.

3. In the *Architecture* tab>Build panel, click ⊞ (Mullion).

4. In the *Modify | Place Mullion* tab>Placement panel, click ⊞ (All Grid Lines).

5. Select each of the curtain walls. Mullions are place on all of the grid lines.

6. Click (Modify).

7. At the two lines where the curtain walls meet, extra mullions are added, as shown in Figure 6–33. These are not needed and should be removed.

Figure 6–33

8. Select one of the mullions.

9. In the View Control Bar, click (Temporary Hide/Isolate) and select **Isolate Category**. This makes selecting the mullions you want to delete easier.

10. Delete the extra mullions. Select one mullion, right-click and select **Select Mullions>On Gridline**.

11. Zoom out until all of the curtain walls are displayed.

12. Select the entire bottom row of mullions. You can use the Window selection box to select the entire row.

13. In the *Modify | Curtain Wall Mullions* tab>Mullion panel, click

    (Make Continuous). This changes the mullion direction, as shown in Figure 6–34.

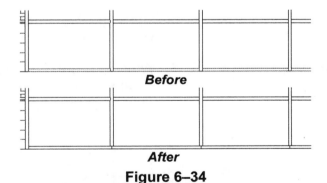

Before

After

Figure 6–34

14. Repeat with the top row of mullions.

15. In the View Control Bar, click (Temporary Hide/Isolate) and select **Reset Temporary Hide/Isolate**.

16. Save the project.

Task 2 - Add the storefront entrance.

1. Open the **Floor Plans: Floor 1** view.

2. In the *Architecture* tab>Build panel, click (Wall).

3. In the Type Selector, select **Curtain Wall:Storefront**.

4. In Properties, enter the following values:

    - *Base Constraint:* **Floor 1**
    - *Base Offset:* **0' 0"**.
    - *Top Constraint:* **Up to level: Floor 2**
    - *Top Offset:* (negative) **-6' 0"**.

5. Draw the storefront within the existing wall **1'-3"** off of the right gridline, as shown in Figure 6–35.

Figure 6–35

- If you draw from right to left, the exterior of the storefront is placed correctly. If you draw from left to right, you need to flip the storefront.

6. Open the **Elevations (Building Elevation): South** view and zoom in on the storefront.

*Type **UP** to unpin the elements.*

7. Window around to select the storefront. Because it was created with a preset type, all of the grids and panels are pinned, as shown on the left in Figure 6–36.

Figure 6–36

8. Modify the storefront, as shown in Figure 6–37. Align the horizontal line with the curtain grid line in the main curtain wall and use temporary dimensions to locate the vertical grid lines.

Ensure you are selecting curtain grid lines as you work and not the mullions. Use <Tab> to cycle through the elements.

Figure 6–37

9. Select the mullions at the top of the storefront and toggle the mullion joins to the top bar so that it is straight across, as shown in Figure 6–38.

Figure 6–38

10. Save the project.

Task 3 - Add a door in the storefront.

---

1. In the *Insert* tab>Load from Library panel, click 🔽 (Load Family). Use this more generic method of loading the curtain wall door family because you cannot use the **Door** command to place doors in curtain walls.

2. In the Load Family dialog box, in the *Doors* folder, select the door **Door-Curtain-Wall-Double-Storefront.rfa**, as shown in Figure 6–39. Click **Open**.

Figure 6–39

3. Select the large panel, as shown in Figure 6–40. Use <Tab> to cycle through the selections and then click to select it.

Figure 6–40

4. In the Type Selector, select **Door-Curtain-Wall-Double-Storefront.** The panel changes to the door. Delete the mullion at the bottom of the door, as shown in Figure 6–41.

Figure 6–41

5. Zoom out until the entire front elevation is displayed.

6. View the project in 3D.

7. Save the project.

Chapter Review Questions

1. Which command do you start with to create a curtain wall?

    a. (Wall)

    b. (Curtain Grid)

    c. (Curtain System)

2. You are placing a curtain grid and it keeps snapping to one dimension, such as the TWO-THIRDS OF CURTAIN PANEL shown in Figure 6–42, when you want it to be another. What should you do?

Figure 6–42

    a. Change the snap settings.

    b. Edit the Curtain Wall Type to permit manual grid placement.

    c. Use a Non-Uniform Curtain Wall Type instead of a Uniform one.

    d. Place the curtain grid anyway, select the temporary dimension, and change it to the required value.

3. How do you select one panel to modify it?

   a. Select the middle of the panel.

   b. Point to the edge of the panel and press <Tab> until it is identified.

   c. Select the curtain wall, right-click and select **Panel Select**.

   d. In the Selection Priority drop-down list, select **Curtain Panel**.

4. Once you select a panel, what can you swap it for? (Select all that apply.)

   a. Empty system panel

   b. Store Front Door

   c. Blank

   d. Wall Type

5. How do you change the way in which two mullions intersect, as shown in Figure 6–43? (Select all that apply.)

Figure 6–43

   a. Select one of the mullions and press <Tab> until the correct intersection displays.

   b. Select one of the mullions and click the **Make Continuous** or **Break at Join** icons in the contextual tab.

   c. Select one of the mullions and click the **Toggle Mullion Join** control.

   d. Select both mullions and select the **Intersect** box in the Options Bar.

Command Summary

Button	Command	Location
	Add/Remove Segments	• **Ribbon:** *Modify	Curtain Wall Grids* tab>Curtain Grid panel
	Curtain Grid	• **Ribbon:** *Architecture* tab>Build panel
	Curtain Grid: All Except Picked	• **Ribbon:** *Modify	Place Curtain Grid* tab>Placement panel
	Curtain Grid: All Segments	• **Ribbon:** *Modify	Place Curtain Grid* tab>Placement panel
	Curtain Grid: One Segment	• **Ribbon:** *Modify	Place Curtain Grid* tab>Placement panel
	Mullion	• **Ribbon:** *Architecture* tab>Build panel
	Mullion: All Grid Lines	• **Ribbon:** *Modify	Place Mullion* tab>Placement panel
	Mullion: Break at Join	• **Ribbon:** *Modify	Curtain Wall Mullions* tab>Mullion panel • **Right-click:** (with mullion selected) Join Conditions>Break at Join
	Mullion: Grid Line	• **Ribbon:** *Modify	Place Mullion* tab>Placement panel
	Mullion: Grid Line Segment	• **Ribbon:** *Modify	Place Mullion* tab>Placement panel
	Mullion: Make Continuous	• **Ribbon:** *Modify	Curtain Wall Mullions* tab>Mullion panel • **Right-click:** (with mullion selected) Join Conditions>Make Continuous

Chapter

7

Working with Views

Views are the cornerstone of working with Autodesk® Revit® models as they enable you to see the model in both 2D and 3D. As you are working, you can duplicate and change views to display different information based on the same view of the model. Callouts, elevations, and sections are especially important views for construction documents.

Learning Objectives in this Chapter

- Change the way elements display in different views to show required information and set views for construction documents.
- Duplicate views so that you can modify the display as you are creating the model and for construction documents.
- Create callout views of parts of plans, sections, or elevations for detailing.
- Add building and interior elevations that can be used to demonstrate how a building will be built.
- Create building and wall sections to help you create the model and to include in construction documents.

7.1 Setting the View Display

Views are a powerful tool as they enable you to create multiple versions of a model without having to redraw building elements. For example, you can have views that are specifically used for working on the model, while other views are annotated and used for construction documents. Different disciplines can have different views that show only the features they require, as shown in Figure 7–1.

Architectural

Mechanical

Figure 7–1

The view display can be modified in the following locations:

- View Control Bar
- Properties
- Right-click menu
- Visibility/Graphic Overrides dialog box

Hiding and Overriding Graphics

Two common ways to customize a view are to:

- Hide individual elements or categories

- Modify how graphics display for elements or categories (e.g., altering lineweight, color, or pattern)

An element is an individual item (i.e., one wall in a view), while a category includes all instances of a selected element (i.e., all walls in a view).

In the example shown in Figure 7–2, a Furniture Plan has been created by turning off the structural grids category, and then graying out all of the walls and columns.

Figure 7–2

How To: Hide Elements or Categories in a view

1. Select the elements or categories you want to hide.
2. Right-click and select **Hide in View>Elements** or **Hide in View>Category**, as shown in Figure 7–3.
3. The elements or categories are hidden in current view only.

*A quick way to hide entire categories is to select an element(s) and type **VH**.*

Figure 7–3

How To: Override Graphics of Elements or Categories in a View

1. Select the element(s) you want to modify.
2. Right-click and select **Override Graphics in View>By Element** or **By Category**. The View-Specific Element (or Category) Graphics dialog box opens, as shown in Figure 7–4.

The exact options in the dialog box vary depending on the type of elements selected.

Figure 7–4

3. Select the changes you want to make and click **OK**.

View-Specific Options

- Clearing the **Visible** option is the same as hiding the elements or categories.

- Selecting the **Halftone** option grays out the elements or categories.

- The options for Projection Lines, Surface Patterns, Cut Lines, and Cut Patterns include **Weight**, **Color**, and **Pattern**, as shown in Figure 7–4.

- **Surface Transparency** can be set by moving the slider bar, as shown in Figure 7–5.

Figure 7–5

- The View-Specific Category dialog box includes the **Open the Visibility Graphics dialog...** button which opens the full dialog box of options.

The Visibility/Graphic Overrides dialog box

The options in the Visibility/Graphic Overrides dialog box (shown in Figure 7–6) control how every category and sub-category of elements is displayed per view.

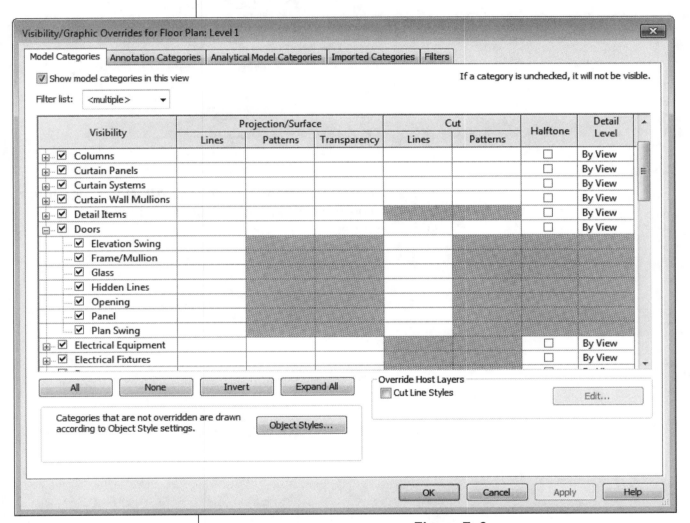

Figure 7–6

To open the Visibility/Graphic Overrides dialog box, type **VV** or **VG**. It is also available in Properties: in the *Graphics* area, beside *Visibility/Graphic Overrides*, click **Edit...**.

- The Visibility/Graphic Overrides are divided into *Model*, *Annotation*, *Analytical Model*, *Imported*, and *Filters* categories.

- Other tabs may be available if specific data has been included in the project, including *Design Options*, *Linked Files*, and *Worksets*.

- To limit the number of categories showing in the dialog box select a discipline from the *Filter list*, as shown in Figure 7–7

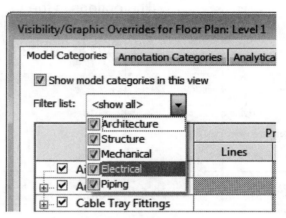

Figure 7–7

- To help you select categories, use the **All**, **None**, and **Invert** buttons. The **Expand All** button displays all of the sub-categories.

Hint: Restoring Hidden Elements or Categories

If you have hidden categories, you can display them using the Visibility/Graphic Overrides dialog box. To display hidden elements, however, you must reveal the elements first.

1. in the View Control Bar, click (Reveal Hidden Elements). The border and all hidden elements are displayed in magenta, while visible elements in the view are grayed out, as shown in Figure 7–8.

Figure 7–8

2. Select the hidden elements you want to restore, right-click, and select **Unhide in View>Elements** or **Unhide in View>Category**. Alternatively, in the *Modify |* contextual tab> Reveal Hidden Elements panel, click (Unhide Element) or (Unhide Category).

3. When you are finished, in the View Control Bar, click (Close Reveal Hidden Elements) or, in the *Modify |* contextual tab> Reveal Hidden Elements panel click (Toggle Reveal Hidden Elements Mode).

View Properties

The most basic properties of a view are accessed using the View Control Bar, shown in Figure 7–9. These include the *Scale*, *Detail Level*, and *Visual Style* options. Additional options include temporary overrides and other advanced settings.

1/8" = 1'-0"

Figure 7–9

Other modifications to views are available in Properties, as shown in Figure 7–10. These options include *Underlays*, *View Range*, and *Crop Regions*.

The options in Properties vary according to the type of view. A plan view has different parameters than a 3D view.

Figure 7–10

View Range

The View Range sets the locations of cut planes and view depths in plans, as shown in a section in Figure 7–11.

Figure 7–11

How To: Set the View Range

1. In Properties, in the *Extents* area, beside *View Range*, select **Edit...**.
2. In the View Range dialog box, as shown in Figure 7–12, modify the Levels and Offsets for the *Primary Range* and *View Depth*.
3. Click **OK**.

If the settings used cannot be represented graphically, a warning displays stating the inconsistency.

Figure 7–12

- A Reflected Ceiling Plan (RCP) is drawn as if the ceiling is reflected by a mirror on the floor so that the ceiling is the same orientation as the floor plan. The cutline is placed just below the ceiling to ensure that any windows and doors below do not display.

Hint: Depth Clipping and Far Clipping

Depth Clipping, shown in Figure 7–13, is a viewing option which sets how sloped walls are displayed if the *View Range* of a plan is set to a limited view.

Figure 7–13

Far Clipping (shown in Figure 7–14) is available for section and elevation views.

Figure 7–14

Crop Regions

Plans, sections, and elevations can all be modified by changing how much of the model is displayed in a view. One way to do this is to set the Crop Region. If there are dimensions, tags, or text near the desired crop region, you can also use the Annotation Crop Region to include these, as shown in Figure 7–15.

Annotation Crop Region

Model Crop Region

Figure 7–15

Zoom out if you do not see the crop region when you set it to be displayed.

- The crop region must be displayed to modify the size of the view. In the View Control Bar, click 🔲 (Show Crop Region) Alternatively, in Properties, in the *Extents* area, select **Crop Region Visible**. **Annotation Crop** is also available in this area.

- Resize the crop region using the ● control on each side of the region.

Breaking the crop region is typically used with sections or details.

- Click ⌇ (Break Line) control to split the view into two regions, horizontally or vertically. Each part of the view can then be modified in size to display what is needed and be moved independently.

- It is a best practice to hide a crop region before placing a view on a sheet. In the View Control Bar, click 🔲 (Hide Crop Region).

Hint: Applying View Templates

A powerful way to use views effectively is to set up a view and then save it as a View Template. To apply a View Template, right-click on a view in the Project Browser and select **Apply View Template Properties....** Then, in the Apply View Template dialog box, select a *Name* in the list (as shown in Figure 7–16) and click **OK**.

Figure 7–16

*   View Templates can be preset in Properties so that changes cannot be made to the view.

7.2 Duplicating Views

Once you have created a model, you do not have to redraw the elements at different scales or copy them so that they can be used on more than one sheet. Instead, you can duplicate the required views and modify them to suit your needs.

Duplication Types

Duplicate creates a copy of the view that only includes the building elements, as shown in Figure 7–17. Annotation and detailing are not copied into the new view. Building model elements automatically change in all views, but view-specific changes made to the new view are not reflected in the original view.

Original   *Duplicate*

Figure 7–17

Duplicate with Detailing creates a copy of the view and includes all annotation and detail elements (such as tags), as shown in Figure 7–18. Any annotation or view-specific elements created in the new view are not reflected in the original view.

Original   *Duplicate with Detailing*

Figure 7–18

Duplicate as a Dependent creates a copy of the view and links it to the original (parent) view, as shown in the Project Browser in Figure 7–19. View-specific changes made to the overall view, such as changing the *Scale*, are also reflected in the dependent (child) views and vice-versa.

Figure 7–19

- Use dependent views when the building model is so large that you need to split the building onto separate sheets, while ensuring that the views are all same scale.

- If you want to separate a dependent view from the original view, right-click on the dependent view and select **Convert to independent view**.

How To: Create Duplicate Views

1. Open the view you want to duplicate.
2. In the *View* tab>Create panel, expand **Duplicate View** and select the type of duplicate view you want to create, as shown in Figure 7–20.

Most types of views can be duplicated.

Figure 7–20

- Alternatively, you can right-click on a view in the Project Browser and select the type of duplicate that you want to use, as shown in Figure 7–21.

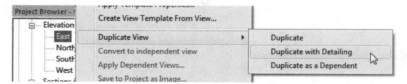

Figure 7–21

*You can also press
<F2> to start the
Rename command.*

- To rename a view, right-click on the new view in the Project Browser and select **Rename**. In the Rename View dialog box, type in the new name, as shown in Figure 7–22.

Figure 7–22

Practice 7a

Duplicate Views and Set the View Display

Practice Objectives

- Duplicate views.
- Modify crop regions.
- Change the visibility and graphic display of elements in views.

In this practice you will duplicate views and then modify them by changing the scale and crop region, hiding some elements, and changing some elements to halftone to prepare them to be used in construction documents. The finished views of the second floor are shown in Figure 7–23, which is a model of the completed building.

Estimated time for completion: 10 minutes

Before

After

Figure 7–23

Task 1 - Duplicate and modify the first floor plan view.

1. Open the project **Modern-Hotel-Display.rvt**.

2. Open the **Floor Plans: Floor 1** view. This view includes a variety of tags.

3. In the Project Browser, right-click on the **Floor Plans: Floor 1** view and select **Duplicate View>Duplicate**. This creates a view without all of the tags, but includes the grids and elevation markers.

4. Right-click on the new view and rename it to **Floor 1 Overall**.

5. In the View Control Bar, change the *Scale* to **1/16"=1'-0"**. All of the annotations become larger, as they need to plot correctly at this scale.

6. In the View Control Bar, click (Show Crop Region).

7. Select the crop region and drag the control on the top until the pool house displays, as shown in Figure 7–24.

Figure 7–24

8. In the View Control Bar, click ▦ (Hide Crop Region)

9. Select the four horizontal pool grid lines (P1-P4).

10. Right-click and select **Hide in View> Elements**. Only the selected grid lines are hidden.

11. Select one of the elevation markers.

12. Right-click and select **Hide in View>Category**. All of the elevation markers are hidden.

13. In the View Control Bar, click ▦ (Hide Crop Region).

14. Zoom out to display the entire view. (Hint: Use the shortcuts **ZF** or **ZE**, or double-click the mouse wheel.)

15. Duplicate **Floor 1** again (without Detailing). Rename this view **Floor 1 - Reference**. You will use this later to place callouts and sections.

16. Save the project.

Task 2 - Duplicate and modify a second floor plan view.

---

1. Open the **Floor Plans: Floor 2** view.

2. In the Project Browser, right-click on the same view and select **Duplicate View>Duplicate**. This creates a new view without any annotation.

3. Rename this view to **Typical Guest Room Floor Plan**.

4. Select one of the grids and type **VH** (Hide in View Category).

5. Turn on the crop region and bring it in close to the building on all sides. If any of the elevation markers still display, hide them.

6. Turn off the crop region.

7. Select one of the railings along the balconies. Right-click and select **Select All Instances>Visible in View**. The railings are selected as shown in Figure 7–25.

Figure 7–25

8. Right-click again and select **Override Graphics in View > By Element...**

9. In the View-Specific Element Graphics dialog box select **Halftone** and click **OK**.

10. Click in the view to release the selection. The railings are now gray and not as prominent.

11. Close any other projects that may be open.

12. In the Quick Access Toolbar, click (Close Hidden Windows). Only the Typical Guest Room Floor Plan view should be open.

13. Open the **Floor Plans: Floor 2** view again.

14. Type **WT** to tile the two windows and then type **ZA** so the model displays fully in the view so that you can see the differences in the views.

15. Save the project.

7.3 Adding Callout Views

Callouts are details of plan, elevation, or section views. When you place a callout in a view, it automatically creates a new view clipped to the boundary of the callout, as shown in Figure 7–26. If you change the size of the callout box in the original view, it automatically updates the callout view and vice-versa. You can create rectangular or sketched callout boundaries.

Figure 7–26

How To: Create a Rectangular Callout

1. In the *View tab>Create panel,* click ⬭ **(Callout)**.
2. Select points for two opposite corners to define the callout box around the area you want to detail.
3. Select the callout and use the shape handles to modify the location of the bubble and any other edges that might need changing.
4. In the Project Browser, rename the callout.

How To: Create a Sketched Callout

1. In the *View tab>Create panel,* expand ⬭ (Callout), and click 🖾 (Sketch).
2. Sketch the shape of the callout using the tools in the *Modify | Edit Profile* tab>Draw panel, as shown in Figure 7–27.

Figure 7–27

3. Click ✔ (Finish) to complete the boundary.
4. Select the callout and use the shape handles to modify the location of the bubble and any other edges that might need to be changed.
5. In the Project Browser, rename the callout

• To open the callout view, double-click on its name in the Project Browser or double-click on the callout bubble (verify that the callout itself is not selected before you double-click on it).

Modifying Callouts

The callout bubble displays numbers when the view is placed on a sheet.

In the original view where the callout is created, you can use the shape handles to modify the callout boundary and bubble location, as shown in Figure 7–28.

Figure 7–28

• You can rotate the callout box by dragging the ○ (Rotate) control or by right-clicking on edge of callout and selecting **Rotate**.

In the callout view, you can modify the crop region with shape handles and view breaks, as shown in Figure 7–29.

Figure 7–29

- If you want to edit the crop region to reshape the boundary of the view, select the crop region and, in the *Modify | Floor Plan* tab>Mode panel, click (Edit Crop).

- If you want to return a modified crop region to the original rectangular configuration, click (Reset Crop).

- You can also resize the crop region and the annotation crop region using the Crop Region Size dialog box as shown in Figure 7–30. In the *Modify | Floor Plan* tab>Crop panel, click (Size Crop) to open the dialog box.

Crop Region Size

Model Crop Size
Width: 28"   Height: 22"

Annotation Crop Offsets
Left: 1"   Top: 1"
Right: 1"   Bottom: 1"
Overall Size: 30" x 24"

OK   Cancel   Apply   Help

Figure 7–30

Practice 7b

Add Callout Views

Practice Objective

- Create callouts.
- Override visibility and graphic styles in views.

Estimated time for completion: 10 minutes

In this practice you will create callout views of a guest room and make modifications to the visibility graphics so that one displays dimensions and the other displays the furniture plan, as shown in Figure 7–31.

Figure 7–31

Task 1 - Add callout views.

1. Open the project **Modern-Hotel-Callouts.rvt**.

2. Open the **Floor Plans: Typical Guest Room Floor Plan** view (if it is not already open).

3. In the *View* tab>Create panel, click (Callout).

4. Place a callout around one of the guest rooms. Using the controls (as shown in Figure 7–32), move the bubble as required. Click in empty space to release the selection.

Figure 7–32

5. Double-click on the callout view bubble. It only opens the view that is enclosed within the callout window. Rename the view to **Typical Guest Room - Dimension Plan**.

6. In Properties, change the *Underlay* to **None**.

7. Duplicate the callout view and rename it to **Typical Guest Room - Furniture Plan**. Both views should look similar to Figure 7–33.

Figure 7–33

8. Save the project.

Task 2 - Override graphics in views.

1. Open the **Floor Plans: Typical Guest Room - Dimension Plan** view.

2. Open the Visibility/Graphic Overrides dialog box by typing **VV**.

3. In the dialog box, set the *Filter list* to **Architecture** (by clearing the check marks for the other options). In the *Visibility* column, clear **Casework**, **Furniture**, **Furniture Systems**, as shown in Figure 7–34 and **Plumbing Fixtures** (not shown).

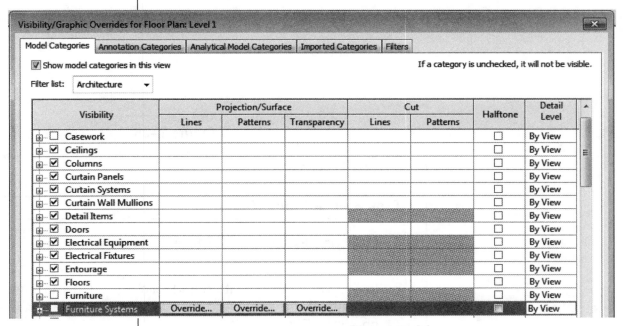

Figure 7–34

4. Click **OK**. While nothing looks different now, when furniture is placed in the model it will not display in this view.

5. Open the **Floor Plans: Typical Guest Room - Furniture Plan** view.

6. Reopen the Visibility/Graphic Overrides dialog box. Below the table, click **All** and place a checkmark in one of the *Halftone* columns. All of the elements are set to halftone.

7. Click **None** to clear all categories.

8. In the *Halftone* column, clear the **Casework**, **Furniture**, **Furniture Systems**, and **Plumbing Fixtures** categories.

9. Click **Apply** to set the changes without exiting the dialog box.

When furniture, casework, and plumbing fixtures are added, they will display in black against the other halftone elements.

10. In the *Annotation Categories* tab, clear **Show annotation categories in this view**. No annotations elements will display in this view.

11. Click **OK** to close the dialog box. The view should display with all existing elements in halftone, as shown in Figure 7–35.

Figure 7–35

12. Save the project.

Task 3 - Additional Callouts

1. Open the **Floor Plans: Floor 1 - Reference** view.

2. In the *View* tab>Create panel, click ⬭⁺ (Callout) and add callouts to the stairs and restrooms. Name the views as shown in Figure 7–36.

Figure 7–36

3. Save the project.

7.4 Elevations and Sections

Elevations and sections are critical elements of construction documents and can assist you as you are working on a model. Any changes made in one of these views (such as the section in Figure 7–37), changes the entire model and any changes made to the project model are also displayed in the elevations and sections.

Figure 7–37

- In the Project Browser, elevations are separated by elevation type and sections are separated by section type as shown in Figure 7–38.

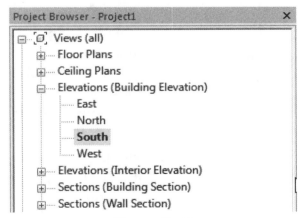

Figure 7–38

- To open an elevation or section view, double-click on the marker arrow or on its name in the Project Browser.

- To give the elevation or section a new name, right-click on it in the Project Browser and select **Rename...**

Elevations

Elevations are *face-on* views of the interiors and exteriors of a building. Four Exterior Elevation views are defined in the default template: **North**, **South**, **East**, and **West**. You can create additional building elevation views at other angles or interior elevation views, such as the Kitchen elevation shown in Figure 7–39.

When you add an elevation or section to a sheet, the detail number and sheet number are automatically added to the view title.

Figure 7–39

- Elevations must be created in plan views.

How To: Create an Elevation

The software remembers the last elevation type used, so you can click the top button if you want to use the same elevation command.

1. In the *View* tab>Create panel, expand ⬆ (Elevation) and click ⬆ (Elevation).
2. In the Type Selector, select the elevation type. Two options that come with the templates are **Building Elevation** and **Interior Elevation**.
3. Move the cursor near one of the walls that defines the elevation. The marker follows the angle of the wall.
4. Click to place the marker.

- The length, width, and height of an elevation are defined by the wall(s) and ceiling/floor at which the elevation marker is pointing.

- When creating interior elevations, ensure that the floor or ceiling above is in place before creating the elevation or you will need to modify the elevation crop region so that the elevation markers do not show on all floors.

Sections

Sections can be created in plan, elevation, and other section views.

Sections are slices through a model. You can create a section through an entire building, as shown in Figure 7–40, or through one wall for a detail.

Figure 7–40

How To: Create a Section

1. In the *View* tab>Create panel or in the Quick Access Toolbar, click ♀ (Section).

2. In the Type Selector, select **Section: Building Section** or **Section: Wall Section.** If you want a section in a Drafting view select **Detail View: Detail.**

3. In the view, select a point where you want to locate the bubble and arrowhead.

4. Select the other end point that describes the section.

5. The shape controls display. You can flip the arrow and change the size of the cutting plane, as well as the location of the bubble and flag.

New
in **2016**

Hint: Selection Box

You can modify a 3D view to display parts of a building, as shown in Figure 7–41.

Section Boxes : Section Box

Figure 7–41

1. In a 3D view, select the elements you want to isolate. In the example shown in Figure 7–41, the front wall was selected.

2. In the *Modify* tab>View panel click   (Selection Box) or type **BX**.
3. The view is limited to a box around the selected item(s).
4. Use the controls of the Section Box to modify the size of the box to show exactly what you want.

*   To turn off a section box and restore the full model, in the view's Properties, in the *Extents* area, clear the check from **Section Box**.

Modifying Elevations and Sections

There are two parts to modifying elevations and sections:

*   Modifying the markers (as shown in Figure 7–42).

*   Modifying the view (as shown in Figure 7–43).

Markers have slightly different options, but the views have the same options as callout views.

Modifying elevation and section markers

Figure 7–42

Modifying elevation and section views

Figure 7–43

Modifying Elevation Markers

When you modify the elevation markers you can specify the length and depth of the clip plane as well as split the section line. Select the arrowhead of the elevation marker (not the circle portion) to display the clip plane. You can adjust the length of the clip planes using the round shape handles (as shown in Figure 7–44) and adjust the depth of the elevation using the

♠ Drag control.

Figure 7–44

To display additional interior elevations from one marker, place an elevation marker and select the circle portion (not the arrowhead). With the elevation marker selected, place a checkmark in the directions that you want to display, as shown in Figure 7–45.

Figure 7–45

*   You can also rotate the marker using ↻ (Rotate) (i.e., for a room with angled walls).

Modifying Section Markers

When you modify the section markers, you can specify the length and depth of the clip plane, flip the orientation, and create a gap as well as split the section line. Various shape handles and controls enable you to modify a section, as shown in Figure 7–46.

Figure 7–46

*   Change the size and location of the cut plane by dragging ↕ (Arrow) on the dashed lines in or out.

*   Change the location of the arrow or flag without changing the cut boundary by dragging the circular controls at either end of the section line.

*   Click ⇆ (Flip) to change the direction of the arrowhead, which also flips the entire section.

- Cycle between an arrowhead, flag, or nothing on each end of the section by clicking ↻ (Cycle Section Head/Tail).

- Create gaps in section lines by clicking ⤳ (Gaps in Segments), as shown in Figure 7–47. Select it again to restore the full section cut.

Figure 7–47

How To: Split an Elevation or Section Line

In some cases, you need to create additional jogs in an elevation or section line so that it displays the most important information along the cut, as shown for a section in Figure 7–48.

Figure 7–48

1. Select the elevation or section line you want to split.
2. In the Section panel, click ▦ (Split Segment).
3. Select the point along the line where you want to create the split, as shown in Figure 7–49.

Figure 7–49

4. Specify the location of the split line, as shown in Figure 7–50.

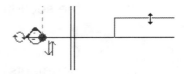

Figure 7–50

- If you need to adjust the location of any segment on the section line, modify it and drag the shape handles along each segment of the line, as shown in Figure 7–51.

Figure 7–51

- To bring a split elevation or section line back into place, use a shape handle to drag it until it is in line with the rest of the elevation or line.

Hint: Using Thin Lines

The software automatically applies line weights to views, as shown for a section on the left in Figure 7–52. If a line weight seems heavy or obscures your work on the elements, turn off the line weights. In the Quick Access Toolbar or in the *View* tab>Graphics panel, click ⧉ (Thin Lines) or type **TL**. The lines display with the same weight, as shown on the right in Figure 7–52.

Thin Lines Off   *Thin Lines On*

Figure 7–52

- The Thin Line setting is remembered until you change it, even if you shut down and restart the software.

Enhanced
in **2016**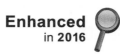

Practice 7c

Create Elevations and Sections

Estimated time for completion: 20 minutes

Practice Objectives

- Create exterior and interior elevations.
- Add building sections and wall sections.

In this practice you will create exterior elevations of the poolhouse and interior elevations of the restrooms. You will also add building sections, as shown in Figure 7–53, and several wall sections to the project.

Figure 7–53

Task 1 - Add exterior elevations.

1. Open the project **Modern-Hotel-Elevations.rvt**.

2. Open the **Floor Plans: Floor 1 Overall** view.

3. In the View Control Bar click ☼ (Reveal Hidden Elements).

4. Select one of the elevation markers. In the Reveal Hidden Element panel click ⊞ (Unhide Category).

5. In the View Control Bar click ▣ (Close Reveal Hidden Elements).

6. In the View Control Bar, click ⊞ (Show Crop Region).

7. Ensure that there is enough space above the pool house to add an elevation mark at this scale, if not, move the crop region up.

8. In the *View* tab>Create panel, expand ⬆ (Elevation) and click ⬆ (Elevation). In the Type Selector, select **Elevation: Building Elevation**.

9. Place an elevation marker outside of the pool building, as shown in Figure 7–54.

Figure 7–54

10. Click ⌖ (Modify) and select the pointed side of the new elevation marker.

Grids are hidden to clarify the view.

11. Change the length and depth of the elevation boundaries so only the poolhouse is displayed, as shown in Figure 7–55.

Figure 7–55

12. Double-click on the pointed side of the elevation marker to open the elevation view.

13. Change the crop region so that the height is up to **Floor 3** and the bottom is just below the floor line. Bring the sides in close to the pool building.

14. Hide the grids and levels so that the elevation is similar to that shown in Figure 7–56.

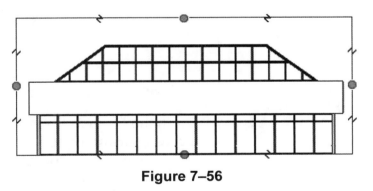

Figure 7–56

15. Hide the crop region.

16. In the Project Browser, rename the elevation (Elevation 1 -a if you selected this direction first) as **Pool-North**.

In this project, North is considered the top of the project.

17. Return to the **Floor Plans: Floor 1 Overall** view.

18. Add elevation markers to the other sides of the poolhouse.

19. Open the new elevations. Resize and rename them as required.

20. Save the project.

Task 2 - Add interior elevations.

1. Open the **Floor Plans: Floor 1 - Restrooms** view.

2. In the *View* tab>Create panel, click 🔼 (Elevation).

3. In the Type Selector, select **Elevation: Interior Elevation**.

4. Place an elevation in one of the restrooms and then in the other restroom.

5. Click ⬉ (Modify and select the circle part of one of the elevation markers and check each of the boxes, as shown in Figure 7–57. This places an elevation in each direction.

Figure 7–57

6. Repeat for the other restroom.

7. In the Project Browser, under *Elevations (Interior Elevation)*, as shown in Figure 7–58, rename the top restroom elevations as **Men's Restroom-North**, **South**, **East**, **West** and the bottom restroom elevations as **Women's Restroom-North**, **South**, **East**, **West**.

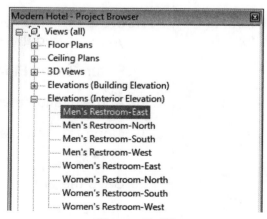

Figure 7–58

8. Open one of the elevations facing the door (**Men's Restroom-East**). The interior elevation automatically stops at the boundaries of the walls and the level above.

9. Move the crop region so that it is tight against the walls, as shown in Figure 7–59

Figure 7–59

10. Save the project.

Task 3 - Clean up a view and add building sections.

1. Open the **Floor Plans: Floor 1- Reference** view.

2. Select all the elements around the restrooms. Use a selection window around the restrooms.

3. In the Status Bar or in the *Modify | Multi-Select* tab>Selection panel, click ▼ (Filter).

4. In the Filter dialog box, clear all of the selections except **Elevations** and **Views** and click **OK**. Only the Interior Elevation markers in the restrooms should be selected.

5. Right-click and select **Hide in View>Elements**.

6. In the View Control Bar, click 🔲 (Do Not Crop View).

7. Move the elevation markers closer to the building.

8. In the View Control Bar, click 🔲 (Crop View).

In this case you do not want to hide the entire category of elevation markers.

9. In the *View* tab>Create panel, click ✐ (Section).

10. In the Type Selector, select **Section: Building Section**.

11. Draw a horizontal section and a vertical section through the building, as shown in Figure 7–60.

Figure 7–60

12. In the Project Browser, under *Sections*, rename them to **East-West Section** and **North-South Section**.

13. View each of the building sections.

Task 4 - Add wall sections.

You are using the ***Floor 2*** *view to place the wall sections, as you want to ensure they go through certain features, such as doors and windows.*

1. Open the **Floor Plans: Floor 2** view.

2. Hide the grids if required and hide by element, any extraneous elevation markers.

3. In the *View* tab>Create panel, click ✐ (Section). In the Type Selector, select **Section: Wall Section**.

4. Draw four wall sections, as shown in Figure 7–61. Ensure that the front wall section passes through a window and the back wall section passes through a door.

Figure 7–61

5. Move the door and window tag over so they do not interfere with the section cut.

6. View each of the wall sections.

7. Open the **Floor Plans: Floor 1** view.

8. Save the project.

Chapter Review Questions

1. Which of the following commands shown in Figure 7–62, creates a view that results in an independent view displaying the same model geometry and containing a copy of the annotation?

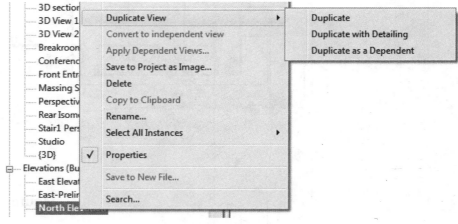

Figure 7–62

  a. Duplicate

  b. Duplicate with Detailing

  c. Duplicate as a Dependent

2. Which of the following is true about the Visibility Graphic Overrides dialog box? (Select all that apply.)

  a. Changes made in the dialog box only affect the current view.

  b. It can only be used to turn categories on and off.

  c. It can be used to turn individual elements on and off.

  d. It can be used to change the color of individual elements.

3. The purpose of callouts is to create a...

  a. Boundary around part of the model that needs revising, similar to a revision cloud.

  b. View of part of the model for export to the AutoCAD® software for further detailing.

  c. View of part of the model that is linked to the main view from which it is taken.

  d. 2D view of part of the model.

4. You placed dimensions in a view and some of them display and others do not (as shown on the left in Figure 7–63) but you were expecting the view to display as shown on the right in Figure 7–63. To display the missing dimensions you need to modify the...

Figure 7–63

a. Dimension Settings

b. Dimension Type

c. Visibility Graphic Overrides

d. Annotation Crop Region

5. How do you create multiple interior elevations in one room?

a. Using the **Interior Elevation** command, place the elevation marker.

b. Using the **Elevation** command, place the first marker, select it and select the appropriate Show Arrow boxes.

c. Using the **Interior Elevation** command, place an elevation marker for each wall of the room you want to display.

d. Using the **Elevation** command, select a Multiple Elevation marker type, and place the elevation marker.

6. How do you create a jog in a building section, such as that shown in Figure 7–64?

Figure 7–64

a. Use the **Split Element** tool in the *Modify* tab>Modify panel.

b. Select the building section and then click the **Split Segment** icon in the contextual tab.

c. Select the building section and click the blue control in the middle of the section line.

d. Draw two separate sections, and use the **Section Jog** tool to combine them into a jogged section.

Command Summary

Button	Command	Location
Views		
	Building Elevation	• **Ribbon:** *View* tab>Create panel> expand Elevation
	Callout: Rectangle	• **Ribbon:** *View* tab>Create panel> expand Callout
	Callout: Sketch	• **Ribbon:** *View* tab>Create panel> expand Callout
	Duplicate	• **Ribbon:** *View* tab>Create panel> expand Duplicate View • **Right-click:** (*on a view in the Project Browser*) expand Duplicate View
	Duplicate as Dependent	• **Ribbon:** *View* tab>Create panel> expand Duplicate View • **Right-click:** (*on a view in the Project Browser*) expand Duplicate View
	Duplicate with Detailing	• **Ribbon:** *View* tab>Create panel> expand Duplicate View • **Right-click:** (*on a view in the Project Browser*) Duplicate View
	Section	• **Ribbon:** *View* tab>Create panel • **Quick Access Toolbar**
	Split Segment	• **Ribbon:** (*when the elevation or section marker is selected*) Modify	*Views* tab>Section panel
Crop Views		
	Crop View	• **View Control Bar** • **View Properties:** Crop View (*check*)
	Do Not Crop View	• **View Control Bar** • **View Properties:** Crop View (*clear*)
	Edit Crop	• **Ribbon:** (*when the crop region of a callout, elevation, or section view is selected*) Modify	*Views* tab>Mode panel
	Hide Crop Region	• **View Control Bar** • **View Properties:** Crop Region Visible (*clear*)
	Reset Crop	• **Ribbon:** (*when the crop region of a callout, elevation or section view is selected*) Modify	*Views* tab>Mode panel
	Show Crop Region	• **View Control Bar** • **View Properties:** Crop Region Visible (*check*)

	Size Crop	• **Ribbon:** *(when the crop region of a callout, elevation or section view is selected)* *Modify	Views* tab>Mode panel
View Display		
	Hide in View	• **Ribbon:** *Modify* tab>View Graphics panel>Hide>Elements *or* By Category • **Right-click:** *(when an element is selected)* Hide in View>Elements *or* Category
	Override Graphics in View	• **Ribbon:** *Modify* tab>View Graphics panel>Hide>Elements *or* By Category • **Right-click:** *(when an element is selected)* Override Graphics in View>By Element *or* By Category • **Shortcut:** *(category only)* VV or VG
	Reveal Hidden Elements	• **View Control Bar**
	Temporary Hide/Isolate	• **View Control Bar**

Chapter
8

Adding Components

As you construct a building model, you add component families such as furniture, lighting fixtures, mechanical equipment, and structural framing elements. These components can be loaded from your company's template, the Autodesk® Revit® library, a custom library, or the Autodesk® Seek service.

Learning Objectives in this Chapter

- Place components in a project to further develop the design.
- Load components from the Autodesk Revit library and the Autodesk Seek service.
- Change component types and locations.
- Purge unused component elements to increase the processing speed of the model.

8.1 Adding Components

Many types of elements are added to a project using component families. These can include freestanding components, such as the furniture, floor lamp, and table lamp shown in Figure 8–1. They can also include wall, ceiling, floor, roof, face and line-hosted components. These components must be placed on the referenced element, such as the fluorescent light fixtures in Figure 8–1.

Figure 8–1

- Several components are included in the default template, making them automatically available in new projects. You can load more components into a project or create your own as required.

- Components are located in family files with the extension RFA. For example, a component family named Desk.rfa can contain several types and sizes.

How To: Place a Component

1. In the *Architecture* tab>Build panel, click ▣ (Place a Component), or type **CM**.
2. In the Type Selector, select the component you want to add to the project.
3. In the view, select a point to place the stand-alone component.

Create Similar works with all elements.

- A fast way to add components that match those already in your project is to select one, right-click on it, and select **Create Similar**. This starts the **Component** command with the same type selected.

Loading Components

If the components you are looking for are not available, you can look in the Autodesk Revit Library, which contains many options. You can also check which components your company has. As you start building a custom library, you can find vendor-specific components on Autodesk Seek.

How To: Load a Family

You can also load a family from the Modify | Place Component tab> Mode panel when placing a component.

1. In the *Insert* tab>Load from Library panel, click

   (Load Family).

2. In the Load Family dialog box, locate the folder that contains the family or families you want to load and select them, as shown in Figure 8–2. To load more than one family at a time, hold <Ctrl> while selecting.

Figure 8–2

3. Click **Open**.

4. Once the family (or families) is loaded, click (Component) and select the type you want to use from the Type Selector, as shown in Figure 8–3.

Figure 8–3

Loading from Autodesk Seek

An Autodesk ID account is required to access content on Autodesk Seek.

Many components are created by manufacturers and other users that are available on-line at Autodesk Seek, as shown in Figure 8–4. You can do a search from within the software or directly on the website and access content for items as diverse as elevator doors, furniture, equipment, details, and materials.

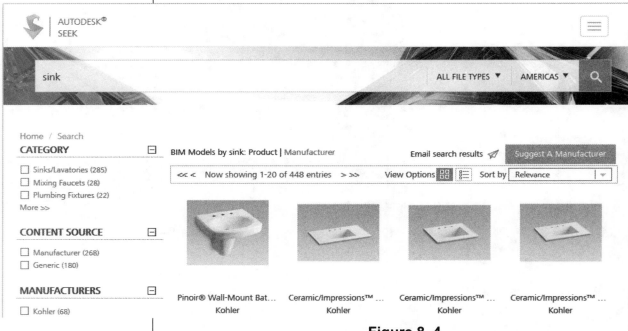

Figure 8–4

How To: Find and Load a Component from Autodesk Seek

1. In the *Insert* tab>Autodesk Seek panel, type the item you are looking for, such as sink, as shown in Figure 8–5. Then click

    (Search Seek Online).

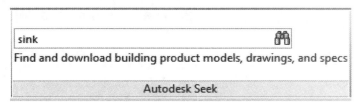

Figure 8–5

2. In the Autodesk Seek website, select the model of the component you want to use.
3. More information about that specific component displays. In the download area (as shown in Figure 8–6), select the file you want to use, specify where you want to save it (locally or on A360 Drive), and click **Download**.

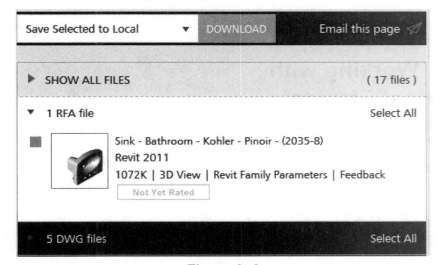

Figure 8–6

Once you have set up a profile in Autodesk Seek you will not see these prompts each time.

4. Once you accept the terms and conditions, the file is downloaded to your computer. It might automatically open in the software depending on your web browser and other settings.
5. Save the family file to the appropriate folder.
6. Use ⬇ (Load Family) to bring it into the current project.

8.2 Modifying Components

Components can be modified when they are selected by changing the type in the Type Selector. For example, you might have placed a task chair in a project (as shown in Figure 8–7), but now you need to change it to an executive chair. With some types, you can use controls to modify the component. You can also select a new host for a component and move components with nearby elements.

Figure 8–7

Working with Host Elements

If you need to move a component from the level on which it was inserted, you can change its host. For example, one of the desks in Figure 8–8 is floating above the floor. It was placed on Level 1 when it was inserted, but needs to be located on the floor that is below the level.

Figure 8–8

How To: Pick a New Host Element

1. Select a component.
2. In the *<component type>* contextual tab>Host panel, click (Pick New Host).
3. Select the new host (e.g., the floor).

- You can select a floor, surface, or level to be the new host for the components depending on the requirements of the component.

Moving with Nearby Host Elements

Components have the capacity to move with nearby host elements (such as walls) when they are moved. Select the component and in the Options Bar select **Moves With Nearby Elements**. The component is automatically assigned to the closest host elements.

For example, a desk near the corner of two walls is linked to those two walls. If you move either wall, the desk moves as well. However, you can still move the desk independently of the walls.

- You cannot specify which elements the component should be linked to; the software determines this automatically. This option only works with host elements (such as walls), not with other components.

Purging Unused Elements

You can remove unused elements from a project, including individual component types, as shown in Figure 8–9.

Figure 8–9

How To: Purge Unused Elements

1. In the *Manage* tab>Settings panel, click 🔲 (Purge Unused).
2. In the Purge unused dialog box, click **Check None** and select the elements you want to purge.
3. Click **OK**.

- Purging unused components not only helps simplify the component list, but more importantly, reduces the project file size.

Practice 8a

Estimated time for completion: 20 minutes

Add Components

Practice Objectives

- Load and add components.
- Load components from Autodesk Seek.

In this practice you will add furniture to the lobby of the hotel, as shown in Figure 8–10. You will load a component from a custom library and use controls to modify the placement. You will also download and use components from Autodesk Seek for the elevator and elevator doors. If you have time, add casework and equipment to the Breakfast and Preparation areas. Finally, you will add footing components to the base of the columns.

Figure 8–10

Task 1 - Add furniture to the lobby.

1. Open the project **Modern-Hotel-Components.rvt**.

2. In the Project Browser, right-click on the **Floor Plans: Floor 1** view and select **Duplicate View>Duplicate**.

3. Rename the new view to **Floor 1 - Furniture Plan**.

4. Hide all annotations and grids, so that only the walls, doors, and columns are displayed.

5. In the *Architecture* tab>Build panel, expand ⬛ (Component) and click ⬛ (Place a Component).

6. In the Type Selector, review the various furniture components that are available for the project. Select **Chair-Corbu** and place it in the lobby area near the curved curtain walls.

7. Open the **Floor Plans: Floor 1** view. The chair displays in this view as well.

8. Open the Visibility/Graphic Overrides dialog box and toggle off the *Visibility* of **Casework**, **Furniture**, **Furniture Systems**, **Planting**, and **Site**. Click **OK**. The chair is no longer displayed in the Floor 1 view.

9. Return to the **Floor Plans: Floor 1 Furniture Plan**.

10. Start the **Component** command.

11. Load the following families:

   - In the *Furniture>Tables* folder: **Table-Dining Round w Chairs.rfa**.
   - In the *Planting* folder: **RPC Plant-Tropical.rfa RPC Tree-Tropical.rfa**.
   - In the *Site>Accessories* folder: **Planter.rfa**.

12. Place and arrange the components as required, placing the dining tables in the breakfast area and other elements in the lobby, as shown in Figure 8–11. Place at least one plant in a planter. You can follow the suggested layout or create your own design.

Figure 8–11

Task 2 - Load and place a countertop component.

1. Zoom in on the office area near the elevator where there is a partial height wall.

2. Start the **Component** command and load **Countertop-Lobby.rfa** from the *Practice Library* subfolder.

Countertops are automatically set to 3'-0" above the level where they are placed. This wall is 4'-0" high and the countertop thickness is about 1 1/2".

3. In Properties, set the *Offset* to **1' 1 5/8"**.

4. Place the Countertop component over the partial height wall. Modify its length using the controls on each end, as shown in Figure 8–12.

Figure 8–12

Task 3 - Load and add elevator components from Autodesk Seek.

If you do not have internet access, these components are available in the Practice Library sub-folder.

1. Pan over to the elevator.

2. In the *Insert* tab>Autodesk Seek panel, type **Electric Elevator**.

3. In Autodesk Seek, find the **Elevator-Electric** component and download it to your practice folder.

   • If a later version of the elevator is not available, select the 2010 version. When you insert an older version, it automatically upgrades to the latest version.

4. While still in Autodesk Seek, search for elevator doors and select **Elevator Door-Center.rfa** to download to your practice folder.

5. Start the **Component** command and load the elevator and elevator door into the project.

6. Place the **Elevator-Electric 2500 lbs** inside the elevator shaft and place the **Elevator Door - Center 42" x 84"** in the wall, as shown in Figure 8–13. (The door is also a component.)

Figure 8–13

7. Select the Elevator Door component.

8. In the *Modify | Floors* tab>Clipboard panel, click 🗐 (Copy to the Clipboard).

9. In the Clipboard panel, expand 📋 (Paste) and click

   📋 (Aligned to Selected Levels).

10. In the Select Levels dialog box, select **Basement** and **Floor 2** through **Floor 8**, as shown in Figure 8–14. Click **OK**. This copies the door to the rest of the levels.

Figure 8–14

11. Save the project.

Task 4 - Add column footings.

1. Open the **Floor Plans: T.O. Footing** view and select everything in the view.

2. In the Status Bar (or in the *Modify | Multi-select* tab>Selection panel), click (Filter).

3. In the Filter dialog box, clear **Structural Columns** and click **OK**.

4. In the Status Bar, expand (Temporary Hide/Isolate) and select **Hide Element.** Everything except the columns should be hidden, as shown in Figure 8–15. It is now easier to identify the locations of the footings.

Figure 8–15

5. In the *Architecture* tab>Build panel, click (Component).

6. In the *Modify | Place Component* tab>Mode panel, click (Load Family).

7. In the *Structural Foundations* folder of the Autodesk Revit Library, select **Footing-Rectangular.rfa** and click **Open**.

8. In the Type Selector, select **Footing-Rectangular:72" x 48" x 18"**. Set the *Level* to **T.O. Footing**.

9. Place a footing at each column. Once you have placed at least one footing, you can use **Copy** to add the others. Ensure that you are copying from the column midpoint, as shown in Figure 8–16.

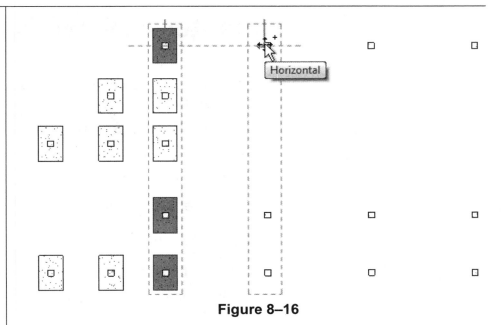

Figure 8–16

10. In the View Control Bar, click ⬗ (Temporary Hide/Isolate) and select **Reset Temporary Hide/Isolate**.

11. In Properties, edit the View Range so that the *Cut plane Offset* is **1' 0"**. This hides any elements that should not part of the foundation plan. as shown in Figure 8–17. (Note: the foundations are highlighted for clarity.)

Figure 8–17

12. Save the project.

Chapter Review Questions

1. When inserting a component, you select the family that you want to use in the...

   a. Quick Access Toolbar

   b. Type Selector

   c. Options Bar

   d. Properties Palette

2. If the component you want to use is not available in the current project, where do you go to get the component? (Select all that apply.)

   a. In another project, copy the component to the clipboard and paste it into the current project.

   b. In the current project, use (Insert from File) and select the family from the list in the dialog box.

   c. In the current project, use (Load Family) and select the family from the list in the dialog box.

   d. Search Autodesk Seek for a component and download it.

3. When you use the **Moves with Nearby Elements** option, can you control which elements move with a component?

   a. Yes, select the element with which you want it to move.

   b. No, it moves with the closest host element.

4. Which of the following commands would you use if you want to move a furniture component to a floor that is lower than the level where it was original placed, as shown in Figure 8–18?

Figure 8–18

a. Use (Level) and add a Level at the height of the lower floor.

b. Use (Ref Plane) and draw a plane aligned with the lower floor.

c. Use (Pick New Host) and select the lower floor.

d. Use (Edit Family) and change the work plane in the family so that it matches the height of the lower floor.

Command Summary

Button	Command	Location
	Load Family	• **Ribbon:** *Modify	Place Component* tab>Load panel or *Insert* tab>Load from Library panel
	Pick New Host	• **Ribbon:** *Modify	Multi-Select* or *component type* contextual tab>Host panel
	Place Component	• **Ribbon:** *Architecture* tab>Build panel> expand Component • **Shortcut:** CM
	Purge Unused	• **Ribbon:** *Manage* tab>Settings panel
	Search Seek Online	• **Ribbon:** *Insert* tab>Autodesk Seek panel

Modeling Floors

Floors in the Autodesk® Revit® software can be used as full depth floors, or as a thin veneer that shows floor material placed on an underlying floor. You can customize floors by creating slopes for drainage, cutting holes, or creating shafts that cut through multiple floors.

Learning Objectives in this Chapter

- Sketch and modify floor boundaries.
- Join Geometry between floors and walls for a cleaner visual presentation.
- Add a shaft opening that cuts through multiple floors.
- Slope a floor in one or more directions for drainage.

9.1 Modeling Floors

The **Floor** command can generate any flat or sloped surface, such as floors, balconies, decks, and patios, as shown in Figure 9–1. Typically created in a plan view, the floor can be based either on bounding walls or on a sketch that you draw to define the outline.

Floors : Floor : Generic

Figure 9–1

- The floor type controls the thickness of a floor.

How To: Add a Floor

1. In the *Architecture* tab>Build panel, expand 🗔 (Floor) and click 🗔 (Floor: Architectural) or 🗔 (Floor: Structural). You are placed in sketch mode where other elements in the drawing are grayed out.
2. In the Type Selector, set the type of floor you want to use. In Properties, set any other options you might need.
3. In the *Modify | Create Floor Boundary* tab>Draw panel, click

   ▯⟍ (Boundary Line).

   - Click ▨ (Pick Walls) and select the walls, setting either the inside or outside edge. If you have selected a wall, you can click ⇆ (Flip) to switch the inside/outside status of the boundary location, as shown in Figure 9–2.

   - Click ⟋ (Line) or one of the other Draw tools and draw the boundary edges.

4. Click ▨ (Slope Arrow) to define a slope for the entire floor.

The lines in the sketch must form a closed loop. You can use tools in the Modify panel to adjust intersections.

5. Click (Span Direction) to modify the direction for floor spans. It comes in automatically when you place the first boundary line, as shown in Figure 9–2.

Span Direction Symbol

Flip Control

Figure 9–2

6. Click ✓ (Finish Edit Mode) to create the floor.

- If you are using 🔲 (Pick Walls), select the **Extend into wall (to core)** option in the Options Bar if you want the floor to cut into the wall. For example, the floor would cut through the gypsum wall board and the air space but stop at a core layer such as CMU.

- If you select one of the boundary sketches, you can also set *Cantilevers* for *Concrete* or *Steel*, as shown in Figure 9–3.

| Offset: 0' 0" | ☐ Defines Slope | ☑ Extend into wall (to core) | Cantilevers : Concrete: 0' 0" | Steel: 0' 0" |

Figure 9–3

- To create an opening inside the sketch, create a separate closed loop inside the first one, as shown in Figure 9–4.

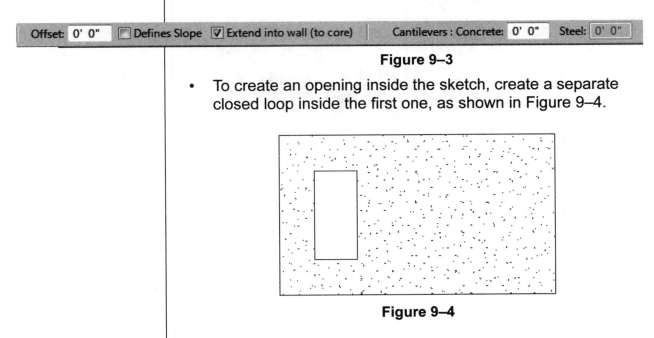

Figure 9–4

- If you create a floor on an upper level, an alert box displays prompting if you want the walls below to be attached to the underside of the floor and its level. If you have a variety of wall heights, it is better to click **No** and attach the walls separately.

- Another alert box might open as shown in Figure 9–5. You can automatically join the geometry or can do so at a later time.

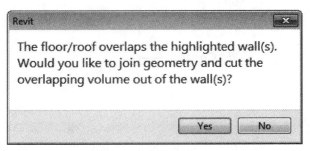

Figure 9–5

- Floors can be placed on top of floors. For example, a structural floor can have a finish floor of tile or carpet placed on top of it, as shown in Figure 9–6. These floors can then be scheduled separately.

Finish floors
Structural floor

Figure 9–6

Modifying Floors

You can change a floor to a different type in the Type Selector. In Properties, you can modify parameters including the *Height Offset From Level*, as shown in Figure 9–7. When you have a floor selected, you can also edit the boundaries.

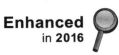

Enhanced
in 2016

Many of the parameters in Properties are used in schedules, including Elevation at Top (Bottom) and Elevation at Top (Bottom) Core for multi-layered floors.

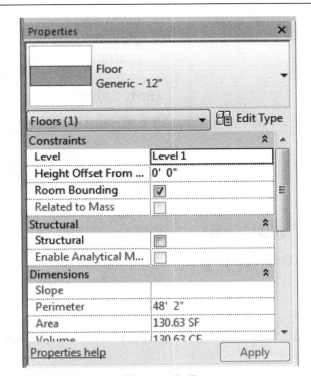

Figure 9–7

How To: Modify the Floor Sketch

1. Select a floor. You might need to highlight an element near the floor and press <Tab> until the floor type displays in the Status Bar or in a tooltip, as shown in Figure 9–8.

Figure 9–8

2. In the *Modify | Floors* tab>Mode panel, click (Edit Boundary). You are placed in sketch mode.
3. Modify the sketch lines using the draw tools, controls, and the various modify tools.

4. Click (Finish Edit Mode).

- Double-click on a floor to move directly to editing the boundary.

- Floor sketches can be edited in plan and 3D views, but not in elevations. If you try to edit in an elevation view, you are prompted to select another view in which to edit.

> **Hint: Selecting Floor Faces**
>
> If it is difficult to select the floor edges, toggle on the Selection Option ⬚ (Select Elements by Face). Then can select the floor face, and not only the edges.

Joining Geometry

Cutting a section through the objects you want to join helps to display them more clearly.

Join Geometry is a versatile command used to clean up intersections. The elements remain separate, but the intersections are cleaned up. It can be used with many types of elements including floors, walls, and roofs. In Figure 9–9, the wall on the left and the floor have been joined, but the wall on the right has not been joined with the floor and therefore does not display the lines that define the intersection edges.

| Geometry joined | Geometry not joined |

Figure 9–9

How To: Join Geometry

1. In the *Modify* tab>Geometry panel, expand ⬚ (Join) and click ⬚ (Join Geometry).
2. Select the elements to join.

- If you toggle on the **Multiple Join** option in the Options Bar, you can select several elements to join to the first selection.

- To remove the join, expand ⬚ (Join), click ⬚ (Unjoin Geometry), and select the elements to unjoin.

Practice 9a

Model Floors

Estimated time for completion: 30 minutes

Practice Objectives

- Add floors.
- Copy a floor to multiple levels.

In this practice you will create or modify floors in the Basement, first floor, and second floor of a project. You then copy the floor on the second floor to other related levels and clean up connections between the floors and wall. The second floor with balconies is shown in Figure 9–10.

Figure 9–10

Task 1 - Add the basement floor.

1. Open the project **Modern-Hotel-Floors.rvt**.

2. Open the **Floor Plans: Basement** view.

3. In the *Architecture* tab>Build panel, click ▱ (Floor).

4. In the Type Selector, select **Floor: Concrete-1-'0"**.

5. In the *Modify | Create Floor Boundary* tab>Draw panel, click
   ▯ (Pick Walls) and select the inside face of the exterior foundation walls.

6. Click ✓ (Finish Edit Mode).

7. If an error dialog box opens, click **Continue**. Use the modify tools to ensure that the boundary is a closed loop. (Hint: On the right side of the building, move the wall end of the stairwell up until it connects with the curved wall.)

8. Click (Finish Edit Mode) again.

9. When the alert box opens, click **Yes**. The floor pattern displays as shown in Figure 9–11.

Figure 9–11

10. Click in empty space to release the floor selection.

Press <Enter> to repeat the last command.

11. Start the **Floor** command again.

12. In the Type Selector, select **Floor: Tile**. In Properties, set the *Height Offset from Level* to **1/4"** to match the thickness of the tile.

13. Draw the boundary around the stair wells and hall as shown in Figure 9–12.

Figure 9–12

14. Click (Finish Edit Mode).

15. When prompted to join overlapping geometry, click **Yes**.

16. Click in empty space to release the selection and zoom in to display the different floor coverings, as shown in Figure 9–13.

Figure 9–13

17. Save the project.

Task 2 - Modify a floor as a platform for the building.

1. Open the **Floor Plans**: **Floor 1 with Pool** view.

2. Hide the grid lines, tags, and elevation markers.

3. Select the existing floor around the pool building. In the *Modify | Floors* tab>Mode panel, click (Edit Boundary).

4. Modify the boundary as shown in Figure 9–14.

Modifying the boundary of this floor creates a platform for the building.

Select this outline to modify

Change the outline to look like this

Remove this line

Figure 9–14

5. Click (Finish Edit Mode).

6. When prompted to attach walls to the floor, click **No**. Some of the walls need to be attached, but not all of them.

7. Click in empty space to release the selection.

8. View the building in 3D. It now has a base to rest on.

9. Save the project.

Task 3 - Add the second floor with balconies.

1. Open the **Floor Plans: Floor 2** view.

2. In the View Control Bar, click ⌗ (Reveal Hidden Elements).

3. Select one of the text notes in the imported CAD file. Right-click and select **Unhide in View>Elements**.

4. Click ⌗ (Close Reveal Hidden Elements).

The linked CAD file has been imported to prevent problems with the software finding the correct information for the practice.

5. Select any element that makes it difficult to display the outline of the floor and balcony. In the View Control Bar, click ↭ (Temporary Hide/Isolate) and select **Hide Category**.

Using Temporary Hide/Isolate cleans up the view temporarily as you create the floor.

6. In the *Architecture* tab>Build panel, click ⬚ (Floor).

7. In the Type Selector, select **Floor: Generic - 12"**.

8. In the *Modify | Create Floor Boundary* tab>Draw panel, click ⌐ (Boundary Line) and ⬚ (Pick Walls).

9. In the Options Bar, set the *Offset* to **0' 0"** and select **Extend into wall (to core)**.

10. Select the main outside walls. The sketch line displays at the core of the wall, as shown in Figure 9–15. Do not select the three curved walls.

Figure 9–15

11. Change to ⚡ (Pick Lines) and select the lines of walkways in the linked CAD file. (The text notes displays as **LINE OF WALKWAYS** and points to it).

12. Use draw and modify tools to fix the connections at the wall and walkway, as shown in Figure 9–16.

Figure 9–16

13. Pan over to one of the balconies.

14. Use ⚡ (Pick Lines) to draw the outline of the balcony.

15. Use drag controls to have the balcony lines meet the floor line.

16. Use ✛ (Split Element) with **Delete Inner Segment** selected on the Options Bar, and cut the line as shown in Figure 9–17.

Figure 9–17

17. Click ▹ (Modify) and select the balcony elements.

18. Copy the elements to the other balconies and split the lines to create one continuous sketch.

19. Click ✔ (Finish Edit Sketch).

20. When the alert box shown in Figure 9–18 displays, click **Yes** to cut overlapping geometry out of the walls.

Figure 9–18

21. Click in empty space to release the floor selection.

22. Hide the imported CAD file in the view.

23. In the View Control Bar, click ↩ (Temporary/Hide Isolate) and select **Reset Temporary/Hide Isolate**. The elements you hid earlier display.

24. Save the project.

Task 4 - Copy the second floor to other floors and clean up floor connections with the walls.

---

1. In the **Floor Plans: Floor 2** view, select the new floor.

2. In the *Modify | Floors* tab>Clipboard panel, click 📋 (Copy to the Clipboard).

3. In the Clipboard panel, expand 📋 (Paste) and click 📋 (Aligned to Selected Levels).

4. In the Select Levels dialog box, select **Floor 3** through **Floor 8**, as shown in Figure 9–19. Click **OK**.

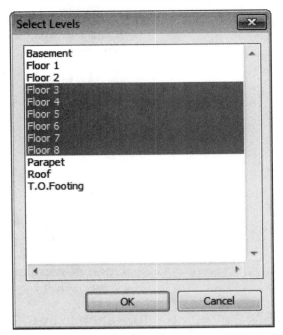

Figure 9–19

5. Open a 3D view and rotate it to display the new floors placed in the building, as shown in Figure 9–20.

Figure 9–20

6. Return to the **Floor Plans: Floor 2** view again.

7. Select all of the interior walls and interior doors of the guest rooms as well as the exterior doors to the balcony. (Hint: You can open the floor plan of any of the floors between Floor 3 and Floor 8 to display the elements that need to be copied.)

- Hold down <Shift> to clear the selection of anything you did not want, such as the exterior walls and the interior stairwell and elevator walls.

- Use ▼ (Filter) to filter out items you do not want to copy, such as the columns, door tags, elevations, and views.

8. Copy the selected elements to the clipboard and paste them to the same levels as the floors.

9. Open several of the floor plan views to verify the placement of the guest room walls and doors.

10. Return to the 3D view to display the building with all of the doors and guest rooms, as shown in Figure 9–21.

Figure 9–21

11. Zoom in on the back of the building. The floor slabs that extend to the balconies are not joined with the walls and therefore do not display a line across the connection between the wall and balcony, as shown in Figure 9–22. Zoom out to display all of the floors.

Figure 9–22

12. In the *Modify* tab>Geometry panel, expand (Join) and click (Join Geometry). In the Options Bar, select **Multiple Join**.

13. Select the back exterior wall and then select each floor with a balcony to join the wall and floors, as shown in Figure 9–23. Floor 2 is already joined and does not need to be selected.

Figure 9–23

14. Zoom out to see the entire building.

15. Save the project.

9.2 Creating Shaft Openings

Openings can be added to floors (as well as roofs and ceilings) by drawing a closed sketch within the existing sketch. When you have elevator shafts or other floor openings that span more than one floor, you can create a Shaft Opening, as shown in plan and 3D in Figure 9–24.

Shaft Openings only cut floors, roofs, and ceilings. They do not cut walls, beams, or other objects.

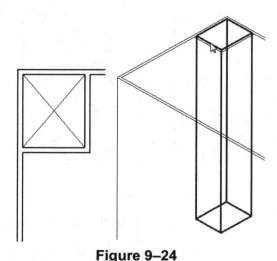

Figure 9–24

How To: Add a Shaft Opening

1. In the *Architecture* tab>Opening panel, click (Shaft).
2. In the *Modify | Create Shaft Opening Sketch* tab>Draw panel, click (Boundary Line) and draw a line to define the opening.
3. In the Draw panel, click (Symbolic Line) and add lines that show the opening symbol in plan view.
4. In Properties, set the following:
   - *Base and Top Constraint*
   - *Base and Top Offset* or *Unconnected Height*
5. Click (Finish Edit Mode) to create the opening.

- A Shaft Opening element can include symbolic lines that repeat on each level, displaying the shaft in a plan view.

- Shafts are a separate element from the floor, roof, ceiling, or wall, and can be deleted without selecting a host element.

Enhanced
in 2016

9.3 Creating Sloped Floors

These tools also work with roofs and structural slabs.

Floors can have slopes applied to them. Slope arrows are added in the sketch of the floor. There are two main types of slopes: slopes added to the entire floor and slopes added to a sketch line in the floor. After the floor is created, you can add multiple drainage points and cause the floor to warp toward them.

How To: Slope a Floor in One Direction

The slope arrow only displays while Sketch mode is active.

To make a floor slope in one direction, you place a *slope arrow* in the sketch of the floor, as shown in Figure 9–25. The direction and properties of the arrow control the slope.

Figure 9–25

1. Select the floor you want to slope. In the *Modify | Floors* tab> Mode panel, click (Edit Boundary).
2. In the *Modify | Floors>Edit Boundary* tab>Draw panel, click (Slope Arrow).
3. Select two points to define the arrow. The first point is the tail and the second is the head. The tail and head locations are points at which you can specify heights. The direction of the arrow determines the orientation of the slope.
4. In Properties, specify the *Level* and *Offset* at the *Tail* and *Head*, as shown in Figure 9–26.

Constraints	⌃
Specify	Height at Tail
Level at Tail	Default
Height Offset at Tail	1' 0"
Level at Head	Default
Height Offset at Head	0' 0"

Figure 9–26

Creating Multiple Slopes for Drainage

Restrooms, labs, garages, and other rooms often need to have floors that slope towards drains, as shown in Figure 9–27. In addition, all flat roofs are not actually flat, but also slope towards drains. Several tools provide ways of creating points for the drain locations, as well as creating lines to define how the slope is going to drain.

Figure 9–27

- These tools work with floors, roofs, and structural floors.

How To: Create Multiple Slopes for Drainage

1. Select the required flat floor, roof, or slab.
2. In the *Modify | Floors* tab>Shape Editing panel, as shown in Figure 9–28, select the tools that you want to use to define the slopes.

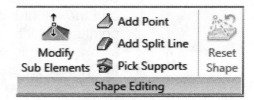

Figure 9–28

Add Point: Specify the location of the low or high points on the surface. In the Options Bar, set the *Elevation*. By default, the elevation is relative to the top of the surface. Clear the **Relative** option if you want to use the project elevation.

displays when you place the point. Slope lines are automatically added from the corners of the surface to the point.

Add Split Line: Define smaller areas on the surface when you place more than one drain. Depending on the size of the area you are working with, you might want to create these before you add the drains.

Select the **Chain** option if you want to draw more than one connected segment.

 Pick Supports: Select structural beams that define the split lines.

 Modify Sub-Elements: Change the elevation of edges and points and change the location of points. You can also move points using

shape handles without clicking (Modify Sub-Elements), as shown below. Press <Tab> to cycle through the options to reach the element you want to modify.

- If you want to remove the slopes from a surface, click

  (Reset Shape).

- Floors, roofs, and slabs use styles set to a constant thickness (where the entire element slopes) or to a variable thickness (where only the top layer slopes), as shown in Figure 9–29.

Figure 9–29

Practice 9b

Add an Elevator Shaft and Slope Floors to Floor Drains

Estimated time for completion: 15 minutes

Practice Objectives

- Create a shaft opening.
- Slope floors.

In this practice you will add a shaft opening for the elevator, as shown on the left in Figure 9–30. You will also slope floors for drainage in the restrooms and janitors closet using the Shape Editing tools, as shown on the right in Figure 9–30.

Shaft Openings : Opening Cut

Figure 9–30

Task 1 - Create a shaft opening.

1. Open the project **Modern-Hotel-Shaft.rvt**.

2. Open the **Floor Plans: Floor 1** view and zoom in to the elevator area.

3. Temporarily hide the elevator.

4. In the *Architecture* tab>Opening panel, click (Shaft).

5. In the *Modify | Create Shaft Opening Sketch* tab>Draw panel, verify that (Boundary Line) is selected.

6. Use ⬚ (Pick Walls) to create the boundary. Then use

    ⬚ (Trim/Extend to Corner) to ensure that the boundary is
    closed, as shown in Figure 9–31.

7. In the Draw panel, click ⬚ (Symbolic Line) and draw two
    lines crossing the opening, as shown in Figure 9–31.

*Shafts do not cut
through structural
elements.*

Opening
Sketch

Symbolic
Lines

Figure 9–31

8. In Properties, verify that the *Base Constraint* is **Floor 1** and
    the *Base Offset* is (negative) **-1' 0"** (the defaults).

9. In Properties, set the *Top Constraint* to **Up to Level:Roof**.

10. Click ✔ (Finish Edit Mode).

11. Reset **Temporary Hide/Isolate** and zoom out to fit the view.

12. Open the **Floor Plans: Floor 2** view.

13. In the View Control Bar, change the *Visual Style* to
    ⬚ (Consistent Colors) to display the opening.

14. Return the *Visual Style* to ⬚ (Hidden Line).

15. Open the 3D view and rotate it to display the shaft as it goes through all of the floors, as shown in Figure 9–32.

Figure 9–32

16. Open a couple other full floor plan views. The symbolic lines display in all views.

17. Return to the **Floor Plans: Floor 1** view.

18. Zoom out to display the entire view if needed.

19. In the Quick Access Toolbar, click (Close Hidden Windows).

20. Save the project.

Task 2 - Slope floors for drainage.

1. Open the **Floor Plans: Floor 1 Restrooms** view.

2. Expand the size of the crop region so the janitor's closet below is also included in the plan.

3. Select one of the elevation markers and hide the category.

4. The edge of the floor does not display in this view, so you cannot select it using the standard method. In the Status Bar, click (Select Elements by Face), and then click on the face of the floor to select it.

5. In the *Modify | Floors* tab>Shape Editing panel, click (Add Split Line). Draw the lines, as shown in Figure 9–33.

*Use the **Chain** option and draw all of the outside edges first.*

Figure 9–33

6. In the Shape Editing panel, click (Add Point). In the Options Bar, set the *Elevation* to (negative) **-1/2"**. Place a point in the center of each room, as shown for one of them in Figure 9–34.

Figure 9–34

7. End the command.

8. Zoom out and save the project.

Chapter Review Questions

1. When creating a floor the boundary sketch must be...

   a. Open

   b. Closed

   c. It does not matter.

2. How do you change the thickness of a floor, such as those shown in Figure 9–35?

   Figure 9–35

   a. In the Type Selector, change the Floor Type.

   b. In the Options Bar, change the Floor Thickness.

   c. In Properties, change the Floor Thickness.

   d. In the contextual ribbon, change the Offset.

3. Which of the following Opening commands cuts an opening in multiple floors at the same time?

   a. **By Face**

   b. **Shaft**

   c. **Wall**

   d. **Vertical**

4. When creating a sloped floor, (Add Point) places a point at...

   a. The end of the floor where you want the slope to end.

   b. The end of the floor where you want the slope to begin.

   c. A point where several slopes converge.

   d. A point where two slopes converge.

Command Summary

Button	Command	Location
	Add Point	• **Ribbon:** *Modify	Floors* tab>Shape Editing panel
	Add Split Line	• **Ribbon:** *Modify	Floors* tab>Shape Editing panel
	Floor: Architectural	• **Ribbon:** *Architecture* tab>Build panel>expand Floor
	Floor: Structural	• **Ribbon:** *Architecture* tab>Build panel>expand Floor
	Modify Sub Elements	• **Ribbon:** *Modify	Floors* tab>Shape Editing panel
	Pick Supports	• **Ribbon:** *Modify	Floors* tab>Shape Editing panel
	Reset Shape	• **Ribbon:** *Modify	Floors* tab>Shape Editing panel
	Shaft	• **Ribbon:** *Architecture* tab>Opening panel

Modeling Ceilings

In the Autodesk® Revit® software, ceilings are modeled using reflected ceiling plans. You can add ceilings by selecting a room boundary, or by sketching ceilings that do not fill an entire room. You can create basic ceilings made of acoustical tile grids, or you can create custom ceilings of different heights with a soffit wall added between. In addition to creating a ceiling, you can also place ceiling fixtures directly onto ceiling elements.

Learning Objectives in this Chapter

- Add automatic ceilings that fill an entire room boundary and sketched ceilings that are customized to suit a design.
- Modify ceiling boundaries and the grid locations for acoustical tiles to ensure that the tiles fit the room correctly.
- Add ceiling components, including lighting and mechanical fixtures.
- Add soffit walls in the gap between ceilings of different heights.

10.1 Modeling Ceilings

Adding ceilings to Autodesk Revit models is a straightforward process. To place a ceiling, click inside areas that are bounded by walls, and the ceiling is created, as shown in the large room on the right in Figure 10–1. You can also sketch custom ceilings when required. Any fixtures you attach to a ceiling displays in reflected ceiling plans, as well as in sections and 3D views.

Figure 10–1

- Ceiling plans are typically created by default when you add a level with a view, as shown in Figure 10–2.

*If you do not want a level to have a ceiling plan, you can right-click on its name in the Project Browser and select **Delete**.*

Figure 10–2

How To: Create an Automatic Boundary Ceiling

1. Switch to the appropriate Ceiling Plan view.

2. In the *Architecture* tab>Build panel, click 📄 (Ceiling).
3. In the Type Selector, select the ceiling type. In Properties, set the *Height Offset from Level*.
4. In the *Modify | Place Ceiling* tab>Ceiling panel, verify that

   📄 (Automatic Ceiling) is selected. Click inside a room to create a ceiling, as shown in Figure 10–3.

Figure 10–3

5. Continue adding ceilings to other rooms, as required.

Hint: Room Bounding Status

Elements (such as walls, floors, ceilings, and roofs) have a *Room Bounding* parameter set in Properties. In most cases, this is turned on by default as these elements typically define areas and volumes.

The **Automatic Ceiling** tool uses this parameter to identify walls that set the outline of a ceiling. If you turn off this parameter for a wall (such as a partial height wall), the **Automatic Ceiling** tool ignores the wall.

Ceilings can also be used as a Room Bounding for volume calculations.

- To modify a ceiling boundary, select a ceiling and either:

  - In the *Modify |Ceilings* tab>Mode panel, click 📝 (Edit Boundary), or
  - Double-click on the ceiling.

Sketching Ceilings

To add a ceiling to part of a room (as shown in Figure 10–4) or to have two different ceiling types at separate levels, you need to sketch a ceiling.

Sketched boundary

Figure 10–4

How To: Sketch a Ceiling

1. In the *Architecture* tab>Build panel, click (Ceiling).
2. In the *Modify | Place Ceiling* tab>Ceiling panel, click

   (Sketch Ceiling).

3. In the Draw panel, click ⟋ (Line) or ⬚ (Pick Walls) and define a closed loop for the ceiling boundary, similar to sketching a floor boundary.

4. Click ✔ (Finish Edit Mode) to create the ceiling.

- To include a hole in a ceiling, draw the hole as part of the sketch. The hole must be a closed loop completely inside the ceiling boundary.

- In the *Architecture* tab>Opening panel, you can also use

  ⬦ (Opening By Face), ⬚ (Shaft Opening) or ⬚ (Vertical Opening) to cut a hole in a ceiling that is separate from the sketch.

> **Hint: Selecting Ceiling Faces**
>
> If it is difficult to select the ceiling without the grids, you can toggle on the Selection Option (Select elements by face). Then you can select the ceiling face, and not only the edges. If you double-click on the ceiling face (or a grid line) the Edit Boundary options are displayed.

Modifying Ceiling Grids

To change a rectangular ceiling tile pattern from horizontal to vertical, select a grid line and rotate it 90 degrees.

When using acoustical tile ceiling types, you can reposition the grid locations by moving or rotating the gridlines, as shown in Figure 10–5.

Move   Rotate

Figure 10–5

How To: Move a Ceiling Grid

1. Select a grid line in the ceiling that you want to modify.
2. In the *Modify | Ceilings* tab>Modify panel, click ✣ (Move).
3. Move the cursor to one side and type a distance, such as **1'-0"** or **6"**.

How To: Rotate a Ceiling Grid

1. Select a grid line in the ceiling that you want to modify.
2. In the *Modify | Ceilings* tab>Modify panel, click ↻ (Rotate).
3. In the Options Bar, type an *Angle* or use ↻ (Rotate) to visually select the angle.

10.2 Adding Ceiling Fixtures

Several groups of components are commonly used with ceilings, such as:

- Lighting fixtures (as shown in Figure 10–6)

- Mechanical equipment (for registers and diffusers)

- Specialty equipment (such as exit signs or sprinklers)

Figure 10–6

After placing a component, press <Spacebar> to rotate it in 90-degree increments.

- Use ⬚ (Component) to place ceiling fixtures in the ceiling view.

- The Autodesk Revit Library contains a variety of light fixtures and mechanical ceiling fixtures. You can also download fixtures from Autodesk Seek.

- Many light fixtures include types that specify the voltage of the lamp, as shown in Figure 10–6.

- Some light fixtures are wall-based, instead of ceiling-based, and need to be placed on a wall in a floor plan view. These include items such as sconces.

- When you delete a ceiling, the associated components (such as light fixtures) are also deleted.

- Components come in based on their center point and respond to the nearby walls, not to the ceiling grid. Therefore, you need to place an instance of the component and then move it to the correct location on the grid. You can then use **Copy** to place additional instances on the grid.

- Some light fixtures can display the light source, as shown in the section in Figure 10–7. To display the light source, in the Visibility/Graphic Overrides dialog box, *in the Model Categories* tab, expand **Lighting Fixtures** and select **Light Source,** as shown on the left in Figure 10–7

Figure 10–7

- The light sources display their true strength in renderings.

Hint: Placing Components in Rooms Without a Ceiling

If you need to place components in a room that does not have a ceiling, you can create a reference plane at the height where you want them and place workplane-based families on it.

1. In a section or elevation view, draw the reference plane at the desired height.
2. Select the reference plane. In Properties, give the reference plane a name.
3. Open the ceiling plan where you want to work.
4. Start the **Component** command and select a workplane-based component.
5. In the *Modify | Place Component* tab>Placement panel, click (Place on Workplane), as shown in Figure 10–8.

Figure 10–8

6. In the Options Bar, specify the named reference plane from the *Placement Plane* drop-down list, as shown in Figure 10–9.

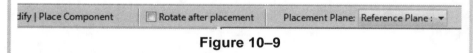

Figure 10–9

7. Place the component.

• These options are only available if you have selected a workplane-based component.

Practice 10a

Model Ceilings and Add Ceiling Fixtures

Estimated time for completion: 15 minutes

Practice Objectives

- Create automatic ceilings with grids.
- Add ceiling components.

In this practice, while working in a reflected ceiling plan, you will add acoustical tile ceilings to several support spaces. You will then add light fixtures and air terminals, as shown in Figure 10–10.

Figure 10–10

Task 1 - Create ceilings with ceiling grids.

1. Open the drawing **Modern-Hotel-Ceilings.rvt**.

2. Open the **Ceiling Plans: Floor 1** view.

   - To clarify the drawing, you might want to hide the grids, elevations, and sections categories. A quick way to do this is to select one of each element and then use the **Visibility Hide** shortcut by pressing <V> and then pressing <H>.

3. In the *Architecture* tab>Build panel, click (Ceiling).

4. In the Type Selector, verify that **Compound Ceiling: 2' x 4' ACT System** is selected.

5. Click inside the four support rooms, as shown in Figure 10–11.

Figure 10–11

6. Start the **Modify** command and select one grid line in each restroom. In the Type Selector, select **Compound Ceiling: 2' x 2' ACT System**. In Properties, set the *Height Offset from Level* to **9' 0"**.

Hold <Ctrl> to select more than one element.

Task 2 - Add ceiling components.

1. In the *Architecture* tab>Build panel, click [icon] (Component).

2. In the Mode panel, click [icon] (Load Family) and load the following components from the associated folders:

    *   Lighting>Architectural>Internal: **Downlight Recessed Can.rfa**, **Troffer Light 2x2 Parabolic.rfa**, and **Troffer Light 2x4 Parabolic.rfa**
    *   Mechanical>MEP>Air-Side Components>Air Terminals: **Return Register.rfa** and **Supply Diffuser.rfa**

The air terminals found in the Architectural folder are only 2D. If you don't have access to the MEP folder, you can use these instead.

3. Add the ceiling fixtures, as shown in Figure 10–12.

- Select a ceiling grid line and use **Move** to modify the grid to suit the location of the fixtures.
- Select a light fixture and place it on the grid. Press <Esc> and select the light fixture. Press <Spacebar> to rotate the light 90 degrees.
- Use snaps or **Align** to place it exactly on the grid.
- Copy it to the other locations.
- Place return registers in each room. Set the *Offset* from the Level to the height of the ceiling before placing them.

Figure 10–12

4. Save the project.

10.3 Creating Ceiling Soffits

Ceiling soffits are parts of a ceiling that have been lowered, as shown in Figure 10–13, or that connect two ceilings of different heights. Creating a ceiling soffit takes two steps. First, you create a ceiling, and then you draw walls using a soffit wall type.

Properties	☒
Basic Wall Soffit - 1/2" GWB & Metal Stud	
New Walls	☐ Edit Type
Constraints	☆
Location Line	Finish Face: Exterior
Base Constraint	1st Floor
Base Offset	9' 0"
Base is Attached	☐
Base Extension Distan...	0' 0"
Top Constraint	Unconnected
Unconnected Height	1' 0"
Top Offset	0' 0"

Figure 10–13

How To: Create a Ceiling with a Soffit

1. Open a ceiling plan.

2. In the *Architecture* tab>Build panel, click 🖼 (Ceiling).
3. In the Type Selector, select the ceiling type. In Properties, set the *Height Offset from Level*.
4. In the *Modify | Place Ceiling* tab>Ceiling panel, click

   🖼 (Sketch Ceiling).
5. Draw the soffit design, such as the example shown in Figure 10–14.

Figure 10–14

6. Click ✔ (Finish Edit Mode).

7. In *Architecture* tab>Build panel, click 🗀 (Wall) to create the soffit wall.

8. In the Type Selector, select a soffit wall type. In Properties, set the *Base Offset* from the floor and set the *Top Constraint/Unconnected Height* as required to establish the height of the soffit.

   • Sometimes it is easier to set the height of the soffit walls by extending or trimming elements in a section view.

9. In the *Modify | Place Wall* tab>Draw panel, click

   ⚞ (Pick Lines). Select the edges of the ceiling to create the walls, as shown in Figure 10–15.

*If the wall is on the outside of the ceiling, flip it using the Flip control and create the rest of the walls using the opposite **Location Line** option.*

Figure 10–15

10. Display the ceiling in 3D to verify that it is displayed correctly.

Hint: Joining Geometry

When you are working with elements that are next to each other, they might need additional modification so that they display as expected. For example, one way to fix connections between walls and ceilings is to join the geometry.

In the *Modify* tab>Geometry panel, click 🔗 (Join Geometry) and then select the elements to join.

Practice 10b | Create Ceiling Soffits

Practice Objective

- Create ceiling soffits.

Estimated time for completion: 15 minutes

In this practice you will sketch a ceiling, add fixtures, and create a soffit wall in the hall, as shown in Figure 10–16. Optionally, you will also add a recessed ceiling and soffit to the breakfast area.

— Soffit wall

Figure 10–16

Task 1 - Sketch a ceiling.

1. Open the drawing **Modern-Hotel-Soffits.rvt**.

2. Open the **Ceiling Plans: Floor 1** view and zoom in on the hallway by the restrooms.

3. In the *Architecture* tab>Build panel, click 📧 (Ceiling).

4. In the Type Selector, select **Compound Ceiling: GWB on Mtl.Stud** and in Properties, set the *Height Offset from Level* to **10' 0"**.

5. In the *Modify | Place Ceiling* tab>Ceiling panel, click

   (Sketch Ceiling) and draw sketch lines, as shown in Figure 10–17 in the hallway.

Figure 10–17

6. Click (Finish Edit Mode).

7. Add a line of four **Downlight - Recessed Can** components down the hallway, set at an elevation of 10'-0". Use

   (Aligned Dimension) with the **EQ** control to space them equally in the hallway.

8. Save the project.

Task 2 - Add a soffit.

---

1. Open the **Sections (Building Section): East-West Section** view and zoom in on the hallway area shown in Figure 10–18.

The area above the ceiling is open to the next floor. A soffit wall should be placed here.

Figure 10–18

2. Return to the **Ceiling Plans: Floor 1** view.

3. Click (Wall). In the Type Selector, select **Basic Wall: Soffit 1/2" GWB & Metal Stud**.

4. In Properties, set the *Location Line* to **Finish Face: Interior**, the *Base Offset* to **10' 0"**, and the *Top Constraint* to **Up to level: Floor 2** with a *Top Offset* of (negative) **-1' 0"**.

5. Draw the wall across the face of the ceiling, as shown in Figure 10–19.

Figure 10–19

6. Open the **Sections (Building Section): East-West Section** view.

7. In the *Modify* tab>Geometry panel, click (Join).

8. Select the soffit wall above the ceiling and then select the ceiling, as shown on the left in Figure 10–20.

9. Select the ceiling again, and then the wall to the left. The elements clean up as shown on the right in Figure 10–20.

Figure 10–20

10. Open the Default 3D view and save the project.

Task 3 - Add a recessed ceiling (optional).

1. In the **Ceiling Plans: Floor 1** view, pan over to the breakfast area.

2. Click (Ceiling) and click (Sketch Ceiling).

3. Create a ceiling, similar to the one shown in Figure 10–21, that has an opening in the center.

*If you have difficulty selecting the center of the curved wall, type **SC** and then select the curved wall. This snaps to the center point of the arc.*

Figure 10–21

4. Click (Finish Edit Mode). The ceiling is still selected.

5. In the Type Selector, select **Compound Ceiling: GWB on Mtl. Stud** and in Properties, set the *Height Offset from Level* to **10' 0"**.

6. Click (Wall). In the type Selector, select **Basic Wall: Soffit - 1/2"GWB & Metal Stud** with the following parameters:

   - Location Line: **Finish Face: Interior**
   - Base Constraint: **Floor 1**
   - Base Offset: **10' 0"**
   - Top Constraint: **Up to level: Floor 1**
   - Top Offset: **12' 0"**

7. In the *Modify | Place Wall* tab>Draw panel, click ✎ (Pick Lines) and select the inside hole of the ceiling, as shown in Figure 10–22.

New soffit walls

Figure 10–22

8. Click ▱ (Ceiling) again and use ▱ (Sketch Ceiling) to draw a ceiling inside the open area. Use ▨ (Pick Walls) to select the soffit walls.

9. Click ✔ (Finish Edit Mode).

10. In the Type Selector, select **Compound Ceiling: GWB on Mtl. Stud** and in Properties, set the *Height Offset from Level* to **12' 0"**.

11. Open the **Floor Plans: Floor 1** view and create a camera view looking toward the Breakfast area, as shown in Figure 10–23.

*Use **Hide in View> Elements** to turn off obstructing elements.*

Figure 10–23

12. Save the project.

Chapter Review Questions

Figure 10–24

1. For the rooms labeled A and B in Figure 10–24, which command do you use to change the position of the ceiling grid?

   a. 🔲 (Align)

   b. ✛ (Move)

   c. ↻ (Rotate)

   d. 🗐 (Copy)

2. For the rooms labeled C and D in Figure 10–24, which command do you use to change the direction of the grids?

   a. 🔲 (Align)

   b. ✛ (Move)

   c. ↻ (Rotate)

   d. 🗐 (Copy)

3. Which of the following component types can be hosted by ceiling elements? (Select all that apply.)

   a. Mechanical Diffusers and Returns

   b. Lighting fixtures

   c. Curtain Grids

   d. Columns

4. Which of the following commands would you use to create a ceiling with a soffit around the edges? (Select all that apply.)

   a. 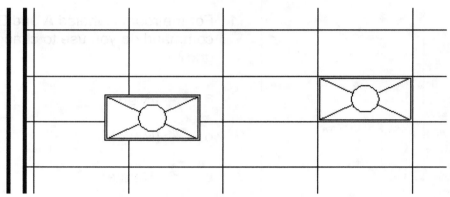 (Automatic Ceiling)

   b. (Sketch Ceiling)

   c. (Wall)

   a. (Join)

5. Which of the following commands can you use to get a light fixture fitted exactly in a ceiling grid as shown in Figure 10–25? (Select all that apply.)

Figure 10–25

   a. (Trim/Extend to Corner)

   b. (Align)

   c. (Join)

   d. (Move)

Command Summary

Button	Command	Location
	Ceiling	• **Ribbon:** *Architecture* tab>Build panel
	Place a Component	• **Ribbon:** *Architecture* tab>Build panel

Modeling Roofs

You can create simple or very complex roofs in the Autodesk® Revit® software using two different methods. The Footprint method enables you to create roofs using a process that is similar to that for creating a floor. You can also use the Extrusion method, which is based on a profile that controls the shape of the roof.

Learning Objectives in this Chapter

- Sketch roofs using the Footprint method for flat, shed, gable, or hip roofs.
- Set Work Planes to help you create extruded roof profiles.
- Draw sketches for extruded roofs that require a special profile.

11.1 Modeling Roofs

The Autodesk Revit software provides two main ways of creating roofs:

- **Footprint:** Created in a floor plan view by defining the area to be covered.

- **Extrusion:** Created in an elevation or section by defining a profile sketch.

The footprint method can generate most common roof types, including flat, shed, gable, and hip roofs. The extrusion method is needed for an odd-shaped roof or a roof with two slopes on the same face, as shown in Figure 11–1.

Roof by Footprint

Extruded Roof

Roof by Footprint

Figure 11–1

- Other roof options, found in the Roof drop-down list, include **Roof by Face**, which is used with Massing elements, **Roof Soffit**, which connects the edge of the roof to the wall, **Fascia**, which places a flat board on the outside edge of the roof and **Gutter**, which adds a gutter on the edge of the roof.

11.2 Creating Roofs by Footprint

To create a flat roof, or any basic single-sloped roofs (hip, shed, or gable), start with a plan view and define a sketch or "footprint" around the area that you want the roof to cover, as shown in Figure 11–2.

Defines Slope

Figure 11–2

You control the type of roof by specifying which edge(s) define the slope:

- No edges sloped = flat roof
- One edge sloped = shed roof
- Two opposing edges sloped = gable roof
- All edges sloped = hip roof

How To: Add a Roof by Footprint

1. Open a plan view at the roof level of the building.

2. In the *Architecture* tab> Build panel, expand � (Roof) and click ▐ (Roof by Footprint).

3. In the *Modify | Create Roof Footprint* tab>Draw panel, click ▐ (Pick Walls) or ╱ (Line) or any other Draw tool to create the roof footprint. You can include arcs in the sketch.

    - The lines must form a closed boundary with no overlapping lines.

    - Use commands such as ▀ (Trim), to modify the lines as required.

4. Select and modify each segment of the sketch as required using the Options Bar, Properties, or controls, as shown in Figure 11–3.

Figure 11–3

5. Click ✔ (Finish Edit Mode).
6. An alert box might open, as shown in Figure 11–4. You can attach the highlighted walls to the roof now or later.

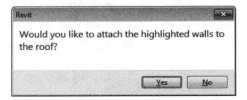

Figure 11–4

7. The roof is still selected and you can set the options for the entire roof in Properties. These include the roof type, *Base Offset from Level*, *Rafter Cut*, and *Cutoff Level* options.

Attaching Walls to Roofs

Attaching walls to the roof extends the walls up to the roof, as shown in Figure 11–5. You attach walls while you are still in the roof command, or you can use the **Attach Top/Base** options later in the design process.

Wall detached from roof   **Wall attached to roof**

Figure 11–5

- **Attach Top/Base** can also be used with walls that are against sloping floors or topographic site features.

How To: Attach Walls to Roofs

1. Select the wall or walls that you want to attach to the roof.

2. In the *Modify | Walls* tab>Modify Wall panel, click ⬚ᵀ (Attach Top/Base). Verify that *Attach Wall* is set to **Top**, as shown in Figure 11–6.

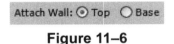

Figure 11–6

3. Select the roof. The walls are trimmed or extended to the roofline.

- To edit a roof, either:

  - Double-click on the edge of the roof

  - With the roof selected, click 🗒 (Edit Footprint).

  You can then modify the sketch and all of the options for each segment.

Hint: Setting Up a Roof Plan

When creating a roof, add a level with a floor plan view where the bottom of the roof should be located. If there are roofs at different heights, create a level for each location.

Most plan views are typically cut at 3'-0" to 4'-0" above the bottom of the level, as shown in Figure 11–7. However, this does not work with pitched roofs, whose structures can reach 20'-0" high or more. To change the height of the area shown in the roof plan, change the *View Range* in View Properties.

View Range Cut Plane @ 4'-0"   *View Range Cut Plane @ 30'-0"*

Figure 11–7

Practice 11a

Create Roofs by Footprint

Estimated time for completion: 25 minutes

Practice Objectives

- Create flat and sloped roofs using Roof by Footprint.
- Create a roof plan view.

In this practice you will create a flat roof on the main part of the hotel, and flat and sloped roofs over the poolhouse, as shown in Figure 11–8.

Figure 11–8

Task 1 - Create a flat roof.

1. Open **Modern-Hotel-Roof-Footprint.rvt**.

2. Open the **Floor Plans: Roof** view and set the *Underlay* to **None**.

3. Hide the grid lines and section and elevation markers.

4. In the *Architecture* tab>Build panel, expand (Roof) and click (Roof by Footprint).

5. In the Options Bar, clear the **Defines slope** option.

6. In the *Modify | Create Roof Footprint* tab>Draw panel, click

   (Pick Walls) and select the inside of the walls around the building, as shown in Figure 11–9.

Figure 11–9

7. Click ✔ (Finish Edit Mode).

8. In the Type Selector, select **Basic Roof: Steel Truss - Insulation on Metal Deck - EPDM**.

9. View the building in 3D to display the roof applied below the parapet wall, as shown in Figure 11–10.

Figure 11–10

10. Save the project.

Task 2 - Create a roof plan.

Hold down <Shift> and the mouse wheel to rotate in 3D view.

1. Rotate the 3D view until the poolhouse at the back of the building displays. It does not yet have a roof, but several features are in place, including the parapet walls and roof soffit, as shown in Figure 11–11.

Figure 11–11

2. Duplicate (without detailing) a copy of the **Floor Plans: Floor 2** view and rename it as **Roof - Poolhouse**.

3. Verify that this view is open.

4. In Properties, edit the *View Range* and set it up as shown in Figure 11–12. Then click **OK**.

Figure 11–12

5. Expand the crop region to display the pool area and then modify it so that only the poolhouse displays, as shown in Figure 11–13. Hide any other elements as required.

Figure 11–13

6. Hide the crop region.

Task 3 - Create roofs on the poolhouse.

1. In the *Architecture* tab>Build panel, click (Roof). The software remembers the most recently used command of **Roof by Footprint**.

2. In the Options Bar, verify that the **Defines slope** option is cleared and there is no overhang.

3. In the *Modify | Create Roof Footprint* tab>Draw panel, click (Pick Walls) and select the inside of the parapet walls.

   Use (Pick Lines) and select the soffit opening, as shown in Figure 11–14. This creates a flat roof with an opening in it.

Figure 11–14

4. Click ✔ (Finish Edit Mode.)

5. With the roof still selected, set the following:

   - *Type:* Basic Roof: Generic - 12"
   - *Base Level:* **Floor 2**
   - *Base Offset from Level:* (negative) **-2' 0"**

6. Click in the view to release the roof.

7. Click 📁 (Wall).

8. In Properties, set the following parameters:

   - Wall Type: **Basic Wall: Exterior - EIFS on Mtl.Stud**
   - Location Line: **Finish Face: Interior**
   - Base Constraint: **Floor 2**
   - Base Offset: (negative) **-1' 0"**
   - Top Constraint: **Unconnected**
   - Unconnected Height: **1' 0"**

9. Draw this short wall around the opening, as shown in Figure 11–15.

Figure 11–15

10. Click ▛ (Roof by Footprint).

11. In the Options Bar, select the **Defines slope** option.

12. Use (Pick Walls) and select the outside of the new walls you just created, as shown in Figure 11–16.

Figure 11–16

13. Click ✔ (Finish Edit Mode). In the Message dialog box, click **No** to not attach any walls to the roof.

14. In the Type Selector, select **Sloped Glazing: Pool Roof** and verify that the *Base Level* is **Floor 2**. In the *Grid 1* area, set the *Justification* to **Center**. The new roof displays as shown in Figure 11–17.

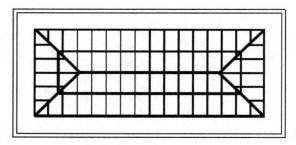

Figure 11–17

15. View the entire model in 3D.

16. Save the project.

Task 4 - Apply slopes to the main flat roof (optional).

If time permits, select the flat roof on the main hotel and use the Shape Editing tools on the *Modify | Floors* tab to add appropriate drainage slopes.

11.3 Establishing Work Planes

In some processes, such as creating a Roof by Extrusion, you are prompted to specify a Work Plane. A Work Plane is the surface you sketch on or extrude from.

- In a plan view, the Work Plane is automatically parallel to the level.

- In an elevation or 3D view, you need to specify the Work Plane before you start sketching.

To see the current Work Plane, in the *Architecture* tab>Work Plane panel, click (Viewer). This opens the Workplane Viewer, a separate window showing the current work plane, as shown in Figure 11–18.

Figure 11–18

- Named reference planes can be used to specify a work plane that would otherwise not be displayed in a view. This is especially helpful when creating extruded roofs.

How To: Select a Work Plane

1. Start a command that requires a work plane or, in the *Architecture* tab>Work Plane panel, click 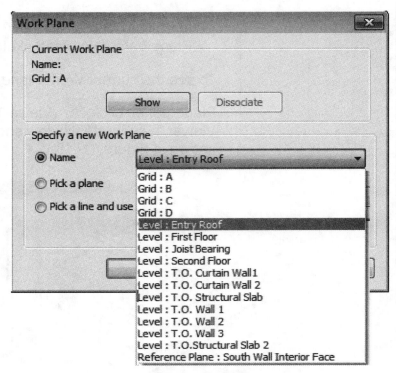 (Set).
2. In the Work Plane dialog box, select one of the options.

Name: Select an existing level, grid, or named reference plane, as shown in Figure 11–19 and click **OK**.

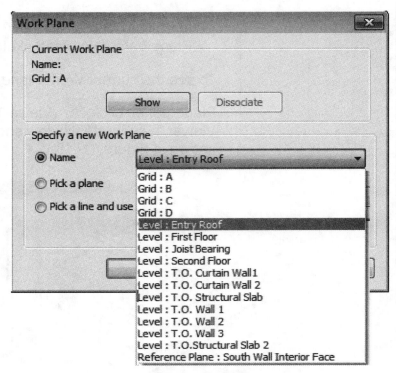

Figure 11–19

Pick a plane: Click **OK** and select a plane in the view, such as a wall face. Ensure the entire plane is highlighted before you select it.

Pick a line and use the work plane it was sketched in: Click **OK** and select a model line such as a room separation line.

- if you are in a view in which the sketch can not be created, the Go To View dialog box opens, as shown in Figure 11–20. Select one of the views and click **Open View**.

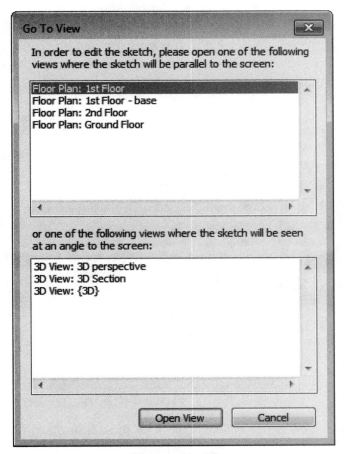

Figure 11–20

11.4 Creating Roofs by Extrusion

Extruded roofs enable you to create complex roof forms, such as the curved roof shown in Figure 11–21. Extruded roofs are based on a sketch of the roof profile in an elevation or section view. The profile is extruded between a start and end point.

Roofs : Basic Roof : Generic

Figure 11–21

How To: Create an Extruded Roof

1. Open an elevation or a section view.

2. In the *Architecture* tab>Build panel, expand ⌐ (Roof) and click ◿ (Roof by Extrusion).

3. In the Work Plane dialog box, select the Work Plane on which you want to sketch the roof profile, and click **OK.**

4. In the Roof Reference Level and Offset dialog box, as shown in Figure 11–22, specify the base *Level* and *Offset* (if any).

By default, this level is set to the highest one in the project. The offset creates a reference plane at that distance.

Figure 11–22

5. Draw reference planes to help you create the roof profile. Reference planes created within sketch mode do not display once the roof is finished.

6. Use the Draw tools to create the profile, as shown in Figure 11–23.

Sketch only the shape of the roof in profile, not the thickness.

Figure 11–23

7. In Properties, set the *Extrusion Start* and *End*.

8. Click ✔ (Finish Edit Mode).

9. In the Type Selector, select the roof type.

   • The thickness, which is determined by the roof type, is added below the profile sketch line.

10. View the roof in 3D and make any other required modifications. For example, you can use the controls on the ends of the roof to extend the overhang (as shown in Figure 11–24), as well as modify the roof using temporary dimensions and the parameters in Properties.

Figure 11–24

11. Attach the walls to the roof.

• You can make changes to the roof's profile in one of the following ways:

   • Double-click on the edge of the roof.

   • Select the roof. In the *Modify | Roofs* tab>Mode panel, click 🔷 (Edit Profile).

How To: Modify the Plan View of an Extruded Roof

1. Open a plan view where the entire roof displays.
2. Select the roof.

3. In the *Modify | Roofs* tab>Opening panel, click ▧ (Vertical).
4. In the *Modify | Create Extrusion Roof Profile* tab>Draw panel, use the tools to create a closed boundary. The boundary can be entirely inside the roof or touching the roof boundaries.

5. Click ✓ (Finish Edit Mode). The extruded view now has a cutout, as shown in Figure 11–25.

Figure 11–25

Joining Roofs

When you want to join an extruded roof to another roof, or a wall face that is taller than the roof, you can use the **Join/Unjoin Roof** command, as shown in Figure 11–26.

Figure 11–26

How To: Use Join/Unjoin Roof

1. In the *Modify* tab>Geometry panel, click (Join/Unjoin Roof).
2. Select one of the roof edges.
3. Select the other roof or the wall.

> **Hint: Join Geometry**
>
> Where roofs overlap walls or other roofs, use **Join Geometry** to clean up the intersections. The elements remain separate, but the intersections are cleaned up as shown in Figure 11–27.
>
>
>
> **Figure 11–27**

Practice 11b | Create Roofs by Extrusion

Practice Objectives

- Create an extruded roof.
- Modify the plan profile of a roof.

Estimated time for completion: 20 minutes

In this practice you will create a curved extruded roof to cover the main entrance of the building and modify its plan profile to cover the side entrance, as shown in Figure 11–28.

Figure 11–28

Task 1 - Create a roof by extrusion.

1. Open **Modern-Hotel-Roof-Extruded.rvt**.

2. Open the **Elevations (Building Elevation): South** view.

3. Zoom in on the area around the front entrance.

4. In the *Architecture* tab>Build panel, expand (Roof) and click (Roof by Extrusion).

5. In the Work Plane dialog box, verify that **Pick a plane** is selected, and click **OK**.

6. Select the front face of the wall.

7. In the Roof Reference Level and Offset dialog box, set the *Level* to **Floor 2** and click **OK**. A reference plane is set at this level and the drawing is grayed out.

The example was created using

 (Spline).

8. Sketch the profile of a roof similar to the one shown in Figure 11–29. It should extend beyond the building to the left but finish at the end of the brick wall on the right.

Figure 11–29

9. In Properties, set the *Extrusion End* to (negative) **-6' 0"**.

10. Click ✔ (Finish Edit Mode).

11. In the Type Selector, select **Basic Roof: Generic - 9"**.

12. View the new roof in 3D. It is mostly inside the building at this point.

Task 2 - Modify the extruded roof.

---

1. Open the **Floor Plans: Site** view. This view displays the entire building in plan including all of the roofs.

2. Hide the grid lines and elevation markers by category.

3. Select the Entrance roof and using controls, move the roof outward so that the length is 20' 0", as shown in Figure 11–30.

Figure 11–30

4. In the *Modify | Roofs* tab>Opening panel, click (Vertical).

5. Create a rectangular cutout of the roof for the portion that passes through the building, as shown in Figure 11–31.

Figure 11–31

6. Click (Finish Edit Mode).

7. View the modified roof in 3D. It now wraps around the side of the building to cover the side entrance, as shown in Figure 11–32.

Figure 11–32

8. Save the project.

Chapter Review Questions

1. To create a roof sloping in one direction only (as shown on the front of the building in Figure 11–33), you would create a roof...

Figure 11–33

   a. By extrusion and rotate the roof to the correct angle.

   b. By footprint and specify the slope along one side.

   c. By extrusion and use the Slope Arrow to define the overall slope of the roof.

   d. By footprint and use the **Shape Editing** tools to create the slope.

2. To create a flat roof, which of the following commands would you use to draw a sketch of the boundary of the roof and to set its thickness?

   a. **Roof by Footprint** with the thickness set by the roof type.

   b. **Roof by Extrusion** with the thickness extruded from the sketch.

3. Which of the following methods makes a wall touch the underside of a roof?

   a. Select the wall and use ⬚⬆ (Attach Top/Base).

   b. Select the roof and use ⬚⬆ (Attach Top/Base).

   c. Select the wall and edit the profile.

   d. Select the roof and use the **By Face** option.

4. Which roof type and view should you use to create a curved roof as shown in Figure 11–34?

Roofs : Basic Roof : Generic

Figure 11–34

a. Roof by Footprint, Plan View

b. Roof by Footprint, Elevation or Section view

c. Roof by Extrusion, Plan View

d. Roof by Extrusion, Elevation or Section view

5. You can name Reference Planes.

a. True

b. False

Command Summary

Button	Command	Location
	Attach Top/Base	• **Ribbon:** *Modify | Walls* tab>Modify Wall panel
	Join Geometry	• **Ribbon:** *Modify* tab>Geometry panel expand Join
	Join/Unjoin Roof	• **Ribbon:** *Modify* tab>Geometry panel
	Ref Plane	• **Ribbon:** *Architecture* tab>Work Plane panel
	Roof by Extrusion	• **Ribbon:** *Architecture* tab>Build panel expand Roof
	Roof by Footprint	• **Ribbon:** *Architecture* tab>Build panel expand Roof
	Set Work Plane	• **Ribbon:** *Architecture* tab>Work Plane panel
	Unjoin Geometry	• **Ribbon:** *Modify* tab>Geometry panel expand Join

Chapter

12

Modeling Stairs, Railings, and Ramps

When modeling in the Autodesk® Revit® software you can easily create basic stairs in straight, u-shaped, and multi-landing configurations. More complex shapes and styles can be used to create custom stairs or ramps for your building. Once created, you can add railings to stairs or modify the stairs to change their run, landing, or supports, as required. Railings can also be added to other elements to create features such as balconies or decks.

Learning Objectives in this Chapter

- Create and modify component-based stairs made of runs, landings, supports, and railings.
- Add and modify railings that are connected to stairs, as well as free standing railings for balconies.
- Sketch custom stairs when using the basic components do not work.
- Create ramps to make your design accessible.

12.1 Creating Component Stairs

As with other Autodesk Revit elements, stairs are *smart* parametric elements. With just a few clicks, you can create stairs of varying heights and designs, complete with railings. Stairs can be created by assembling stair components (as shown in Figure 12–1), or by sketching a custom layout.

Figure 12–1

When creating component-based stairs, there are three parts of a stair that can be assembled, as shown in Figure 12–1:

- **Runs:** The actual stair tread and riser elements. These include straight runs which can be combined for multi-landing stairs, spiral stairs and L-shaped and U-shaped Winders.

- **Landings:** The platform between runs. These are typically created automatically and then modified if required.

- **Supports:** The stringer or carriage that structurally holds the stair elements. These can be created automatically or you can pick the edges where you want the different types to go. These can be placed on either side of the stairs or in the center of the stairs.

- Railings are typically added within the **Stair** command. They display after you complete the stair.

- You can select and edit each of the components while you are in edit mode, or after the stair has been created.

- Each component of the stair is independent but also has a relationship to the other components. For example, if steps are removed from one run they are added to connected runs to maintain the overall height, as shown in Figure 12–2.

Before   **After**

Figure 12–2

Hint: Stairs and Views

When creating stairs you can work in either plan or 3D views. It can help to have the plan view and a 3D view open and tiled side by side. Only open the views in which you want to work and type **WT** to tile the views.

Creating Runs

To create a component stair, you must first place the run elements. There are six different options available in the Components panel, as shown in Figure 12–3, and described as follows:

Figure 12–3

🏛	**Straight**	Draws a straight run by selecting the start and end points of the run.
◎	**Full-Step Spiral**	Draws a spiral run based on a start point and radius.
⌇	**Center-Ends Spiral**	Draws a spiral run based on a center point, start point, and end point.
⌐	**L-Shape Winder**	Draws an L-shaped winder based on the lower end.

	U-Shape Winder	Draws a U-shaped winder based on the lower end.
	Create Sketch	Opens additional tools where you can sketch stair boundary and risers individually.

- Component stairs can include a mix of the different types of runs.

How To: Create a Component-based Stair with Straight Runs

1. In the *Architecture* tab>Circulation panel, click 🪜 (Stair by Component).
2. In the Type Selector, select the stair type, as shown in Figure 12–4.

The stair type can impact all of the other settings. Therefore, it is important to select it first.

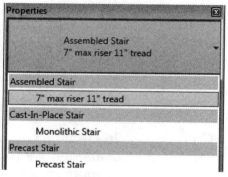

Figure 12–4

3. In Properties (shown in Figure 12–5), set the parameters for the *Base Level* and *Top Level*, and any other information that is needed.

Multistory Top Level enables you to create multiple runs of stairs based on Levels. The levels need to be the same height for this to work.

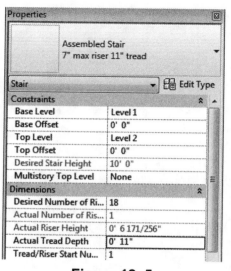

Figure 12–5

4. In the *Modify | Create Stairs* tab>Tools panel, click

   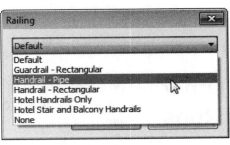 (Railing), select a railing type in the Railings dialog box as shown in Figure 12–6, and specify whether the *Position* is on the **Treads** or **Stringer**. Click **OK**.

Railings can also be added and modified after the stair has been placed.

Figure 12–6

5. In the *Modify | Create Stair* tab>Components panel, click

   (Run) and then click (Straight).

6. In the Options Bar (shown in Figure 12–7), specify the following options:

   • **Location Line:** Select **Exterior Support: Left**, **Run: Left**, **Run: Center**, **Run: Right**, or **Exterior Support: Right**.

   • **Offset:** Specify a distance from the Location Line. This is typically used if you are following an existing wall but do not need to have the stairs directly against them.

   • **Actual Run Width:** Specify the width of the stair run (not including the supports).

   • **Automatic Landing:** Creates landings between stair runs (recommended).

Location Line: Run: Center   Offset: 0' 0"   Actual Run Width: 3' 0"   ☑ Automatic Landing

Figure 12–7

7. Click on the screen to select a start point for the run. A box displays, indicating the stair orientation and the number of risers created and remaining, as shown in Figure 12–8.

*If you are creating a complex stair pattern, sketch reference planes in the **Stairs** command to help you select the start and end points of each run.*

Figure 12–8

If the stair is going in the wrong direction, click

(Flip) in the Modify | Create Stair tab>Tools panel.

- For straight stairs of a single run, select a second point anywhere outside the box to create the run.
- For multi-landing or u-shaped stairs, select a second point inside the box for the length of the first run. Then select a start point and an end point for the next run.

8. Click ✔ (Finish Edit Mode) to create the stairs, complete with railings.

Creating Other Types of Runs

While most stairs are created using straight runs there are times when you need to create specialty runs, such as spirals and winders.

How To: Create a Full-Step Spiral Run

1. Start the **Stair** command and set up the Properties as required.
2. In the Components panel, click ⚙ (Full-Step Spiral).
3. Select the center point of the spiral.
4. Select (or type) the radius of the spiral. The run is created as shown in Figure 12–9.

18 RISERS CREATED, 0 REMA N NG

In process   *Completed*

Figure 12–9

How To: Create a Center-Ends Spiral Run

1. Start the **Stair** command and set up the Properties as required.
2. In the Components panel, click 🍥 (Center-Ends Spiral).
3. Select the center of the spiral.
4. Select (or type) the radius of the spiral, as shown on the left in Figure 12–10.

5. Drag the cursor to display the number of risers as shown on the right in Figure 12–10.

You can create spiral stairs with landings with this option.

0 RISERS CREATED, 18 REMAINING   18 RISERS CREATED, 0 REMAINING

Select the radius   **Select the end of the run**

Figure 12–10

How To: Create Winder-based stairs.

1. Start the **Stair** command and set up the Properties as required.

2. In the Components panel, click ▨ (L-Shape Winder) or

   ▨ (U-Shape Winder).

3. Click a start point to place the overall stair.

4. Select the stair and use the arrow controls to modify the length as shown in Figure 12–11.

Figure 12–11

Hint: Trouble Shooting

When working with stairs and other elements, Warnings (such as the one shown in Figure 12–12), display when something is wrong, but you can keep on working. In many cases you can close the dialog box and fix the issue or wait and do it later.

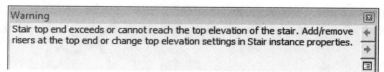

Warning ⊠
Stair top end exceeds or cannot reach the top elevation of the stair. Add/remove risers at the top end or change top elevation settings in Stair instance properties.

Figure 12–12

Sometimes Errors display where you must take action. These force you to stop and fix the situation.

When you select an element for which there has been a warning ⚠ (Show Related Warnings) displays in the Ribbon. It opens a dialog box in which you can review the warning(s) related to the selected element. You can also display a list of all of the warnings in the project by clicking 🗏 (Review Warnings) in the *Manage* tab>Inquiry panel.

Creating Landings

Landings are typically created automatically between any breaks in runs. Once finishing the stair, you can easily modify the landings to create custom designs. There are two additional options to create landings, as shown in Figure 12–13:

- **Pick Two Runs:** Places the landing at the correct height between the runs.

- **Create Sketch:** Enables you to draw the shape of the landing, but you must place it at the correct height.

Pick Two Runs   *Create Sketch*

Figure 12–13

- You can connect runs with a landing as long as the start level and end level of the runs are at the same height.

Adding Supports

Stair supports are included in the stair type if required. However, you might want to delete them and add them later. (This only works if the stair type has supports that are specified in the Type properties.)

How To: Add Stair Support Components

1. If there are no supports, in the *Modify | Create Stair* tab>

   Components panel, click 🦴 (Support) and then click

   ⚡ (Pick Edges).
2. Select the edge on which you want to place the support. Hover over the first support and press <Tab> if you have more than one connected edge on which you want to place the supports.
3. Finish the stair assembly as required.

12.2 Modifying Component Stairs

Stairs created by the **Stair by Component** command can be modified in a variety of ways. For example, in Figure 12–14 a straight stair with a landing has been modified to make one run wider than the other and the landing wider than both runs, creating a balcony. The landing has been further customized by changing it to a sketch and creating a curved feature.

Figure 12–14

- Modifying stair components can be done when you first create the stair or later when you edit a stair.

Editing Stair Assemblies

When working with a finished stair assembly, you can change the type and properties, as well as flip the stair direction and use temporary dimensions to modify the width of individual runs, as shown in Figure 12–15.

Flip Stairs Up Direction

Stairs : Assembled Stair : Stair

Assembly Selected   ***One Run Selected***

Figure 12–15

- To select a stair run, hover over the stair and press <Tab> to cycle through until the one you want highlights.

Editing Individual Components in a Stair Assembly

There are two ways to edit the stair assembly:

• Double-click on the stairs.

• In the *Modify | Stairs* tab>Edit panel, click ✎ (Edit Stairs)).

You can make more significant modification to individual components using temporary dimensions and shape handles as shown in Figure 12–16. Numerous snaps and alignment lines are also available as you modify the components.

Figure 12–16

• The arrow shape handle at the end of a run lengthens or shortens the run and modifies the other run so that the overall number of steps stays consistent and retains the start and end level.

• The circle shape handle at the end of a run lengthens or shortens the run, does not modify any other runs, but changes the start and end level.

• The arrow shape handle on the sides of the runs or landings can be used to modify the width.

• You can use temporary dimensions for the run width and connections to other elements, but not for run lengths. Use the shape handles instead.

• When you have finished modifying the stair, click

   ✓ (Finish Edit Mode).

Converting Components to Sketches

To customize a run or landing with more options, convert it into a sketch and modify the outline of the sketch as shown for a curved landing in Figure 12–17.

Figure 12–17

How To: Turn Stair Component into a Sketch

1. Select a stair created using the **Stair by Component** command.

2. In the *Modify | Stairs* tab>Edit panel, click 📚 (Edit Stairs).

3. Select the run or landing that you want to customize.

4. In the Tools panel, click ▦ (Convert to sketch-based). Doing so turns the component into a custom sketched element.

5. In the Tools panel, click 🖉 (Edit Sketch).

6. In the *Modify | Create Stair>Sketch Landing (or Run)* tab>

   Draw panel, click ⌐ (Boundary) and use the **Draw** tools to modify the boundary of the landing (or run) as shown in Figure 12–18.

This is the easiest way to create a custom landing.

Landing
Boundary

Figure 12–18

7. Click ✔ (Finish Edit Mode) to complete the sketch. Click again to return to the stair assembly.

Practice 12a

Estimated time for completion: 25 minutes

Create Component Stairs

Practice Objectives

- Create a component stairs.
- Cut out floors where stairs penetrate them.

In this practice you will create u-shaped stairs, including multi-story stairs in the stairwell, as shown in Figure 12–19. You will also modify the floors for stair openings and (if you have time) add a shaft to create an opening for the upper floors.

Figure 12–19

Task 1 - Create the stairs on the first floor.

1. Open the project **Modern-Hotel-Stairs.rvt**.

2. Open the **Floor Plans**: **Floor 1 - Stair 1** view. This is a callout from the main floor plan.

3. Hide the grid lines, sections, and crop region.

4. In the *Architecture* tab>Circulation panel, click (Stair).

5. In Properties, set or verify the following parameters:

- Stair Type: **Assembled Stair: Hotel Stairs**
- Base Level: **Floor 1**
- Top Level: **Floor 2**
- Base Offset: **0' 0"**
- Top Offset: **0' 0"**

6. In the *Modify | Create Stair* tab>Tools panel, click

   (Railing). In the Railings dialog box, select **Hotel Stair Guardrail-Floor 1**, as shown in Figure 12–20. Verify that the *Position* is set to **Treads** and click **OK**.

The Guardrails are different for the upper floors. Therefore, there are two different stair guardrail styles.

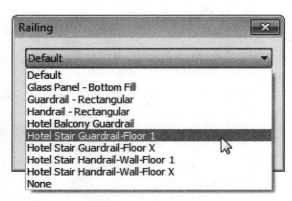

Figure 12–20

7. In the *Modify | Create Stair* tab>Work Plane panel, click

   (Ref Plane). Draw a horizontal reference plane **4' 0"** from the inner edge of the top wall of the stairwell, as shown in Figure 12–21. Click   (Modify).

Figure 12–21

8. In the *Modify | Create Stair* tab>Components panel, click

   (Run).

9. In the Options Bar, set the *Location Line* to **Run: Left**, set *Offset* to **0' 0"**, the *Actual Run Width* to **3' 8"**, and select **Automatic Landing**.

10. Pick the start point of the first run on the wall close to the door, as shown in Figure 12–22. The exact location is not important at this point. Pick a second point near the reference plane.

11. Pick the start point for the second run at the intersection of the wall and reference plane as shown in Figure 12–22. Pick the second point past the ghost image of the completed number of stairs.

Figure 12–22

12. The run on the left wall might not be in the right place. Select the run and click ✛ (Move). Select a point on the top riser and then on the reference plane, as shown in Figure 12–23.

Figure 12–23

13. Depending on how you drew the runs you might also need to modify the run lengths. The left should have 1 to 16 steps and the right should have Steps 17 to 31. Select the stairs on the left and use the arrow shape handle at the base of the stairs, to change the number of stairs as required.

14. Click ✔ (Finish Edit Mode).

15. Save the project.

Task 2 - Create the Upper Floor stairs.

---

1. Open the **Floor Plans: Floor 2** view and zoom in on the left stairwell. You should see the **DN** annotation and part of the stairs from the level below.

2. Use **Temporary/Hide** to clean up the view to have it display more clearly.

3. Click 🗇 (Stair).

All of the floor heights are the same between the 2nd and 8th floors, so you can create a multistory stair.

4. In Properties, verify that the *Base Level* is set to **Floor 2** and the *Top Level* is set to **Floor 3** and set the *Multistory Top Level* to **Floor 8**. Note the *Desired Number of Risers*, as shown in Figure 12–24. This number is much smaller because the height between Floor 2 and Floor 3 is only 12' 0".

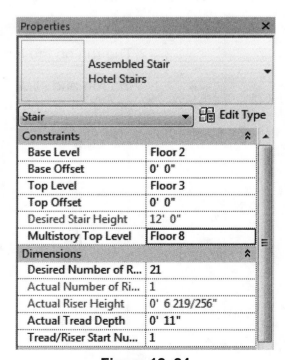

Figure 12–24

5. In the *Modify | Create Stair* tab> Tools panel, click

    (Railing). In the Railing dialog box, set the *Railing Type* to **Hotel Stair Guardrail-Floor X**. Click **OK**.

6. In the Work Plane panel, click (Reference Plane) and add a horizontal reference plane **4' 0"** from the inner side of back wall. Click (Modify).

7. Add the stair runs as in Task 1, modifying the runs as required to display stairs 1 to 11 on the left and 12 to 21 on the right as shown in Figure 12–25.

Figure 12–25

8. Click (Finish Edit Mode).

9. To see the stairs on all of the floors, open the **Sections (Building Section): East-West Section** and set the Visual Style to ⬚ (Consistent Colors), as shown in Figure 12–26.

Figure 12–26

10. If you have time at the end of the practice, create stairs from the Basement to Floor 1 and save the project.

Task 3 - Modify the second floor stair openings.

1. Open the **Floor Plans: Floor 2** view.

2. Select the floor. (It is easiest to select one of the balconies.)

3. In the *Modify | Floors* tab>Mode panel, click ▱ (Edit Boundary).

4. Modify the boundary line so that it creates an opening for the stairs, as shown in Figure 12–27.

Figure 12–27

5. Click ✔ (Finish Edit Mode). Do not attach the walls to the floor.

6. Zoom out to display the entire second floor.

7. Save the project.

8. If you have time at the end of the practice, modify the floor for the Floor 1 stair opening to the Basement. Place a shaft for the Floor 3 through Floor 8. You can use a shaft here because the openings are the same on all of the floors.

9. Save the project.

12.3 Working with Railings

Railings are automatically created with stairs, but you can modify or delete them independently of the stair element. You can also add railings separate from the stairs for other locations, as shown in Figure 12–28.

Figure 12–28

- You can add railings to existing stairs and ramps if they were not included when they were created.

How To: Add Railings by Sketching

1. Open a plan or 3D view.
2. In the *Architecture* tab>Circulation panel, expand
   (Railing) and click (Sketch Path).
3. In the Type Selector, specify the railing type.
4. In the *Modify | Create Railing Path* tab>Tools panel, click

   (Pick New Host) and select the element with which the railing is associated, such as a stair or floor. (This makes the railing take on the slope of the host, and is not required if the host is flat.)

5. Use the Draw tools to draw the lines that define the railings.

6. Click ✔ (Finish Edit Mode) to create the railing.

• The railing must be a single connected sketch. If it is not, you are prompted with a warning, such as that shown in Figure 12–29.

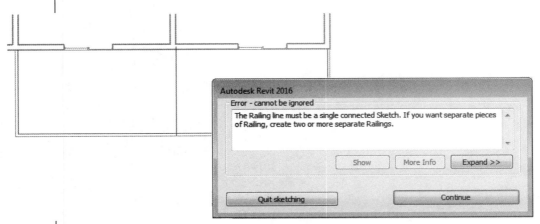

Figure 12–29

How To: Add Railings by Selecting a Host

1. In the *Architecture* tab>Circulation panel, expand

   ▨ (Railing) and click ▨ (Place on Host).

2. In the *Modify | Create Railing Place on Host* tab>Position

   panel, click ▯ (Treads) or ▯ (Stringer).

3. Select the stair or ramp where you want to add the railings.

• **Place on Host** only works if there are no railings on the stair. If you want to add an additional railing (e.g., down the middle of a wide stair) you need to sketch the railing.

Modifying Railings

Modifying railings can be as simple as changing their type in the Type Selector or as complex as creating custom railing styles. A few of the basic methods include editing the path of a railing, joining railings at different heights, and setting the extensions for the top rails, as shown in Figure 12–30.

Extension Style: Wall

Extension Style: Post

Figure 12–30

- You can delete railings separately from stairs or ramps. However, deleting a stair or ramp automatically deletes related railings.

Editing the Path of a Railing

To edit the path of a railing, double-click on the railing or select the railing and in the *Modify | Railings* tab>Mode panel, click

(Edit Path). This places you in edit mode, in which you can modify the individual lines that define the railing, as shown in Figure 12–31. You can create additional lines, but they must be connected to the existing lines.

Unlike many other elements in edit mode, railings do not have to be in a closed loop.

UP

Railing path modified

Figure 12–31

Railing Joins

If two railing segments meet in a plan, but are two different heights, you can specify how they interact. While still in edit mode, you can modify each intersection as shown in Figure 12–32.

Figure 12–32

How To: Join Railings at Different Heights

1. Select the railing and in the *Modify | Railings* tab click

   (Edit Path).
2. In the *Modify | Railings>Sketch Path* tab>Tools panel, click

   (Edit Joins).
3. Select the intersection.
4. In the Options Bar, specify the *Rail Join*, as shown in Figure 12–33. The default is **ByType**.
5. If using the default does not produce the required result, select another option in the *Rail Join* drop-down list.

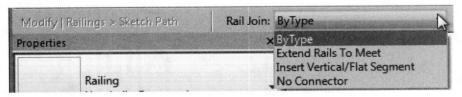

Figure 12–33

- When the *Rail Join* is set to **ByType**, this means that the method of joining the selected intersection is based on parameters in the Type Properties.

Editing the Top Rail or Handrail

The top rail or handrail of railings can be modified separately from the rest of the railing. This is the first step in customizing the railing system to match many code requirements. For example, you often need to have the handrail extend from the stair as shown in Figure 12–34.

Figure 12–34

How To: Add an Extension to a Top Rail Handrail

1. In a 3D view, hover the cursor over the top rail or handrail. Press <Tab> until it is highlighted and then select it as shown in Figure 12–35.

Figure 12–35

2. In the Properties dialog box, click 🔲 (Edit Type). You are editing the type properties of the rail, but not the entire railing system.

3. In the Type Properties dialog box, in the *Extension (Beginning/Bottom)* area, set the *Extension Style*. The options are **None**, **Wall**, **Floor**, and **Post** as shown in Figure 12–36.

Wall

Floor

Post

Figure 12–36

4. Set the *Length* and select **Plus Tread Depth** if required by the local codes.
5. Click **Apply** to check the addition.
6. Repeat the process for the *Extension (End/Top)*.
7. Make any other changes and click **OK** to finish.

• A Termination can be added if needed. The default rectangular termination works best with the Floor Extension Style but you can also create custom ones.

Practice 12b | Modify and Add Railings

Practice Objectives

- Modify railings and handrails.
- Add stand-alone railings.

Estimated time for completion: 25 minutes

In this practice you will modify the railings in the stairwells by changing the railings against the wall to a new type. You will also modify the extensions and terminations at the end of the railings. You will then add railings to the interior balconies (as shown in Figure 12–37), and to exterior balconies.

Figure 12–37

Task 1 - Modify the stairwell railings.

1. Open the project **Modern-Hotel-Railings.rvt**.

2. Open the **Floor Plans: Floor 1 - Stair 1** view.

3. Create a camera view looking from the door into the stairwell to display the new stairs and railings.

Use <Ctrl>+<Tab> to move between the 3D Camera view and the Floor Plan view.

4. In the Project Browser, in *3D Views*, right-click on the new 3D view and rename it as **Stair 1 - Floor 1.**

5. Modify the controls as required to show the first run of the stair. and set the *Visual Style* to 🗖 (Shaded). The top rail and hand rail of the railings display a different material.

6. Select the railing that is against the wall and in the Type Selector, select **Railing: Hotel Stair Handrail-Wall-Floor 1**. The railing type changes as shown in Figure 12–38.

Figure 12–38

7. With the handrail still selected, in Properties set the *Tread/String Offset* to **0**. This prevents the handrail from sitting too far off the wall.

8. Open the **Floor Plans: Floor 2** view.

9. Zoom in on the stairwell and select the outside railing. In the Type Selector, change the type to **Railing: Hotel Stair Handrail-Wall-Floor X** and the *Tread/Stringer Offset* to **0**.

10. Create a camera view to display the stairs and railings of the stair going up as shown in Figure 12–39. Select the railing that is partially displayed and hide it. Shade the view to display the components of the railings more clearly.

Figure 12–39

11. Rename this view as **Stair 1 - Floor 2**.

12. Click inside the camera view. In the inner guardrail, hover the cursor over the separate handrail (not the top rail). Press <Tab> so that only this handrail is highlighted and click to select it.

13. In Properties, click (Edit Type).

14. In the Type Properties dialog box, in both the *Extension (Beginning/Bottom)* area and the *Extension (End/Top)* area, set the *Extension Style* to **Floor** and the *Length* to **1' 0"**.

15. In the *Terminations* area, set the *Beginning/Bottom* and *End/Top* to **Termination - Wood - Rectangular**.

16. Click **OK**. The handrail changes as shown in Figure 12–40.

The railing of the other stair is hidden in this view.

Figure 12–40

17. Open one of the other upper floor plans, as shown for Floor 5 in Figure 12–41. The stairs are in place and the guardrail handrail is modified at both ends.

Figure 12–41

18. Open a different upper floor view. The changes to the handrails display because it is part of the multi-story stair system.

19. You can also use the **Railing** command to add a guardrail at the floor openings on the stairs.

20. Save the project.

Task 2 - Add stand-alone railings.

---

1. Open the **Floor Plans: Floor 2** view and pan and zoom over to the interior balcony (walkway line) as required.

2. In the *Architecture* tab>Circulation panel, expand (Railing) and click (Sketch Path).

3. In the Type Selector, select **Railing: Hotel Balcony Guardrail**.

4. Draw a sketch line that is **3"** from the edge of the balcony floor over the lobby of the hotel, as shown in Figure 12–42. Ensure that you include the curved portion at the far end.

Edge of floor ⟍   *Draw this line*

Figure 12–42

5. Click ✔ (Finish Edit Mode).

6. Zoom in on one of the outdoor balconies on the back of the building.

7. Add balcony railings, as shown in the sketch in Figure 12–43, using the same parameters as the inside balcony railing.

Figure 12–43

8. Click ✔ (Finish Edit Mode).

9. Copy the completed railing to the other balconies.

10. Copy all of the railings, inside and out, to the other floors.

11. Open an exterior 3D view and verify the placement of all of the railings.

12. Save the project.

12.4 Sketching Custom Stairs

To create custom stairs with irregular boundaries or risers, draw individual boundary and riser lines. For example, you can use this method to create a circular stair, as shown in Figure 12–44.

Figure 12–44

How To: Sketch Custom Stairs

1. Open a plan or 3D view.

2. In the *Architecture* tab>Circulation panel, expand 🕸 (Stair) and click 🔲 (Stair by Sketch).

3. In the Type Selector, select the stair type.

4. In Properties, set the *Base Level* and *Top Level*. By default, a stair height is from level to level. In many cases, a custom stair is shorter and should be set using an offset from a level as shown in Figure 12–45.

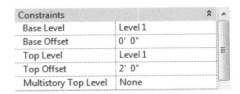

Figure 12–45

5. In the *Modify | Create Stairs Sketch* tab>Draw panel, click

   🔲 (Boundary) and draw the outline of the stairs. Do not put boundaries at the top and bottom of the stairs.

In this example the boundaries are up against the wall. If it were a free standing stair, the boundaries would be along the sides of the stairs.

6. In the Draw panel, click 🔳 (Riser) and draw the risers. The risers must touch the boundary at each end. The number of risers still needed is displayed below the sketch, as shown in Figure 12–46.

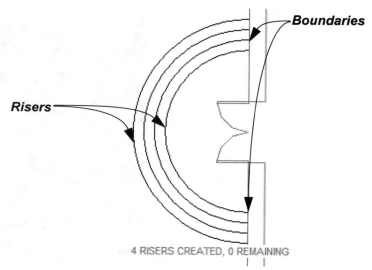

Figure 12–46

7. Click ✔ (Finish Edit Mode).

- In edit mode, riser lines are black and boundaries are green. The number of risers must be appropriate for the properties of the stair type.

- When you use the 🔳 (Run) option of sketched stairs, you can modify the sketch as shown in Figure 12–47.

The blue line in the middle is the run length and can be modified as well. It adds or removes risers as you lengthen or shorten it.

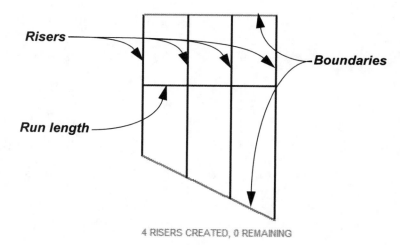

Figure 12–47

Editing Sketched Stairs

As with component stairs, you can edit stair properties and modify the type when you select a stair but you cannot select individual components. Using controls, you can move the *UP* text or flip the stair direction, as shown in Figure 12–48.

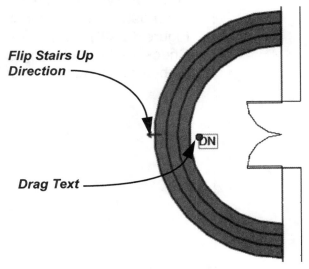

Flip Stairs Up Direction

Drag Text

Figure 12–48

To edit the boundary of the stairs, double-click on the stair or in the *Modify | Stairs* tab>Mode panel, click (Edit Sketch).

* You can modify the Boundaries and Risers and also use standard editing commands, such as **Move** and **Trim** to edit the stair sketch.

12.5 Creating Ramps

The process of creating ramps is similar to that of creating stairs with runs and automatic landings. You can also sketch a boundary with risers at the start and end of each slope. Ramps are most often used for short vertical distances (as shown in Figure 12–49), as they require a lot of space for their runs. Check the local building codes to determine how long a run can be before a landing is required.

Figure 12–49

How To: Create a Ramp using Runs

1. In the *Architecture* tab>Circulation panel, click ⬦ (Ramp).
2. In the Type Selector, select the ramp type.
3. In the *Modify | Create Ramp Sketch* tab>Tools panel, click

   (Railing) and select a railing type in the Railing Types dialog box. Click **OK**.
4. In Properties, specify the *Constraints,* especially **Base Level** and **Top Level** and their offsets as shown in Figure 12–50, and other parameters. The **Width** of the ramp is set in the *Dimensions* area.

Figure 12–50

5. Draw reference planes to specify the locations of the run start and end points before creating the ramp. The run is based on the centerline of the ramp.

6. In the Draw panel, click 🔛 (Run) and select a start point for the run. A preview box displays the ramp's orientation and length. Click ╱ (Line) or ⌒ (Center-ends Arc) to switch between linear and curved runs.

- Landings are automatically created between runs, as shown in Figure 12–51.

Figure 12–51

7. Click ✔ (Finish Edit Mode). The ramp (including railings) is created.

How To: Sketch a Ramp using Boundary and Riser

1. Click ⬙ (Ramp) and set up the ramp type and Properties.
2. In the *Modify | Create Ramp Sketch* tab>Draw panel, click 🔛 (Boundary).
3. Use the Draw tools to outline the sides (not the ends) of the ramp, as shown by the green lines in Figure 12–52.
4. In the *Modify | Create Ramp Sketch* tab>Draw panel, click 🔛 (Riser).
5. Use the Draw tools to specify the ends of the slope of each ramp, as shown by the black lines in Figure 12–52.

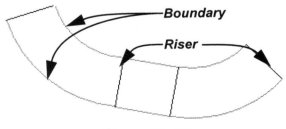

Figure 12–52

6. Click ✔ (Finish Edit Mode).

Practice 12c

Sketch Custom Stairs and Ramps

Practice Objectives

- Create a custom stair using boundaries and risers.
- Add a ramp.

Estimated time for completion: 15 minutes

In this practice you will sketch a custom entrance stair and create a sketched ramp with railings, as shown in Figure 12–53.

Figure 12–53

Task 1 - Create a custom entrance stair.

1. Open the project **Modern-Hotel-Ramp.rvt**.

2. Open the **Floor Plans: Floor 1** view.

3. Hide the gridlines and annotations by selecting one of each and using the shortcut by pressing <V> and then pressing <H>.

4. Set the *Underlay* to **Floor 2**. This displays the outline of the entrance roof that you will use to create custom stairs.

5. In the *Architecture* tab>Circulation panel, expand ⬗ (Stair), and click ⬚ (Stair by Sketch).

6. In the Type Selector, select **Stair: Monolithic Stair - Hotel**.

7. In Properties, set the *Base Level* to **Floor 1,** with a *Base Offset* of (negative) **-1'-0",** and set the *Top Level* to **Floor 1,** with a *Top Offset* of **0'-0".**

8. In the *Modify | Create Stairs Sketch* tab>Tools panel, click

    (Railing). In the Railing dialog box, select **None** and click **OK**.

9. In the Draw panel, click (Boundary), and click (Pick Lines). Select the ends of the roof outline, as shown in Figure 12–54.

10. Click (Riser). Use the **Pick Lines** tool to select the other sides of the roof outline, including right up against the building.

11. With (Riser) still selected, use the **Pick Lines** tool and set the offset to **1'-0"**. Offset another set of risers outside the outline, as shown in Figure 12–54.

The sketch lines have been widened for emphasis.

Figure 12–54

12. Use (Trim/Extend to Corner) to clean up the intersections.

13. Click (Finish Edit Mode) to complete the stair.

14. Verify that the stairs are in the right direction. If the arrow is not pointing the same direction as that shown in Figure 12–55, click the **Flip Stairs Up Direction** control, which might be located near the main door.

Flip Stairs Up Direction

Figure 12–55

15. There is a DN annotation that you do not need. With the stair still selected, in Properties, in the *Graphics* section clear **Down label**.

16. Set the *Underlay* to **None**.

17. View the new stairs in 3D.

18. Save the project.

Task 2 - Adding a Ramp

1. Return to the **Floor Plans: Floor 1** view.

2. In the *Architecture* tab>Circulation panel, click ⬦ (Ramp).

3. In the Type Selector, select **Ramp: Hotel Ramp**.

4. In Properties, set the *Base Level* to **Floor 1**, with a *Base Offset* of (negative) **-1'-0"**. Set the *Top Level* to **Floor 1**, with a *Top Offset* of **0'-0"**. Set the *Width* to **6'-0"**.

5. In the *Modify | Create Ramp Sketch* tab>Tools panel, click 🏛 (Railing), select the Railing type **Hotel Ramp Guardrail**, and click **OK**.

6. In the Work Plane panel, click ⬈ (Ref Plane).

7. Draw the reference planes shown in Figure 12–56.

Figure 12–56

8. Click ⟶ (Modify) to return to the *Modify | Create Ramp Sketch* tab in the ribbon.

9. In the Draw panel, click ⊞ (Run). Start the run as shown in Figure 12–57. Use the reference plane intersections to end the first run, and then draw the second run.

Figure 12–57

10. Click ✔ (Finish Edit Mode).

11. The Railings need to be moved so that they are fixed on the ramp. Select both of the railings and in Properties, change the *Tread/Stringer Offset* to (negative) **-2"**.

12. Open the 3D View and check that the ramp displays as shown in Figure 12–58.

Figure 12–58

13. Zoom out and save the project.

Chapter Review Questions

1. Which of the following is NOT a stair component?

    a. Runs

    b. Landings

    c. Treads

    d. Supports

2. How do you modify a stair so that it is wider at the bottom than at the top as shown in Figure 12–59?

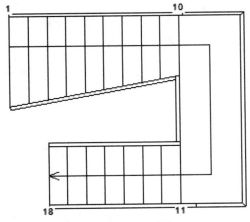

Figure 12–59

    a. Use the grips located at each corner of the stair and drag them to a new location.

    b. Convert the run to a sketch and modify the boundary and riser lines.

    c. Use <Tab> to cycle through components so that you only select the tread that you want to modify.

    d. Explode the stair into components, and then use grips to modify the stair width.

3. When do you need to use the 🪜 (Railing) command? (Select all that apply.)

    a. When you want an extra railing in the middle of very wide stairs.

    b. When you create a stair or ramp.

    c. When you create railings that are not attached to stairs or ramps.

    d. When you use the **Stair by Sketch** command.

4. To draw a stair that covers multiple floors of equal height (as shown in Figure 12–60), you need to select a stair created at the bottom level of the floors and...

Figure 12–60

a. In Properties, select the **Multistory Top Level** from the drop-down list of levels.

b. Also select a stair created at the top level of the floors, right-click and select **Multistory Stair**.

c. Copy it to the clipboard. Then use **Paste Aligned to Selected Levels** and specify the levels where you want the stairs.

5. Which of the following elements is most helpful in specifying the start and end runs of ramps?

a. Walls

b. Stairs

c. Sketch Lines

d. Reference Planes

Command Summary

Button	Command	Location
	Boundary (Stairs by Sketch)	• **Ribbon:** *Modify | Create Stairs Sketch* tab> Draw panel
	Convert to sketch-based	• **Ribbon:** *Modify | Create Stair* tab> Tools panel
	Edit Path (Railings)	• **Ribbon:** *Modify | Railings* tab>Mode panel
	Edit Sketch	• **Ribbon:** *Modify | Create Stair* tab> Tools panel
	Edit Stairs	• **Ribbon:** *Modify | Stairs* tab>Edit panel
	Flip	• **Ribbon:** *Modify | Create Stair* tab> Tools panel
	Landing (Stair by Component)	• **Ribbon:** *Modify | Create Stair* tab> Components panel
	Pick New Host	• **Ribbon:** *Modify | Create Railing Path (Railings)* tab>Tools Panel
	Railing	• **Ribbon:** *Modify | Create Stair (Create Stairs Sketch) (Create Ramp)* tab> Tools panel
	Railing>Place on Host	• **Ribbon:** *Architecture* tab>Circulation panel>expand Railing
	Railing>Sketch Path	• **Ribbon:** *Architecture* tab>Circulation panel>expand Railing
	Riser (Stairs by Sketch)	• **Ribbon:** *Modify | Create Stairs Sketch* tab>Draw panel
	Run (Stair by Component)	• **Ribbon:** *Modify | Create Stair* tab> Components panel
	Run (Stairs by Sketch)	• **Ribbon:** *Modify | Create Stairs Sketch* tab> Draw panel
	Stair by Component	• **Ribbon:** *Architecture* tab>Circulation panel>expand Stair
	Stair by Sketch	• **Ribbon:** *Architecture* tab>Circulation panel>expand Stair
	Support (Stair by Component)	• **Ribbon:** *Modify | Create Stair* tab> Components panel

Construction Documents Phase

The third section of this training guide continues to teach the Autodesk® Revit® tools, focusing on tools that help you to create accurate construction documents for a design.

This section includes the following chapters:

- Chapter 13: Creating Construction Documents

- Chapter 14: Annotating Construction Documents

- Chapter 15: Adding Tags and Schedules

- Chapter 16: Creating Details

Creating Construction Documents

The accurate creation of construction documents in the Autodesk® Revit® software ensures that the design is properly communicated to downstream users. Construction documents are created primarily in special views call sheets. Knowing how to select titleblocks, assign titleblock information, place views, and print the drawing are essential steps in the creation process.

Learning Objectives in this Chapter

- Add Sheets with titleblocks and views of a project.
- Enter the titleblock information for individual sheets and for an entire project.
- Place and organize views on sheets.
- Print sheets using the default Print dialog box.

13.1 Setting Up Sheets

While you are modeling a project, the foundations of the working drawings are already in progress. Any view (such as a floor plan, section, callout, or schedule) can be placed on a sheet, as shown in Figure 13–1.

Figure 13–1

- Company templates can be created with standard sheets using the company (or project) titleblock and related views already placed on the sheet.

- The sheet size is based on the selected title block family.

- Sheets are listed in the *Sheets* area in the Project Browser.

- Most information on sheets is included in the views. You can add general notes and other non-model elements directly to the sheet.

How To: Set Up Sheets

1. In the Project Browser, right-click on the *Sheets* area header and select **New Sheet...** or in the *View* tab>Sheet Composition panel, click (Sheet).

---

2. In the New Sheet dialog box, select a titleblock from the list as shown in Figure 13–2. Alternatively, if there is a list of placeholder sheets, select one or more from the list.

*Click **Load...** to load a sheet from the Library.*

Hold <Ctrl> to select multiple sheets.

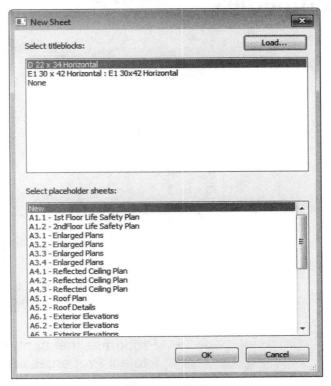

Figure 13–2

3. Click **OK**. A new sheet is created using the preferred title block.
4. Fill out the information in the title block as required.
5. Add views to the sheet.

*   When you create sheets, the next sheet is incremented numerically.

*   When you change the Sheet Name and/or Number in the title block, it automatically changes the name and number of the sheet in the Project Browser.

*   The plot stamp on the side of the sheet automatically updates according to the current date and time. The format of the display uses the regional settings of your computer.

Sheet (Title Block) Properties

A new sheet includes a title block. You can change the title block information in Properties or by selecting any blue label you want to edit (Project Name, Project Number, etc.), as shown in Figure 13–3.

Figure 13–3

- Properties that apply to all sheets can be entered in the Project Properties dialog box (as shown in Figure 13–4). In the *Manage* tab>Settings panel, click (Project Information).

Figure 13–4

13.2 Placing and Modifying Views on Sheets

The process of adding views to a sheet is simple. Drag and drop a view from the Project Browser onto the sheet. The new view on the sheet is displayed at the scale specified in the original view. The view title displays the name, number, and scale of the view, as shown in Figure 13–5.

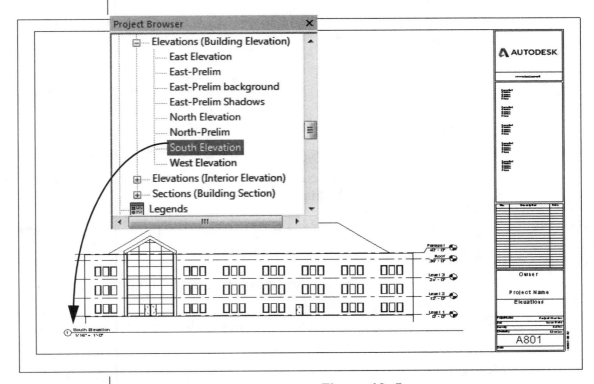

Figure 13–5

How To: Place Views on Sheets

Alignment lines from existing views display to help you place additional views.

1. Set up the view as you want it to display on the sheet, including the scale and visibility of elements.
2. Create or open the sheet where you want to place the view.
3. Select the view in the Project Browser, and drag and drop it onto the sheet.
4. The center of the view is attached to the cursor. Click to place it on the sheet.

Placing Views on Sheets

- Views can only be placed on a sheet once. However, you can duplicate the view and place that copy on a sheet.

- Views on a sheet are associative. They automatically update to reflect changes to the project.

- Each view on a sheet is listed under the sheet name in the Project Browser, as shown in Figure 13–6.

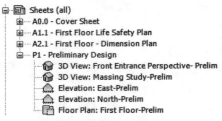

Figure 13–6

- You can also use two other methods to place views on sheets:

  - In the Project Browser, right-click on the sheet name and select **Add View...**

  - In the *View* tab>Sheet Composition panel click ⬚ (Place View).

  Then, in the Views dialog box (shown in Figure 13–7), select the view you want to use and click **Add View to Sheet.**

This method lists only those views which have not yet been placed on a sheet.

Figure 13–7

*You can also use the **Move** command or the arrow keys to move a view.*

- To remove a view from a sheet, select it and press <Delete>. Alternatively, in the Project Browser, expand the individual sheet information to show the views, right-click on the view name and select **Remove From Sheet**.

Moving Views and View Titles

- To move a view on a sheet, select the edge of the view and drag it to a new location. The view title moves with the view.

- To move only the view title, select the title and drag it to the new location.

- To modify the length of the line under the title name, select the edge of the view and drag the controls, as shown in Figure 13–8.

Figure 13–8

- To change the title of a view on a sheet without changing its name in the Project Browser, in Properties, in the *Identity Data* area, type a new title for the *Title on Sheet* parameter, as shown in Figure 13–9.

Identity Data	
View Name	South
Dependency	Independent
Title on Sheet	South Elevation
Sheet Number	A6.1

Figure 13–9

Rotating Views

- When creating a vertical sheet, you can rotate the view on the sheet by 90 degrees. Select the view and set the direction of rotation in the *Rotation on Sheet* drop-down list in the Options Bar, as shown in Figure 13–10.

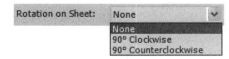

Figure 13–10

- To rotate a view to an angle other than 90 degrees, open the view, turn on and select the crop region and use the **Rotate** command to change the angle.

Working Inside Views

To make small changes to a view while working on a sheet:

- Double-click *inside* the view to activate it.
- Double-click *outside* the view to deactivate it.

Only elements within the viewport are available for modification. The rest of the sheet is grayed out, as shown in Figure 13–11.

Only use this method for small changes. Significant changes should be made directly in the view.

Figure 13–11

- You can activate and deactivate views by right-clicking on the view or by using the tools found on the *Modify | Viewports* and *Views* tab>Sheet Composition panel.

- Changes you make to elements when a view is activated also display in the original view.

Enhanced in 2016

- If you are unsure which sheet a view is on, right-click on the view in the Project Browser and select **Open Sheet**. This item is grayed out if the view has not been placed on a sheet and is not available for schedules and legends which can be placed on more than one sheet.

Resizing Views on Sheets

Each view displays the extents of the model or the elements contained in the crop region. If the view does not fit on a sheet (as shown in Figure 13–12), you might need to crop the view or move the elevation markers closer to the building.

If the extents of the view change dramatically based on a scale change or a crop region, it is easier to delete the view on the sheet and drag it over again.

Figure 13–12

Hint: Add an Image to a Sheet

Company logos and renderings saved to image files (such as .JPG and .PNG) can be added directly on a sheet or in a view.

1. In the *Insert* tab>Import panel, click ![icon] (Image).
2. In the Import Image dialog box, select and open the image file. The extents of the image display as shown in Figure 13–13.

Figure 13–13

3. Place the image where you want it.
4. The image is displayed. Pick one of the grips and extend it to modify the size of the image.

- In Properties, you can adjust the height and width and also set the *Draw Layer* to either **Background** or **Foreground**, as shown in Figure 13–14.

Dimensions		❖
Width	1' 5 185/256"	
Height	1' 1 41/64"	
Horizontal Scale	1.000000	
Vertical Scale	1.000000	
Lock Proportions	☑	
Other		❖
Draw Layer	Background	

Figure 13–14

- You can select more than one image at a time and move them as a group to the background or foreground.

Practice 13a	# Create Construction Documents

Practice Objectives

- Set up project properties.
- Create sheets individually and use placeholder sheets.
- Modify views to prepare them to be placed on sheets.
- Place views on sheets.

Estimated time for completion: 20 minutes

In this practice you will complete the project information, add new sheets and use placeholder sheets to add sheets to the project. You will fill in title block information. You will then add views to sheets, such as the Wall Sections sheet shown in Figure 13–15. Complete as many sheets as you have time for.

Figure 13–15

Task 1 - Complete the project information.

1. Open the project **Modern-Hotel-Sheets.rvt**. This file contains some additional elements that are required for the practice.

2. In the *Manage* tab>Settings panel, click ⬛ (Project Information).

3. In the Project Properties dialog box, in the *Other* area, set the following parameters:

These properties are used across the entire sheet set and do not need to be entered on each sheet.

- Project Issue Date: **Issue Date**
- Project Status: **Design Development**
- Client Name: **Ascent Properties**
- Project Address: Click **Edit...** and enter your address
- Project Name: **Modern Hotel**
- Project Number: **1234-567**

4. Click **OK**.

5. Save the project.

Task 2 - Create sheets.

1. In the *View* tab>Sheet Composition panel, click 🗂 (Sheet).

2. In the New Sheet dialog box click **Load...**.

3. In the Load Family dialog box, navigate to the *Titlesblocks* folder and select **D 22 x 34 Horizontal**. Click **Open**.

4. In the *Select placeholder sheets:* area, **New** is selected by default. Click **OK**.

5. Zoom in on the lower right corner of the title block. The Project Properties filled out earlier are automatically added to the sheet.

*The Scale is automatically entered when a view is inserted onto a sheet. If a sheet has multiple views with different scales, the scale displays **As Indicated**.*

6. Continue filling out the title block, as shown in Figure 13–16. Changing the sheet number and sheet name also changes the name in the Project Browser. Certain labels can be entered on a per sheet basis, such as the *Sheet Name*, *Sheet Number*, *Drawn by*, and *Checked by*. Leave the *Issue Date* as is.

Figure 13–16

7. In the Sheet Composition panel, click (Sheet). Using the D-sized title block, create the following new sheets:

   - A2.1 - 1st Floor Plan Overall
   - A2.2 - 1st Floor Plan
   - A2.3 - 2nd-8th Floor Plan (Typical)

8. Click (Sheet). This time, in the *Select placeholder sheets:* area, select one of the placeholder sheets and click **OK**.

9. In the Project Browser, expand *Sheets (all)*. Note that the selected placeholder sheet and the other sheets that you created are displayed.

10. Click (Sheet) again. Select all of the other placeholder sheets (use <Ctrl> or <Shift> to select multiple sheets) and click **OK**.

The rest of the sheets are placed in the project, as shown in Figure 13–17.

Having typical placeholder sheets created in the company template is a timesaver. Another option is having the sheets already in the template project.

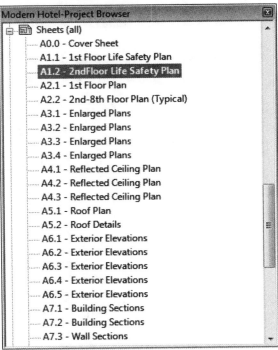

Figure 13–17

Task 3 - Set up and add views to sheets.

1. Duplicate (no detailing) the **Floor Plans: Floor 1** and **Floor 2** views and name them **1st Floor-Life Safety Plan** and **2nd-8th Floor-Life Safety Plan**.

2. Open the new views and do the following:

    - Hide all elements except the actual building elements.
    - Turn on the crop region and ensure it is tight up against the building.
    - Turn the crop region off.

The crop region defines the extent of the view on the sheet.

3. Open the appropriate sheet and drag and drop the corresponding Life Safety Plans onto it.

4. Rename sheet **2nd Floor Life Safety Plan** as **2nd-8th Floor Life Safety Plan**.

5. Repeat the process of adding views to sheets using the views you have available.

- Modify crop regions and hide unnecessary elements in the views, as shown in Figure 13–18. Turn off crop regions after you have modified them.

Figure 13–18

- Verify the scale of a view in Properties before placing it on a sheet.
- Use alignment lines to help place multiple views on one sheet, as shown in Figure 13–19.

Figure 13–19

- Change the view title, if required, to more accurately describe what is on the sheet.
- To make minor changes to a view once it is on a sheet, double-click inside the viewport to activate the view. To return to the sheet, double-click outside the viewport to deactivate the view.

6. Once you have added callout, section, or elevation views to sheets, switch back to the **Floor Plans: Floor 1** view. Zoom in on one of the markers. Note that it has now been automatically assigned a detail and sheet number, as shown in Figure 13–20.

Figure 13–20

7. Save the project.

13.3 Printing Sheets

With the **Print** command, you can print individual sheets or a list of selected sheets. You can also print an individual view or a portion of a view for check prints or presentations. To open the Print dialog box (shown in Figure 13–21), in the Application Menu, click 🖶 (Print).

Figure 13–21

Printing Options

The Print dialog box is divided into the following areas: *Printer, File, Print Range, Options*, and *Settings*. Modify them as required to produce the plot you want.

- **Printing Tips**: Opens Autodesk WikiHelp online in which you can find help with troubleshooting printing issues.

- **Preview**: Opens a preview of the print output so that you can see what is going to be printed.

Printer

Select from the list of available printers, as shown in Figure 13–22. Click **Properties...** to adjust the properties of the selected printer. The options vary according to the printer. Select the **Print to file** option to print to a file rather than directly to a printer. You can create .PLT or .PRN files.

You must have a ,PDF print driver installed on your system to print to PDF.

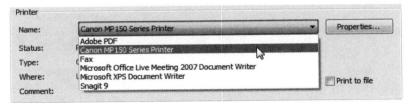

Figure 13–22

File

The *File* area is only available if the **Print to file** option has been selected in the *Printer* area or if you are printing to an electronic-only type of printer. You can create one file or multiple files depending on the type of printer you are using, as shown in Figure 13–23. Click the **Browse...** button to select the file location and name.

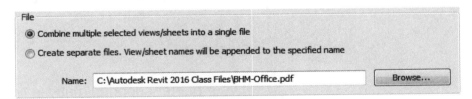

Figure 13–23

Print Range

The *Print Range* area, as shown in Figure 13–24, enables you to print individual views/sheets or sets of views/sheets.

Figure 13–24

- **Current window**: Prints the entire current sheet or view you have open.
- **Visible portion of current window**: Prints only what is displayed in the current sheet or view.
- **Selected views/sheets**: Prints multiple views or sheets. Click **Select...** to open the View/Sheet Set dialog box to choose what to include in the print set. You can save these sets by name so that you can more easily print the same group again.

Options

If your printer supports multiple copies, you can specify the number in the *Options* area, as shown in Figure 13–25. You can also reverse the print order or collate your prints. These options are also available in the printer properties.

Figure 13–25

Settings

Click **Setup**... to open the Print Setup dialog box, as shown in Figure 13–26. Here, you can specify the *Orientation* and *Zoom* settings, among others. You can also save these settings by name.

Figure 13–26

- In the *Options* area specify the types of elements you want to print or not print. Unless specified, all of the elements in a view or sheet print.

Chapter Review Questions

1. How do you specify the size of a sheet?

    a. In the Sheet Properties, specify the **Sheet Size**.

    b. In the Options Bar, specify the **Sheet Size**.

    (c) In the New Sheet dialog box, select a title block to control the Sheet Size.

    d. In the Sheet view, right-click and select **Sheet Size**.

2. How is the title block information filled in as shown in Figure 13–27? (Select all that apply.)

Figure 13–27

    (a.) Select the title block and select the label that you want to change.

    (b.) Select the title block and modify it in Properties.

    c. Right-click on the Sheet in the Project Browser and select **Information**.

    d. Some of the information is filled in automatically.

3. On how many sheets can a view be placed?

    (a) 1

    b. 2-5

    c. 6+

    d. As many as you want.

4. Which of the following is the best method to use if the size of a view is too large for a sheet, as shown in Figure 13–28?

Figure 13–28

a. Delete the view, change the scale and place the view back on the sheet.

b. Activate the view and change the View Scale.

5. How do you set up a view on a sheet that only displays part of a floor plan, as shown in Figure 13–29?

Figure 13–29

a. Drag and drop the view to the sheet and use the crop region to modify it.

b. Activate the view and rescale it.

c. Create a callout view displaying the part that you want to use and place the callout view on the sheet.

d. Open the view in the Project Browser and change the View Scale.

Command Summary

Button	Command	Location
	Activate View	• **Ribbon:** *(select the view) Modify | Viewports* tab>Viewport panel • **Double-click:** *(in viewport)* • **Right-click:** *(on view)* Activate View
	Deactivate View	• **Ribbon:** *View* tab>Sheet Composition panel>expand Viewports • **Double-click:** *(on sheet)* • **Right-click:** *(on view)* Deactivate View
	Guide Grid	• **Ribbon:** *View* tab>Sheet Composition panel • **Properties:** *(when a sheet is selected)*
	Place View	• **Ribbon:** *View* tab>Sheet Composition panel
	Sheet	• **Ribbon:** *View* tab>Sheet Composition panel

Annotating Construction Documents

When you create construction documents, annotations are required to show the design intent. Annotations such as dimensions and text can be added to views at any time during the creation of a project. Detail lines and symbols can also be added to views as you create the working drawing sheets, while Legends can be created to provide a place to document any symbols that are used in a project

Learning Objectives in this Chapter

- Add dimensions to the model as a part of the working drawings.
- Add text to a drawing and use leaders to create notes pointing to a specific part of the model.
- Create Text Types using different fonts and sizes to suit your company standards.
- Draw detail lines to further enhance the documentation view.
- Add view-specific annotation symbols for added clarity.
- Create legend views and populate them with symbols of elements in the project.

14.1 Working with Dimensions

You can create permanent dimensions using aligned, linear, angular, radial, diameter, and arc length dimensions. These can be individual or a string of dimensions, as shown in Figure 14–1. With aligned dimensions, you can also dimension entire walls with openings, grid lines, and/or intersecting walls.

Figure 14–1

- Dimensions referencing model elements must be drawn on a model in an active view. You can dimension on sheets, but only to items drawn directly on the sheets.

- Dimensions are available in the *Annotate* tab>Dimension panel and the *Modify* tab>Measure panel, as shown in Figure 14–2.

Figure 14–2

How To: Add Aligned Dimensions

1. Start the ✐ (Aligned) command or type **DI.**
2. In the Type Selector, select a dimension style.

✐ *(Aligned) is also located in the Quick Access Toolbar.*

3. In the Options Bar, select the location line of the wall to dimension from, as shown in Figure 14–3.

- This option can be changed as you add dimensions.

Figure 14–3

4. In the Options Bar, select your preference from the *Pick* drop-down list:

- **Individual References**: Select the elements in order (as shown in Figure 14–4) and then click in empty space to position the dimension string.

Figure 14–4

- **Entire Walls**: Select the wall you want to dimension and then click the cursor to position the dimension string, as shown in Figure 14–5.

Figure 14–5

- When dimensioning entire walls you can specify how you want *Openings*, *Intersecting Walls*, and *Intersecting Grids* to be treated by the dimension string. In the Options Bar, click **Options**. In the Auto Dimension Options dialog box (shown in Figure 14–6), select the references you want to have automatically dimensioned.

*If the **Entire Wall** option is selected without additional options, it places an overall wall dimension.*

Figure 14–6

How To: Add Other Types of Dimensions

*When the **Dimension** command is active, the dimension methods are also accessible in the Modify | Place Dimensions tab> Dimension panel.*

1. In the *Annotate* tab>Dimension panel, select a dimension method.

	Aligned	Most commonly used dimension type. Select individual elements or entire walls to dimension.
	Linear	Used when you need to specify certain points on elements.
	Angular	Used to dimension the angle between two elements.
	Radial	Used to dimension the radius of circular elements.
	Diameter	Used to dimension the diameter of circular elements.
	Arc Length	Used to dimension the length of the arc of circular elements.

2. In the Type Selector, select the dimension type.
3. Follow the prompts for the selected method.

Modifying Dimensions

When you move elements that are dimensioned, the dimensions automatically update. You can also modify dimensions by selecting a dimension or dimension string and making changes, as shown in Figure 14–7.

Toggle dimension equality

Click to edit dimension text

Move (dimension line)

Drag text

Lock/Unlock

Move witness line

Set gap between witness line and reference

Figure 14–7

- To move the dimension text, select the **Drag text** control under the text and drag it to a new location. It automatically creates a leader from the dimension line if you drag it away. The style of the leader (arc or line) depends on the dimension style.

- To move the dimension line (the line parallel to the element being dimensioned) simply drag the line to a new location or select the dimension and drag the ⊹ (Move) control.

- To change the gap between the witness line and the element being dimensioned, drag the control at the end of the witness line.

- To move the witness line (the line perpendicular to the element being dimensioned) to a different element or face of a wall, use the **Move Witness Line** control in the middle of the witness line. Click repeatedly to cycle through the various options. You can also drag this control to move the witness line to a different element, or right-click on the control and select **Move Witness Line**.

Adding and Deleting Dimensions in a String

- To add a witness line to a string of dimensions, select the dimension and, in the *Modify | Dimensions* tab>Witness Lines panel, click ⌐ (Edit Witness Lines). Select the element(s) you want to add to the dimension. Click in space to finish.

- To delete a witness line, drag the **Move Witness Line** control to a nearby element. Alternatively, you can hover the cursor over the control, right-click, and select **Delete Witness Line**.

- To delete one dimension in a string and break the string into two separate dimensions, select the string, hover over the dimension that you want to delete, and press <Tab>. When it highlights (as shown on top in Figure 14–8), pick it and press <Delete>. The selected dimension is deleted and the dimension string is separated into two elements as shown on the bottom in Figure 14–8.

Figure 14–8

Modifying the Dimension Text

Because the Autodesk® Revit® software is parametric, changing the dimension text without changing the elements dimensioned would cause problems throughout the project. These issues could cause problems beyond the model if you use the project model to estimate materials or work with other disciplines.

You can append the text with prefixes and suffixes (as shown in Figure 14–9), which can help you in renovation projects.

Figure 14–9

Double-click on the dimension text to open the Dimension Text dialog box, as shown in Figure 14–10, and make modifications as required.

Figure 14–10

Setting Constraints

The two types of constraints that work with dimensions are locks and equal settings, as shown in Figure 14–11.

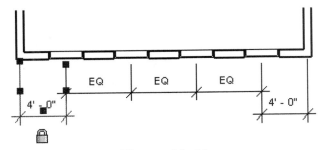

Figure 14–11

- When you lock a dimension, the value is set and you cannot make a change between it and the referenced elements. If it is unlocked, you can move it and change its value.

- For a string of dimensions, select the **EQ** symbol to constrain the elements to be at an equal distance apart. This actually moves the elements that are dimensioned.

- The equality text display can be changed in Properties as shown in Figure 14–12. The style for each of the display types is set in the dimension type.

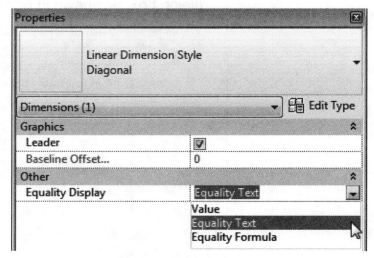

Figure 14–12

- To find out which elements have constraints applied to them, in the View Control Bar click (Reveal Constraints). Constraints display as shown in Figure 14–13.

Figure 14–13

New in **2016**

Practice 14a | Add Dimensions

Practice Objectives

- Add a string of dimensions.
- Dimension using the **Entire Walls** option.
- Edit the witness lines of dimensions.

Estimated time for completion: 10 minutes

In this practice you will add dimensions using several different methods to a floor plan view, as shown on the sheet in Figure 14–14. You will also modify the dimensions so that they show what you are expecting. Note that some additional elements including storefront curtain walls and windows have been added at the back of the building.

Figure 14–14

Task 1 - Add dimensions to the column grid.

1. Open the project **Modern-Hotel-Dimensions.rvt**.

2. In the Project Browser, duplicate the **Floor Plans: Floor 1** view (without detailing so that the door and window tags do not display),

3. Rename the new view to **Floor 1-Dimensioned Plan**.

4. Move the location of the grid bubbles so that there is enough room for dimensioning.

5. In the Quick Access Toolbar, click ✗ (Aligned).

6. Dimension the column grid lines in each direction, as shown in Figure 14–15.

Figure 14–15

Task 2 - Dimension the exterior and interior walls.

1. Click ✗ (Aligned).

2. In the Options Bar, select **Wall faces** and set *Pick* to **Entire Walls**.

3. Click **Options** and set the *Openings* to **Widths** (as shown in Figure 14–16). Click **OK**.

Figure 14–16

4. Select the back wall and place the dimension above it.

5. Zoom in on the upper left corner of the building. Use the **Move Witness Line** control to relocate the line from the end of the wall (as shown in Figure 14–17), to Grid Line C, the closest grid line on the right that passes through the corner column.

Figure 14–17

6. Click ⌖ (Modify)

7. In the same wall, pan over to the right between Grid Lines E, F, and G where the storefront openings are displayed. These were not dimensioned automatically.

8. Select the wall dimension line. In the *Modify | Dimensions* tab> Witness Lines panel, click ⊢⌐ (Edit Witness Lines).

9. Select the outside edges of each side of the storefront openings to add the witness lines and then click in empty space to apply the changes. The modified dimension string displays as shown in Figure 14–18.

Figure 14–18

10. Move the elevation and section markers as well as the dimension line to keep the dimensions clear. You might also want to move the dimension text away from the grid lines.

11. Use the various dimensioning commands and methods to dimension the interior spaces, as shown in Figure 14–19. (Hint: don't forget to change from **Pick: Entire Walls** to **Pick: Individual References**.) The dimensions might not be exactly as shown.

Figure 14–19

12. Save the project.

13. If time permits, dimension the **Floor Plans: Typical Guest Room - Dimension Plan** view. Make adjustments as required to the locations of the walls and doors.

14.2 Working With Text

The **Text** command enables you to add notes to views or sheets, such as the detail shown in Figure 14–20. The same command is used to create text with or without leaders.

(3) 9" SQUARE, (1) 10" x 12"
CUT OUT IN COUNTERTOP
(SEE PLAN)

W-3 & W-1 DOOR
PANELS AND TOE
KICK ARE ATTACHED
AND SWING OUT AS
ONE PANEL

SEAL EDGE

SCHEDULED
FLOORING TO
RUN UNDER
CABINET

Figure 14–20

The text height is automatically set by the text type in conjunction with the scale of the view (as shown in Figure 14–21, using the same size text type at two different scales). Text types display at the specified height, both in the views and on the sheet.

32"CLEAR

WHEELCHAIR ACCESSIBLE
EXIT DISCHARGE

64" CLEAR

Scale: 1/8"=1'-0"

Scale: 1/4"=1'-0"

Figure 14–21

How To: Add Text

1. In the *Annotate* tab>Text panel, click **A** (Text).
2. In the Type Selector, set the text type.

3. In the *Modify | Place Text* tab>Format panel, select the method you want to use: **A** (No Leader), **←A** (One Segment), **↙A** (Two Segments), or **⌐A** (Curved).

4. In the Format panel, set the justification for the text and leader, as shown in Figure 14–22.

Figure 14–22

5. Select the location for the leader and text.

   • If the **No leader** option is selected, select the start point for the text and begin typing.

   • If using a leader, the first point places the arrow and you then select points for the leader. The text starts at the last leader point.

   • To set a word wrapping distance, click and drag to set the start and end points of the text.

*The **Bold**, **Italic**, and **Underline** options only apply to that instance of text. If you want a specific type of text to have this formatting, create a new text type.*

6. Type the required text. In the Format panel, as shown in Figure 14–23, you can apply bold, italic, or underlined formatting to the text, as well as set a paragraph format.

Figure 14–23

7. Click outside the text box to complete the text element.

   • Pressing <Enter> after a line of text starts a new line of text in the same text window.

8. Click in a new location to start another text element, or finish the command.

• Use the controls shown in Figure 14–24 to position, rotate, or edit the text as required.

text with a two segment leader

Figure 14–24

- When placing text, alignment lines help you align the text with other text elements based on the justification of the original text.

- You can add leaders to text when it is selected. Click the related icon in the Format panel, as shown in Figure 14–25. Use the grips to move the leader once it is placed.

More than one leader can be applied to each side.

Figure 14–25

Setting the Paragraph Format

While entering text, you can set up individual lines of text using the paragraph formats shown in Figure 14–26. Change the text format option before you type the line of text. When you press <Enter> to start the next line, it continues to use the new format.

Figure 14–26

- To change a line that has already been typed, click anywhere on the line of text and change the paragraph format.

- You can also select several lines of text by dragging the cursor to highlight them and then change the paragraph format.

Hint: Model Text

Model text is different from annotation text. It is designed to create full-size text on the model itself. For example, you would use model text to create a sign on a door, as shown in Figure 14–27. One model text type is included with the default template. You can create other types as required.

Figure 14–27

- Model text is added from the *Architecture* tab>Model panel, by clicking (Model Text).

Spell Checking

The Spelling dialog box displays any misspelled words in context and provides several options for changing them, as shown in Figure 14–28.

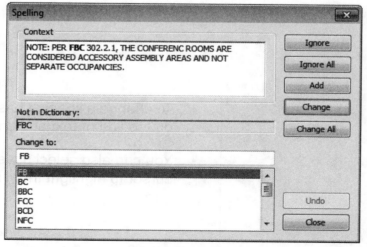

Figure 14–28

- To spell check all text in a view, in the *Annotate* tab>Text panel, click ^{ABC}✓ (Spelling) or press <F7>. As with other spell checkers, you can **Ignore**, **Add**, or **Change** the word.

- You can also check the spelling in selected text. With text selected, in the *Modify | Text Notes* tab>Tools panel, click ^{ABC}✓ (Check Spelling).

Creating Text Types

If you need new text types with a different text size or font (such as for a title or hand-lettering), you can create new ones, as shown in Figure 14–29. It is recommended that you create these in a project template so they are available in future projects.

General Notes

1. This project consists of
furnishing and installing...

Figure 14–29

- You can copy and paste text types from one project to another or use **Transfer Project Standards**.

How To: Create Text Types

1. In the *Annotate* tab>Text panel, click **A** (Text). You can also start by selecting an existing text element.

2. In Properties, click ⊞ (Edit Type).
3. In the Type Properties dialog box, click **Duplicate**.
4. In the Name dialog box, type a new name and click **OK**.

5. Modify the text parameters as required. The parameters are shown in Figure 14–30.

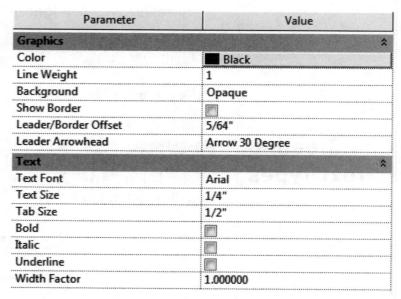

Parameter	Value
Graphics	⌃
Color	■ Black
Line Weight	1
Background	Opaque
Show Border	☐
Leader/Border Offset	5/64"
Leader Arrowhead	Arrow 30 Degree
Text	⌃
Text Font	Arial
Text Size	1/4"
Tab Size	1/2"
Bold	☐
Italic	☐
Underline	☐
Width Factor	1.000000

Figure 14–30

- The **Background** parameter can be set to **Opaque** or **Transparent**. An opaque background includes a masking region that hides lines or elements beneath the text.

- In the *Text* area, the **Width Factor** parameter controls the width of the lettering, but does not affect the height. A width factor greater than **1** spreads the text out and a width factor less than **1** compresses it.

- The Show Border parameter, when selected, draws a rectangle around the text.

6. Click **OK** to close the Type Properties dialog box.

14.3 Adding Detail Lines and Symbols

While annotating views for construction documents, you might need to add detail lines and symbols to clarify the design intent or show information, such as the life safety plan exit information, as shown in Figure 14–31.

Figure 14–31

- Detail lines and symbols are view-specific, which means that they only display in the view in which they were created.

How To: Draw Detail Lines

1. In the *Annotation* tab>Detail panel, click (Detail Line).
2. In the *Modify | Place Detail Lines* tab>Line Style panel, select the type of line you want to use, as shown in Figure 14–32.

Figure 14–32

3. Use the tools in the Draw panel to create the detail lines.

Using Symbols

Symbols are 2D elements that only display in one view, while components can be in 3D and display in many views.

Many of the annotations used in architectural drawings are frequently repeated. Several of them have been saved as symbols in the Autodesk Revit software, such as the North Arrow, Center Line, and Graphic Scale annotations as shown in Figure 14–33.

Figure 14–33

- You can also create or load custom annotation symbols.

How To: Place a Symbol

1. In the *Annotate* tab>Symbol panel, click (Symbol).
2. In the Type Selector, select the symbol you want to use.
3. In the *Modify | Place Symbol* tab>Mode panel, click

    (Load Family) if you want to load other symbols.
4. In the Options Bar, as shown in Figure 14–34, set the *Number of Leaders* and select the **Rotate after placement** option if you want to rotate the symbol as you insert it.

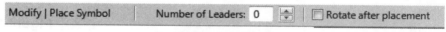

Figure 14–34

5. Place the symbol in the view. Rotate it if you selected the **Rotate after placement** option. If you specified leaders, use the controls to move them into place.

Specialty Symbols

There are three element-specific symbols that are found on the *Annotate* tab>Symbol panel. These symbols may also display when the element is placed:

- (Span Direction Symbol): Labels the span direction of structural floors. It can be used to change the orientation of the steel deck.

- (Beam System Symbol): Labels beam systems and includes the structural framing type and spacing.

- (Stair Path): Labels the slope direction and walk line of a stair, as shown in Figure 14–35.

Figure 14–35

Practice 14b

Annotate Construction Documents

Practice Objectives

- Add detail lines and symbols.
- Add text.

Estimated time for completion: 30 minutes

In this practice you will create a Life Safety Plan. You will use detail lines and symbols to show safety diagonals and travel distances, and add text for labels and notes, as shown in Figure 14–36.

Figure 14–36

Task 1 - Create a Life Safety Plan (lines and symbols).

1. Open the project **Modern-Hotel-Annotations.rvt**.

2. Open the **Floor Plans: 1st Floor Life Safety Plan** view.

3. In the View Control Bar or in Properties, change the *View Scale* to **1/16"=1'-0"**.

4. Type **VV** (or **VG**) to open the Visibility/Graphic Overrides dialog box.

5. In the *Model Categories* tab, select **Casework**, **Furniture**, and **Furniture Systems** to toggle them on. Select the **Halftone** option for each of these items as well.

6. Click **OK** to close the dialog box.

7. In the *Annotate* tab>Detail panel, click ⬜ (Detail Line).

8. In the *Modify | Place Detail Lines* tab>Line Style panel, set the *Line Style:* to **Life Safety Diagonal**.

9. In the Options Bar, clear the **Chain** option.

10. Draw a diagonal line from the lower left corner of the building to the upper right corner of the building, and another diagonal line from exit to exit, as shown in Figure 14–37.

Figure 14–37

11. In the Options Bar, select the **Chain** option.

12. Using the **Life Safety Travel Distance** line type, draw the detail lines shown in Figure 14–38.

Figure 14–38

13. Zoom in on the front entrance.

14. In the *Annotate* tab>Symbol panel, click ⊕ (Symbol).

15. In the *Modify | Place Symbol* tab>Mode panel, click

    (Load Family).

16. In the *Practice Library* folder of your practice folder, select the **Life-Safety-Line-Arrowhead.rfa** symbol and click **Open**.

Press <Spacebar> to rotate the symbol as it is placed. Highlight the end point of the line to rotate to a specific angle.

17. Insert an arrowhead at the end of each travel line and outside the door, as shown in Figure 14–39. Rotate them as required.

Figure 14–39

18. Add arrows to the ends of the other travel lines, pointing the travel direction toward the doors.

Task 2 - Create a Life Safety Plan (text).

1. In the *Annotate* tab>Text panel, click **A** (Text).

2. Create two new text types. In Properties, click (Edit Type). In the Type Properties dialog box, click **Duplicate**. For the first new text type, enter **1/8" Arial Narrow** as the name and click **OK**.

3. Set the following properties:

   • Text Font: **Arial**
   • Text Size: **1/8"**
   • Width Factor: **0.9**

4. Click **OK** to save the settings and close the dialog box.

5. Click ⬛ (Edit Type) again to open the Type Properties dialog box. Click **Duplicate** and create another text type named **1/8" Arial Narrow Italic**.

6. Select the **Italic** option and click **OK**.

7. Zoom in on the front entrance and add text using the **1/8" Arial Narrow** text type, as shown in Figure 14–40. Adjust the Annotation Crop Region as necessary to place the text. Add similar notes for the door sizes at the other exits.

Figure 14–40

8. Add a note to the breakfast room, as shown in Figure 14–41.

Figure 14–41

9. Using the **1/8" Narrow Italic** text type, add text to each diagonal distance line, as shown in Figure 14–42. Enter the text first and then click in empty space to exit the text box.

- Use the ✛ (Move) control at the start of the line of text and the ↻ (Rotate) control at the other end of the text line to get the text on top of the appropriate diagonal line. The text automatically masks the line.

Figure 14–42

10. Save the project.

14.4 Creating Legends

A legend is a separate view in which you can list the symbols used in your project and provide explanatory notes next to them. They are typically in a table format. Legends can include a list of all annotation symbols you use in your drawings, such as door, window, and wall tags (as shown in Figure 14–43), as well as a list of materials, or elevations of window types used in the project.

Annotation Legend	
(grid bubble symbol)	Grid Bubble
Name Elevation (level symbol)	Level
Room name 101 150SF	Room Tag with Area
(section bubble symbol)	Section Bubble
(window tag symbol)	Window Tag
(wall tag symbol)	Wall Tag
(door tag symbol)	Door Tag
(callout bubble symbol)	Callout Bubble
Room name 150SF	Area Tag

Figure 14–43

- You use ⌐ (Detail Lines) and **A** (Text) to create the table and explanatory notes. Once you have a legend view, you can use commands, such as (Legend Component), (Detail Component), and (Symbol), to place elements in the drawing.

- Unlike other views, legend views can be attached to more than one sheet.

- You can set a legend's scale in the View Status Bar.

- Elements in legends can be dimensioned.

How To: Create a Legend

1. In the *View* tab>Create panel, expand ▦ (Legends) and click ▦ (Legend) or in the Project Browser, right-click on the *Legends* area title and select **New Legend**.
2. In the New Legend View dialog box, enter a name and select a scale for the legend, as shown in Figure 14–44, and click **OK**.

Figure 14–44

3. Place the components in the view first, and then sketch the outline of the table when you know the sizes. Use **Ref Planes** to line up the components.

How To: Use Legend Components

1. In the *Annotate* tab>Detail panel, expand ▨ (Component) and click ▦ (Legend Component).
2. In the Options Bar, select the *Family* type that you want to use, as shown in Figure 14–45.

   • This list contains all of the elements in a drawing that can be used in a legend. For example, you might want to display the elevation of all door types used in the project.

Figure 14–45

3. Select the *View* of the element that you want to use. For example, you might want to display the section of the floors or roofs, and the front elevation of the doors (as shown in Figure 14–46) and windows.

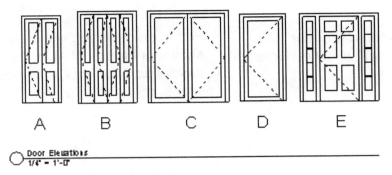

Figure 14–46

4. For section elements (such as walls, floors, and roofs), type a distance for the *Host Length*.

• Elements that are full size, such as planting components or doors, come in at their full size.

Practice 14c

Estimated time for completion: 10 minutes

Create Legends

Practice Objective

- Create legends using legend components and text.

In this practice you will create door and window legends (as shown in Figure 14–47), by creating legend views, adding legend components, and labeling the door and window types with text.

13

A   B   C   D   E   F

Figure 14–47

Task 1 - Add window and door legends.

1. Open the project **Modern-Hotel-Legends.rvt**.

2. In the *View* tab>Create panel, expand [image] (Legends) and click [image] (Legend) to create a new Legend view.

3. Name it **Window Elevations** and set the *Scale* to **1/4"=1'-0"**.

4. In the *Annotate* tab>Detail panel, expand [image] (Component) and click [image] (Legend Component).

5. In the Options Bar, set *Family* to **Windows : Casement 3 x 3 with Trim: 48" x 48"** and *View* to **Elevation: Front**. Place the component in the view. The window displays, as shown in Figure 14–48.

6. In the *Annotate* tab>Text panel, click **A** (Text).

7. In the Type Selector, select **Text: 1/8" Arial Narrow** and add the window number 13 under the window, as shown in Figure 14–48.

13

Figure 14–48

8. Create another Legend view. Name it **Door Elevations** and set the *Scale* to **1/4"=1'-0"**.

9. In the Legend view, click (Legend Component) and add the elevations of the doors used in the project.

10. Label the doors as shown in Figure 14–49.

A   B   C   D   E   F

Figure 14–49

11. Save the project.

Chapter Review Questions

1. When a wall is moved (as shown in Figure 14–50), how do you update the dimension?

Figure 14–50

   a. Edit the dimension and move it over.

   b. Select the dimension and then click the **Update** button in the Options Bar.

   c. The dimension automatically updates.

   d. Delete the existing dimension and add a new one.

2. How do you create new text styles?

   a. Using the **Text Styles** command.

   b. Duplicate an existing type.

   c. They must be included in a template.

   d. Using the **Format Styles** command.

3. When you edit text, how many leaders can be added using the leader tools shown in Figure 14–51?

Figure 14–51

   a. One

   b. One on each end of the text.

   c. As many as you want at each end of the text.

4. Detail Lines created in one view also display in the related view.

   a. True

   b. False

5. Which of the following describes the difference between a symbol and a component?

   a. Symbols are 3D and only display in one view. Components are 2D and display in many views.

   b. Symbols are 2D and only display in one view. Components are 3D and display in many views.

   c. Symbols are 2D and display in many views. Components are 3D and only display in one view.

   d. Symbols are 3D and display in many views. Components are 2D and only display in one view.

6. When creating a Legend, which of the following elements cannot be added?

   a. Legend Components

   b. Tags

   c. Rooms

   d. Symbols

Command Summary

Button	Command	Location
Dimensions and Text		
	Aligned (Dimension)	• **Ribbon:** *Annotate* tab>Dimension panel or *Modify* tab>Measure panel, expanded drop-down list • **Quick Access Toolbar** • **Shortcut:** DI
	Angular (Dimension)	• **Ribbon:** *Annotate* tab>Dimension panel or *Modify* tab>Measure panel, expanded drop-down list
	Arc Length (Dimension)	• **Ribbon:** *Annotate* tab>Dimension panel or *Modify* tab>Measure panel, expanded drop-down list
	Diameter (Dimension)	• **Ribbon:** *Annotate* tab> Dimension panel or *Modify* tab>Measure panel, expanded drop-down list
	Linear (Dimension)	• **Ribbon:** *Annotate* tab>Dimension panel or *Modify* tab>Measure panel, expanded drop-down list
	Radial (Dimension)	• **Ribbon:** *Annotate* tab>Dimension panel or *Modify* tab>Measure panel, expanded drop-down list
A	**Text**	• **Ribbon:** *Annotate* tab>Text panel • **Shortcut:** TX
Detail Lines and Symbols		
	Beam System Symbol	• **Ribbon:** *Annotate* tab>Symbol panel
	Detail Line	• **Ribbon:** *Annotate* tab>Detail panel • **Shortcut:** DL
	Span Direction Symbol	• **Ribbon:** *Annotate* tab>Symbol panel
	Stair Path	• **Ribbon:** *Annotate* tab>Symbol panel
	Symbol	• **Ribbon:** *Annotate* tab>Symbol panel
Legends		
	Legend (View)	• **Ribbon:** *View* tab>Create panel> expand Legends
	Legend Component	• **Ribbon:** *Annotate* tab>Detail panel> expand Component

Adding Tags and Schedules

Adding tags to your views helps you to identify elements such as doors, windows, or rooms in the model. Tags are typically added when you insert an element, but can also be added at any point of the design process. The information captured in the elements in a project is used to populate schedules, which can be added to sheets to complete the construction documents..

Learning Objectives in this Chapter

- Add tags to elements in 2D and 3D views to prepare the views to be placed on sheets.
- Load tags that are needed for projects.
- Add room elements and tags that display finish information, room name, and room number.
- Modify schedule content including the instance and type properties of related elements.
- Add schedules to sheets as part of the construction documents.

15.1 Adding Tags

Tags identify elements that are listed in schedules. Door and window tags are inserted automatically if you use the **Tag on Placement** option when inserting the door or window or other elements. You can also add them later to specific views as required. Many other types of tags are available in the Autodesk® Revit® software, such as wall tags and furniture tags, as shown in Figure 15–1.

Additional tags are stored in the Library in the Annotations folder.

Figure 15–1

- The **Tag by Category** command works for most elements, except for a few that have separate commands.

- Tags can be letters, numbers, or a combination of the two.

You can place three types of tags, as follows:

- (Tag by Category): Tags according to the category of the element. It places door tags on doors and wall tags on walls.

- (Multi-Category): Tags elements belonging to multiple categories. The tags display information from parameters that they have in common.

- (Material): Tags that display the type of material. They are typically used in detailing.

How To: Add Tags

1. In the *Annotate* tab>Tag panel, click [icon] (Tag by Category), [icon] (Multi-Category), or [icon] (Material Tag) depending on the type of tag you want to place.
2. In the Options Bar, set the options as required, as shown in Figure 15–2.

Figure 15–2

3. Select the element you want to tag. If a tag for the selected element is not loaded, you are prompted to load it from the Library.

Tag Options

- You can set tag options for leaders and tag rotation, as shown in Figure 15–3. You can also press <Spacebar> to toggle the orientation while placing or modifying the tag.

Figure 15–3

- Leaders can have an **Attached End** or a **Free End**, as shown in Figure 15–4. The attached end must be connected to the element being tagged. A free end has an additional drag control where the leader touches the element.

Figure 15–4

- The **Length** option specifies the length of the leader in plotting units. It is grayed out if the **Leader** option is not selected or if a **Free End** leader is defined.

- If a tag is not loaded a warning box opens as shown in Figure 15–5. Click **Yes** to open the Load Family dialog box in which you can select the appropriate tag.

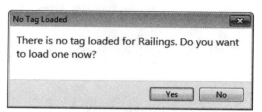

Figure 15–5

How To: Add Multiple Tags

1. In the *Annotate* tab>Tag panel, click 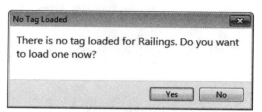 (Tag All).
2. In the Tag All Not Tagged dialog box (shown in Figure 15–6), select one or more categories to tag,

*To tag only some elements, select them before starting this command. In the Tag All Not Tagged dialog box, select the **Only selected objects in current view** option.*

Figure 15–6

3. Set the *Leader* and *Tag Orientation* as required.
4. Click **Apply** to apply the tags and stay in the dialog box. Click **OK** to apply the tags and close the dialog box.

New
in **2016**

- When you select a tag, the properties of that tag display. To display the properties of the tagged element, in the

  Modify | <contextual> tab>Host panel click (Select Host).

How To: Load Tags

1. In the *Annotate* tab, expand the Tag panel and click

    (Loaded Tags And Symbols) or, when a Tag command is active, in the Options Bar click **Tags...**

2. In the Loaded Tags And Symbols dialog box (shown in Figure 15–7), click **Load Family...**

Loaded Tags And Symbols

Select an available Tag or Symbol Family for each Family Category listed

Note: Multi-Category Tag Families are not shown below.

Filter list: Architecture ▼   Load Family...

Category	Loaded Tags	Loaded Symbols
Areas	Area Tag	
Assemblies		
Casework		
Ceilings		
Curtain Panels		
Detail Items		
Doors	Door Tag	
Electrical Equi...		
Electrical Fixtu...		
Floors		Span Direction : One
Furniture		
Furniture Syste...		

OK   Cancel   Help

Figure 15–7

3. In the Load Family dialog box, navigate to the appropriate *Annotations* folder, select the tag(s) needed and click **Open**.
4. The tag is added to the category in the dialog box. Click **OK**.

Instance vs.Type Based Tags

Doors are tagged in a numbered sequence, with each instance of the door having a separate tag number. Other elements (such as windows and walls) are tagged by type, as shown in Figure 15–8. Changing the information in one tag changes all instances of that element.

*An additional window tag (**Window Tag-Number.rfa**) is stored in the Annotations> Architectural folder in the Library. It tags windows using sequential numbers.*

Figure 15–8

- To modify the number of an instance tag (such as a door or room), double-click directly on the number in the tag and modify it, or, you can modify the *Mark* property as shown in Figure 15–9. Only that one instance updates.

Figure 15–9

- To modify the number of a type tag (such as a window or wall), you can either double-click directly on the number in the tag and modify it, or select the element and, in Properties, click 🔲 (Edit Type). In the Type Properties dialog box, in the *Identity Data* area, modify the *Type Mark*, as shown in Figure 15–10. All instances of this element then update.

Figure 15–10

- When you change a type tag, an alert box opens to warn you that changing a type parameter affects other elements. If you want this tag to modify all other elements of this type, click **Yes**.

- If a type tag displays with a question mark, it means that no Type Mark has been assigned yet.

Tagging in 3D Views

You can add tags (and some dimensions) to 3D views, as shown in Figure 15–11, as long as the views are locked first. You can only add tags in isometric views.

Figure 15–11

How To: Lock a 3D View

1. Open a 3D view and set it up as you want it to display.

2. In the View Control Bar, expand 🏠 (Unlocked 3D View) and click 🏠 (Save Orientation and Lock View).

- If you are using the default 3D view and it has not been saved, you are prompted to name and save the view first.

- You can modify the orientation of the view, expand 🏠 (Locked 3D View) and click 🏠 (Unlock View). This also removes any tags you have applied.

- To return to the previous locked view, expand 🏠 (Unlocked 3D View) and click 🏠 (Restore Orientation and Lock View).

Hint: Stair and Railing Tags

Tag by Category can be used to tag the overall stair, stair runs, landings, and railings, as shown in Figure 15–12. An additional type of tag, **Stair Tread/Riser Number**, creates a sequence of numbers for each tread or riser.

8 R @ 0' - 6 21/32"

A

Non-Monolithic Landing

Stringer - 2" Width

UP

10 R @ 0' - 6 21/32"

18 R @ 0' - 6 21/32"

Figure 15–12

How To: Add Tread/Riser Number Tags to Stairs

1. Open a plan, elevation, or section view.
2. In the *Annotate* tab>Tag panel, click (Stair Tread/Riser Number).
3. In Properties setup the *Tag Type*, *Display Rule* and other parameters. These remain active for the project.
4. Select a reference line of a stair to place the numbers, as shown in Figure 15–13.

Runs : Monolithic Run

Figure 15–13

5. Continue selecting runs as required.

Enhanced
in **2016**

Practice 15a | Add Tags

Practice Objectives

- Add tags to a model.
- Use the Tag All Not Tagged dialog box.
- Set the Type Mark parameter for tags.

Estimated time for completion: 10 minutes

In this practice you will add wall tags in a floor plan and modify the Type Mark numbers for the walls. You will also tag all of the walls using the Tag All Not Tagged dialog box, as shown in Figure 15–14.

Figure 15–14

Task 1 - Add tags to a floor plan.

1. Open the project **Modern-Hotel-Tags.rvt**.

2. In the **Floor Plans: Floor 1** view, zoom into the elevator and stair area near the left side of the building.

3. In the *Annotate* tab>Tag panel, click ⌗ (Tag by Category). In the Options Bar, select **Leader** and verify that the **Attached End** option is selected.

4. Select the exterior wall, as shown in Figure 15–15.

Figure 15–15

5. The tag comes in with a question mark because the wall does not have a *Type Mark* set yet. Click on the **?** in the tag and change the tag number to **1** and press <Enter>.

6. When alerted that you are changing a type parameter, click **Yes** to continue.

7. You are still in the **Tag** command. Add a tag to another exterior wall. This time, the tag number 1 comes in automatically as it is the same wall type as the first one.

8. Click (Modify).

9. Select the masonry wall dividing the stairs from the lobby.

10. In Properties, click (Edit Type).

11. In the Type Properties dialog box, in *Identity Data* area, set *Type Mark* to **2**, as shown in Figure 15–16. Click **OK**.

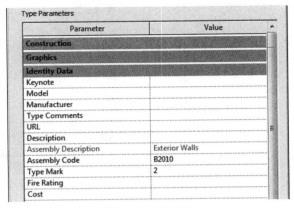

Figure 15–16

12. Select one of the interior partitions and set the *Type Mark* to **3**.

13. Use (Tag By Category) to tag one of each of the wall types. The Type Mark displays as set in the Type Properties.

14. Zoom out to display the entire floor plan.

15. Save the project.

Task 2 - Tag all the rest of the walls and modify tag locations.

---

1. In the *Annotate* tab>Tag panel, click (Tag All).

2. In the Tag All Not Tagged dialog box, set the *Wall Tags* category to the **1/2"** tag type and select **Leader** as shown in Figure 15–17.

Figure 15–17

3. Click **OK** to add wall tags where they have not already been added.

4. Many of the tags overlap other annotation objects. Use the controls to move the tags and/or leaders to a more visible location, as shown in Figure 15–18.

Figure 15–18

5. Update the tag for the main curtain wall to type number **4**.

6. Delete the wall tags that identify the storefront (inset) curtain walls along the back of the building and at the entrance. Delete any other wall tags you do not need to fully annotate the floor plan.

7. Save the project.

15.2 Adding Rooms and Tags

Room tags are a special type of tag associated with room elements. Room elements are important for room names and numbers as well as adding room information to schedules. You can place a room element in any space bounded by walls, as shown in Figure 15–19, or by room separation lines. Room separation lines enable you to divide an open space into more rooms.

Figure 15–19

- Rooms are on, but are not visible in most views. To display the rooms, in the Visibility/Graphic Overrides dialog box, expand **Rooms** and select **Interior Fill** and/or **Reference**, as shown in Figure 15–20.

Color Fill is used when a color scheme is applied to a view.

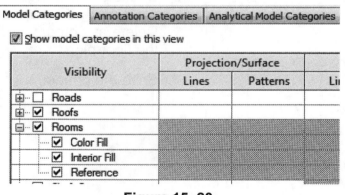

Figure 15–20

- If these two options are cleared (not on), and Rooms are turned on, you can select rooms by hovering the cursor over them.

How To: Add Rooms

1. In the *Architecture* tab>Room & Area panel, click ⊠ (Room) or type **RM**.
2. Move the cursor inside a boundary and click to place a room element. If you have **Tag on Placement** active, it also places the tag at the point you selected.
3. Continue clicking inside boundaries to add other rooms.

New in **2016**

- To add multiple rooms at once, in the *Modify | Place Room* tab>Room panel, click 🗺 (Place Rooms Automatically). Rooms are added in every bounded area that does not already have a room.

- Numbers increment automatically as you place rooms. Select the first room on a floor, change the number as required, and then add the rest of the room locations.

How To: Add Room Separation Lines

1. In the *Architecture* tab>Room & Area panel, click 🗺 (Room Separator).
2. Use the Draw tools to place lines that divide the spaces.
3. After creating the room separation lines use the **Room** command to add the rooms, as shown in Figure 15–21.

Before Room Separation Lines   **With Room Separation Lines**

Figure 15–21

Room Tags

If you did not add tags to rooms when you created them, or want to add tags to another view, you need to use a specific command. In the *Architecture* tab>Room & Area panel, click ⊠ (Tag Room) or type **RT**. You can also use 🏷 (Tag All Not Tagged).

- Tags are inserted with the default name of *Room*. You can change the name or number by clicking on the tag text to edit it, as shown in Figure 15–22.

Figure 15–22

Hint: Customize Double-click Settings

When you are changing information in a tag, double-clicking on the tag might open the tag family. To change this behavior:

1. Expand the Application Menu and click **Options**.
2. In the Options dialog box, select the *User Interface* pane.
3. In the *Configure* area, beside *Double-click Options:,* click **Customize...**
4. In the Customize Double-click Settings dialog box, change the *Double-click action:* for the *Element Type: Family* to **Do Nothing**, as shown in Figure 15–23.

Figure 15–23

5. Click **OK** twice to exit out of the dialog boxes.

- To change the names of several room tags to the same name, select the room elements and change the *Name* parameter in Properties, as shown in Figure 15–24

Figure 15–24

- Other information, such as finishes, can also be added in the room properties. This information is made available to schedules.

Practice 15b

Add Rooms and Room Tags

Practice Objectives

- Set up a view that displays rooms.
- Add rooms and room separation lines.
- Add room tags.

Estimated time for completion: 10 minutes

In this practice you will set up a view that displays rooms and add rooms to the model. You will then change the names and numbers of rooms using tags and Properties and add room separation lines to break up the larger open areas, as shown in Figure 15–25. You will also add room tags to a view where the room elements are not displayed.

Figure 15–25

Task 1 - Set up a view that displays rooms.

1. Open the project **Modern-Hotel-Rooms.rvt**.

2. In the Project Browser, right-click on the **Floor Plans: Floor 1** view and select **Duplicate View>Duplicate**.

3. Rename the new view to **Floor 1 - Rooms**.

4. Hide the gridlines and all elevation and section markers.

5. Open the Visibility/Graphic Overrides dialog box. In the *Model Categories* tab, expand **Rooms,** and select **Interior Fill**, as shown in Figure 15–26.

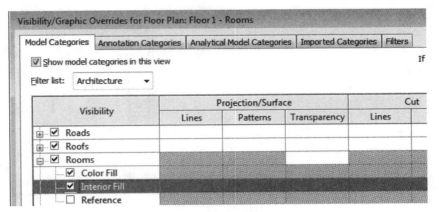

Figure 15–26

6. Nothing displays in the view as there are no rooms in the project.

7. Save the project.

Task 2 - Add rooms and room tags.

1. In the *Architecture* tab>Room & Area panel, click ⬛ (Tag Room). Click inside the lobby area. You cannot place the room tag because a room element is not assigned to the area.

2. Click ⬏ (Modify) to end the command.

3. In the *Architecture* tab>Room & Area panel, click ⬛ (Room).

4. In the *Modify | Place Room* tab>Tag panel, verify that ⬚① (Tag on Placement) is selected.

5. Place a room element inside the lobby area.

6. Return to the **Modify** command and change the name of the room and the room number, as shown in Figure 15–27. Click in empty space to finish the command.

Figure 15–27

7. Click 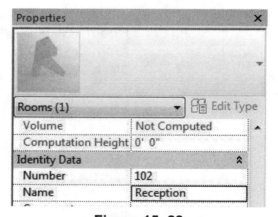 (Room) again. In the *Modify | Place Room* tab, toggle off the **Tag on Placement** option. Place the room element in the check in area (the small room next to the elevator) and finish the command. Select the room element.

8. In Properties, in the *Identity Data* area, note that the *Number* is automatically set to **102**. Set the *Name* as **Reception** (as shown in Figure 15–28) and click **Apply**.

Properties	✕
Rooms (1)	▾ Edit Type
Volume	Not Computed
Computation Height	0' 0"
Identity Data	⌃
Number	102
Name	Reception

Figure 15–28

9. In the *Architecture* tab>Room & Area panel, click (Tag Room).

10. Tag the new room and press <Esc>. The tag is displayed with the name you specified in Properties, as shown in Figure 15–29.

Figure 15–29

11. Add a room and tag in the room to the right of the Reception room and name it **Office**.

12. Save the project.

Task 3 - Add Room Separation Lines and additional rooms.

1. In the *Architecture* tab>Room & Area panel, click (Room Separator).

2. Draw room separation lines to separate the breakfast area from the main lobby as shown in Figure 15–30.

Figure 15–30

3. Start the **Room** command and verify that **Tag on Placement** is on. In Properties, in the *Name* field, type **Breakfast Area, and** then place the room in the location shown in Figure 15–30.

4. Continue to add room elements and room tags to the rest of the rooms on the first floor. Rename the rooms as required.

- If a room tag is too large for the room, toggle on the **Leader** option and move the tag. If the **Leader** option is not toggled on, the tag is orphaned from the room.

5. Save the project.

Task 4 - Add Room Tags to another view.

1. Open the **Floor Plans: Floor 1** view.

2. Although you do not see the rooms in the view, you can roll the cursor over the rooms in the plan and select the room elements, as shown in Figure 15–31.

Figure 15–31

3. In the *Annotate* tab>Tag panel click (Tag All).

4. In the Tag All Not Tagged dialog box, select **Room Tags: Room Tag,** and click **OK**. Room tags are added to all of the rooms in the view.

5. Zoom in and clean up the view by moving the various tags so that they do not overlap, as shown in Figure 15–32.

Figure 15–32

6. Save the project.

15.3 Working with Schedules

Schedules extract information from a project and display it in table form. Each schedule is stored as a separate view and can be placed on sheets, as shown in Figure 15–33. Any changes you make to the project elements that affect the schedules are automatically updated in both views and sheets.

Schedules are typically included in project templates. Ask your BIM Manager for more information about your company's schedules.

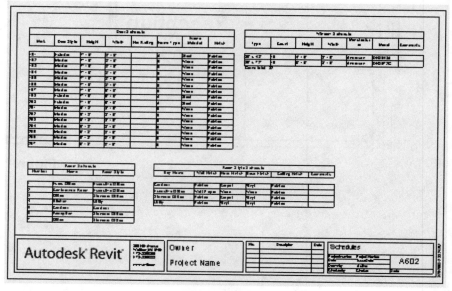

Figure 15–33

How To: Work with Schedules

1. In the Project Browser, expand the *Schedules/Quantities* area, as shown in Figure 15–34, and double-click on the schedule you want to open.

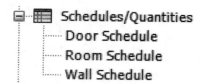

Figure 15–34

2. Schedules are automatically filled out with the information stored in the instance and type parameters of related elements that are added to the model.
3. Fill out additional information in either the schedule or Properties.
4. Drag and drop the schedule onto a sheet.

Modifying Schedules

Information in schedules is bi-directional:

- If you make changes to elements, the schedule automatically updates.

- If you change information in the cells of the schedule, it automatically updates the elements in the project.

How To: Modify Schedule Cells

1. Open the schedule view.
2. Select the cell you want to change. Some cells have drop-down lists, as shown in Figure 15–35. Others have edit fields.

If you change a Type Property in the schedule, it applies to all elements of that type. If you change an Instance Property, it only applies to that one element.

A	B	C	D
			Dimensions
Mark	Type	Width	Height
	Store Front Double	8' - 3 1/2"	9' - 4 1/4"
101	36" x 84"	3' - 0"	7' - 0"
102	24" x 82"	3' - 0"	7' - 0"
103	30" x 80"	3' - 0"	6' - 8"
104	30" x 84"	3' - 0"	6' - 8"
105	32" x 84"	3' - 0"	6' - 8"
106	36" x 80"	3' - 0"	6' - 8"
107	36" x 84"	3' - 0"	6' - 8"
108	36" x 84"	3' - 0"	7' - 0"
109	36" x 84"	3' - 0"	7' - 0"
110	72" x 84"	6' - 0"	7' - 0"
111	72" x 82"	6' - 0"	6' - 10"

Figure 15–35

3. Add the new information. The change is reflected in the schedule, on the sheet, and in the elements of the project.

- If you change a Type Property, an alert box opens, as shown in Figure 15–36.

Figure 15–36

- When you select an element in a schedule, in the *Modify Schedule/Quantities* tab>Element panel, you can click

  (Highlight in Model). This opens a close-up view of the element with the Show Element(s) in View dialog box, as shown in Figure 15–37. Click **Show** to display more views of the element. Click **Close** to finish the command.

Figure 15–37

Modifying a Schedule on a Sheet

Once you have placed a schedule on a sheet, you can manipulate it to fit the information into the available space. Select the schedule to display the controls that enable you to modify it, as shown in Figure 15–38.

Figure 15–38

- The blue triangles modify the width of each column.

- The break mark splits the schedule into two parts.

- In a split schedule you can use the arrows in the upper left corner to move that portion of the schedule table. The control at the bottom of the first table changes the length of the table and impacts any connected splits, as shown in Figure 15–39.

Figure 15–39

- To unsplit a schedule, drag the Move control from the side of the schedule that you want to unsplit back to the original column.

Practice 15c | Work with Schedules

Practice Objectives

- Update schedule information.
- Add a schedule to a sheet.

Estimated time for completion:10 minutes

In this practice you will add information to a door schedule and to elements that are connected to the schedule. You will then place the schedule on a sheet, as shown in Figure 15–40.

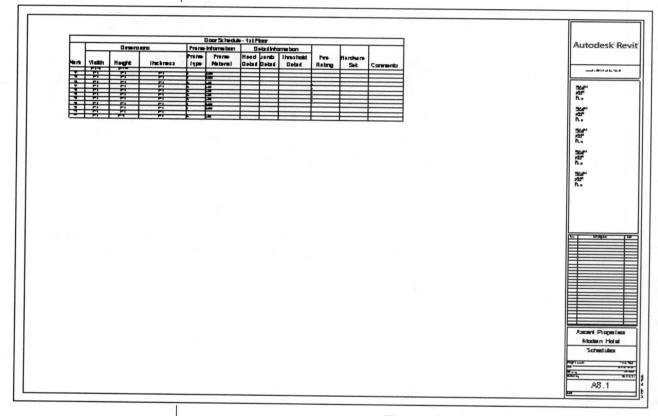

Figure 15–40

Task 1 - Fill in schedules.

1. Open the project **Modern-Hotel-Schedules.rvt**.

2. In the Project Browser, expand *Schedules/Quantities*. Four schedules have been added to this project.

3. Double-click on **Door Schedule - 1st Floor** to open it. The existing doors in the project are already populated with some of the basic information included with the door, as shown in Figure 15–41.

Mark	Dimensions			Frame Information		Detail Information		
	Width	Height	Thickness	Frame Type	Frame Material	Head Detail	Jamb Detail	Threshold Detail
	8' - 3 1/2"	9' - 4 1/4"						
101	3' - 0"	7' - 0"	0' - 2"					
102	3' - 0"	7' - 0"	0' - 2"					
103	3' - 0"	6' - 8"	0' - 2"					
104	3' - 0"	6' - 8"	0' - 2"					
105	3' - 0"	6' - 8"	0' - 2"					
106	3' - 0"	6' - 8"	0' - 2"					
107	3' - 0"	6' - 8"	0' - 2"					

Figure 15–41

4. The first door in the list does not have a mark associated with it. Click in the empty *Mark* cell. In the *Modify Schedules/ Quantities* tab>Element panel, click ⬚ (Highlight in Model). The front door that is part of a curtain wall displays and is highlighted, even though storefront doors are typically not included in Door Schedules. There are no other views to display. Click **Close** in the Show Element(s) in View dialog box.

5. Select one of the single exterior doors other than the front door.

6. In Properties, set a *Frame Type* as **A**, *Frame Material* as **Steel**, and *Finish* as **Coated**.

7. Click ⬚ (Edit Type).

8. In the Type Properties dialog box, in the *Identity Data* area, set the *Fire Rating* to **A**.

9. Click **OK** to finish.

10. Return to the Door Schedule. (Press <Ctrl>+<Tab> to switch between open windows.)

11. Note that the *Frame Type* and *Frame Material* display for one door and the matching exterior doors also have a fire rating. Use the drop-down list and change the options for the matching doors, as shown in Figure 15–42.

\<Door Schedule - 1st Floor\>

	A	B	C	D	E	F	G	H	I
	Mark	Dimensions			Frame Information		Detail Information		
		Width	Height	Thickness	Frame Type	Frame Material	Head Detail	Jamb Detail	Threshold Detail
		8' - 3 1/2"	9' - 4 1/4"						A
	101	3' - 0"	7' - 0"	0' - 2"	A	Steel			A
	102	3' - 0"	7' - 0"	0' - 2"	A	Steel ▾			
	103	3' - 0"	6' - 8"	0' - 2"					
	104	3' - 0"	6' - 8"	0' - 2"					

Figure 15–42

12. In the Door Schedule view, specify the *Fire Rating* for some other doors in the schedule. When you change the fire rating, you are prompted to change all elements of that type. Click **OK**.

13. Open the **Floor Plans: Floor 1** view.

14. Select the door to the office, then right-click and select **Select All Instances>In Entire Project**.

15. Look at the Status Bar beside ▼ (Filter) and note that more doors have been selected than are in the current view.

No visual changes to the door display because these are just text properties.

16. In Properties, set the *Frame Type* and *Frame Material* for these doors.

17. Press <Esc> to clear the selection when you are finished.

18. Switch back to the schedule view to see the additions. Not all of the doors are showing because the schedule has been limited to the 1st floor doors.

19. Save the project.

Task 2 - Add schedules to a sheet.

1. In the Project Browser, open the sheet **A8.1 - Schedules**.

2. Drag and drop the **Door Schedule - 1st Floor** view onto the sheet, as shown in Figure 15–43.

Your schedule may look different then the one shown in Figure 15–43.

Figure 15–43

3. Zoom in and use the arrows at the top to modify the width of the columns so that the titles display correctly.

4. Click in empty space on the sheet to finish placing the schedule.

5. Switch back to the **Floor Plans: Floor 1** view and select the double-swing door at the kitchen.

6. In the Type Selector, change the size to **72" x 82"**. In Properties, add a Frame Type, Frame Material, and Finish.

7. Return to the Door Schedule sheet. The information is automatically populated, as shown in Figure 15–44.

				Door Sc	
	Dimensions			**Frame Information**	
Mark	**Width**	**Height**	**Thickness**	**Frame Type**	**Frame Material**
	8' - 3 1/2"	9' - 4 1/4"			
101	3' - 0"	7' - 0"	0' - 2"	A	Steel
102	3' - 0"	7' - 0"	0' - 2"	A	Steel
103	3' - 0"	6' - 8"	0' - 2"		
104	3' - 0"	6' - 8"	0' - 2"		
105	3' - 0"	6' - 8"	0' - 2"	B	Wood
106	3' - 0"	6' - 8"	0' - 2"	B	Wood
107	3' - 0"	6' - 8"	0' - 2"	B	Wood
108	3' - 0"	7' - 0"	0' - 2"		
109	3' - 0"	7' - 0"	0' - 2"		
110	6' - 0"	7' - 0"	0' - 2"		
111	6' - 0"	6' - 10"	0' - 2"	C	Aluminum

Figure 15–44

8. Return to the 3D view.

9. In the Quick Access Toolbar, click ▤ (Close Hidden Windows.

10. Save the project.

Chapter Review Questions

1. Which of the following elements cannot be tagged using **Tag by Category**?

    a. Rooms

    b. Floors

    c. Walls

    d. Doors

2. What happens when you delete a door in an Autodesk Revit model, as shown in Figure 15–45?

16' - 0"   13' - 6"   8' - 4"

Figure 15–45

    a. You must delete the door on the drawing sheet.

    b. You must delete the door from the schedule.

    c. The door is removed from the model, but not from the schedule.

    d. The door is removed from the model and the schedule.

3. In a schedule, if you change type information (such as a Type Mark) all instances of that type update with the new information.

    a. True

    b. False

4. If you want to add rooms to a project (as shown in Figure 15–46), but they are not displayed, what do you have to do?

Figure 15–46

a. Create a new Room Plan view.

b. In the View Control Bar, turn on **Rooms**.

c. In the Visibility/Graphic Overrides dialog box, under Rooms turn on **Interior Fill**.

d. While the **Room** command is active, in the *Place Room* tab, verify that **Interior Fill** is selected.

Command Summary

Button	Command	Location
	Material Tag	**Ribbon:** *Annotate* tab>Tag panel
	Multi-Category	**Ribbon:** *Annotate* tab>Tag panel
	Room	**Ribbon:** *Architecture* tab>Room & Area panel **Shortcut: RM**
	Room Separator	**Ribbon:** *Architecture* tab>Room & Area panel
	Stair Tread/ Riser Number	**Ribbon:** *Annotate* tab>Tag panel
	Tag All Not Tagged	**Ribbon:** *Annotate* tab>Tag panel
	Tag by Category	**Ribbon:** *Annotate* tab>Tag panel **Shortcut: TG**
	Tag Room	**Ribbon:** *Architecture* tab>Room & Area panel **Shortcut: RT**

Creating Details

Creating details is a critical part of the design process, as it is the step where you specify the exact information that is required to build a construction project. The elements that you can add to a model include detail components, detail lines, text, keynotes, tags, symbols, and filled regions for patterning. Details can be created from views in the model, but you can also draw 2D details in separate views.

Learning Objectives in this Chapter

- Create drafting views where you can draw 2D details.
- Add detail components that show the typical elements in a detail.
- Annotate details using detail lines, text, tags, symbols, and patterns that define materials.
- Place keynotes in a detail and add keynote legends that describe the full content of the keynotes.

16.1 Setting Up Detail Views

Most of the work you do in the Autodesk® Revit® software is exclusively with *smart* elements that interconnect and work together in the model. However, the software does not automatically display how elements should be built to fit together. For this, you need to create detail drawings, as shown in Figure 16–1.

Details are created either in 2D drafting views, or in callouts from plan, elevation, or section views.

Figure 16–1

How To: Create a Drafting View

1. In the *View* tab>Create panel, click (Drafting View).
2. In the New Drafting View dialog box, enter a *Name* and set a *Scale*, as shown in Figure 16–2.

Drafting views are listed in their own section in the Project Browser.

Figure 16–2

3. Click **OK**. A blank view is created with space in which you can draw the detail.

How To: Create a Detail View from Model Elements

1. Create a section or a callout of the area you want to use for the detail.
2. In the Type Selector, select the **Detail View: Detail** type.
   - The marker indicates that it is a detail, as shown for a section in Figure 16–3.

Callouts also have a Detail View Type that can be used in the same way.

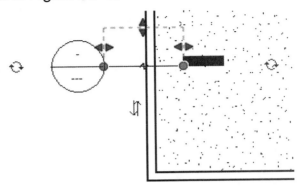

Figure 16–3

3. Open the new detail. Use the tools to draw on top of or add to the building elements.

   - In this type of detail view when the building elements change, the detail changes as well, as shown in Figure 16–4.

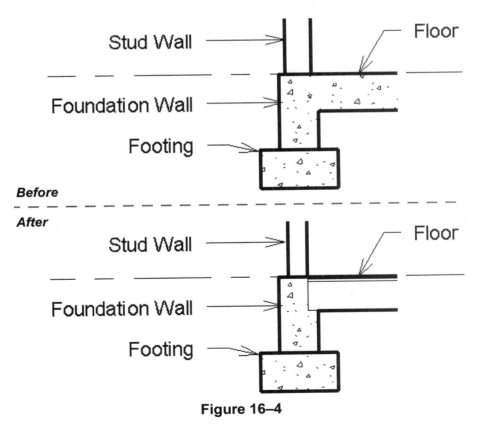

Figure 16–4

- You can create detail elements on top of the model and then turn the model off so that it does not show in the detail view. In Properties, in the *Graphics* area, change *Display Model* to **Do not display**. You can also set the model to **Halftone**, as shown in Figure 16–5.

Figure 16–5

Referencing a Drafting View

Enhanced
in **2016**

Once you have created a drafting view, you can reference it in another view (such as a callout, elevation, or section view), as shown in Figure 16–6. For example, in a section view, you might want to reference an existing roof detail. You can reference drafting views, sections, elevations, and callouts.

Figure 16–6

- You can use the search feature to limit the information displayed.

How To: Reference a Drafting View

1. Open the view in which you want to place the reference.
2. Start the **Section, Callout,** or **Elevation** command.
3. In the *Modify | <contextual>* tab>Reference panel select **Reference Other View**.
4. In the drop-down list, select **<New Drafting View>** or an existing drafting view.
5. Place the view marker.

6. When you place the associated drafting view on a sheet, the marker in this view updates with the appropriate information.

- If you select **<New Drafting View>** from the drop-down list, a new view is created in the *Drafting Views (Detail)* area in the Project Browser. You can rename it as required. The new view does not include any model elements.

- When you create a detail based on a section, elevation, or callout, you do not need to link it to a drafting view.

- You can change a referenced view to a different referenced view. Select the view marker and in the ribbon, select the new view from the list.

Saving Drafting Views

To create a library of standard details, save the non-model specific drafting views to your server. They can then be imported into a project and modified to suit. They are saved as .RVT files.

Drafting views can be saved in two ways:

- Save an individual drafting view to a new file.
- Save all of the drafting views as a group in one new file.

How To: Save One Drafting View to a File

1. In the Project Browser, right-click on the drafting view you want to save and select **Save to New File...**, as shown in Figure 16–7.

Figure 16–7

2. In the Save As dialog box, specify a name and location for the file and click **Save**.

You can save sheets, drafting views, model views (floor plans), schedules, and reports.

How To: Save a Group of Drafting Views to a File

1. In the Application Menu, expand (Save As), expand
 (Library), and click (View).
2. In the Save Views dialog box, in the *Views:* pane, expand the list and select **Show drafting views only**.
3. Select the drafting views that you want to save as shown in Figure 16–8.

Figure 16–8

4. Click **OK**.
5. In the Save As dialog box, specify a name and location for the file and click **Save**.

How To: Use a Saved Drafting View in another Project

1. Open the project to which you want to add the drafting view.

2. In the *Insert* tab>Import panel, expand (Insert from File) and click (Insert Views from File).
3. In the Open dialog box, select the project in which you saved the detail and click **Open**.
4. In the Insert Views dialog box, limit the types of views to **Show drafting views only**, as shown in Figure 16–9.

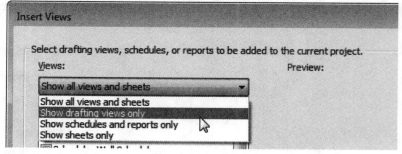

Figure 16–9

5. Select the view(s) that you want to insert and click **OK**.

Hint: Importing Details from Other CAD Software

You might already have a set of standard details that have been used in various projects. You can reuse them in the Autodesk Revit software, even if they were created in other software, such as the AutoCAD® software. Import the detail into a new project, clean it up, and save it as a view before bringing it into your project.

1. Create a drafting view and make it active.

2. In the *Insert* tab>Import panel, click (Import CAD).
3. In the Import CAD dialog box, select the file to import. Most of the default values are what you need. You might want to change the *Layer/Level colors* to **Black and White**.
Click **Open**.

- If you want to modify the detail, select the imported data. In the *Modify | [filename]* tab>Import Instance panel, expand (Explode) and click (Partial Explode) or (Full Explode). Click (Delete Layers) before you explode the detail. A full explode greatly increases the file size.

- Modify the detail using tools in the Modify panel. Change all the text and line styles to Autodesk Revit specific elements.

16.2 Adding Detail Components

Autodesk Revit elements, such as the casework section shown on the left in Figure 16–10, typically require additional information to ensure that they are constructed correctly. To create details such as the one shown on the right in Figure 16–10, you add detail components, detail lines, and various annotation elements. These elements are not directly connected to the model, even if model elements display in the view.

Section   *Detail Built on Section*

Figure 16–10

Detail Components

Detail components are families made of 2D and annotation elements. Over 500 detail components organized by CSI format are found in the *Detail Items* folder of the library, as shown in Figure 16–11.

Figure 16–11

How To: Add a Detail Component

1. In the *Annotate* tab>Detail panel, expand ▨ (Component) and click ▨ (Detail Component).
2. In the Type Selector, select the detail component type. You can load additional types from the Library.

3. Many detail components can be rotated as you insert them by pressing <Spacebar>. Alternatively, select the **Rotate after placement** option in the Options Bar, as shown in Figure 16–12.

☐ Rotate after placement

Figure 16–12

4. Place the component in the drawing. Rotate it if needed.

Adding Break Lines

The Break Line is a detail component found in the *Detail Items\ Div 01-General* folder. It consists of a rectangular area (shown highlighted in Figure 16–13) which is used to block out elements behind it. You can modify the size of the area that is covered and change the size of the cut line using the controls.

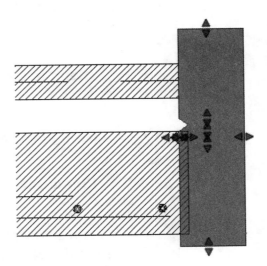

Figure 16–13

Hint: Working with the Draw Order of Details

When you select detail elements in a view, you can change the draw order of the elements in the *Modify | Detail Items* tab> Arrange panel. You can bring elements in front of other elements or place them behind elements, as shown in Figure 16–14.

Draw order: front　　　　　　　**Draw order: back**

Figure 16–14

- 🗗 **(Bring to Front):** Places element in front of all other elements.

- 🗗 **(Send to Back):** Places element behind all other elements.

- 🗗 **(Bring Forward):** Moves element one step to the front.

- 🗗 **(Send Backward):** Moves element one step to the back.

- You can select multiple detail elements and change the draw order of all of them in one step. They keep the relative order of the original selection.

Repeating Details

Instead of having to insert a component multiple times (such as with a brick or concrete block), you can use 🗊 (Repeating Detail Component) and draw a string of components, as shown in Figure 16–15.

Figure 16–15

How To: Insert a Repeating Detail Component

1. In the *Annotate* tab>Detail panel, expand (Component)
   and click ▤ (Repeating Detail Component).
2. In the Type Selector, select the detail you want to use.

3. In the Draw panel, click ✏ (Line) or ✎ (Pick Lines).
4. In the Options Bar, type a value for the *Offset* if needed.
5. The components repeat as required to fit the length of the sketched or selected line, as shown in Figure 16–16. You can lock the components to the line.

Existing Line ———   ———***Repeating Detail***

Figure 16–16

Hint: ⊗ (Insulation)

Adding batt insulation is similar to adding a repeating detail component, but instead of a series of bricks or other elements, it creates the linear batting pattern, shown in Figure 16–17.

Figure 16–17

Before you place the insulation in the drawing, specify the *Width* and other options in the Options Bar, as shown in Figure 16–18.

| Modify | Place Insulation | | Width 0' 3 1/2 | ☐ Chain | Offset: 0' 0" | to center ▼ |

Figure 16–18

16.3 Annotating Details

After you have added components and drawn detail lines, you need to add annotations to the drawing. You can use standard annotation tools to place text notes, dimensions and symbols, as shown in Figure 16–19. You can also fill regions with a pattern and add detail tags to the region.

Figure 16–19

Creating Filled Regions

Many elements include material information that displays in plan and section views, while other elements need such details to be added. For example, the concrete wall shown in Figure 16–20 includes material information, while the earth to the left of the wall needs to be added using the **Filled Region** command.

Filled region

Wall material

Figure 16–20

The patterns used in details are *drafting patterns*. They are scaled to the view scale and update if you modify it. You can also add full-size *model patterns*, such as a Flemish Bond brick pattern, to the surface of some elements.

• Fill patterns can be applied to all surfaces in a model. If the surface is warped, the patterns display as planar surfaces to keep the visual integrity of the geometry.

How To: Add a Filled Region

1. In the *Annotate* tab>Detail panel, expand (Region) and click (Filled Region).
2. Create a closed boundary using the Draw tools.
3. In the Line Style panel, select the line style for the outside edge of the boundary. If you do not want the boundary to display, select the <Invisible lines> style.
4. In the Type Selector, select the fill type, as shown in Figure 16–21.

Figure 16–21

5. Click (Finish Edit Mode).

- You can modify a region by changing the fill type in the Type Selector or by editing the sketch.

- Double-click on the edge of the filled region to edit the sketch.

  If you have the Selection option set to (Select elements by face) you can select the pattern.

Hint: Creating a Filled Region Pattern Type

You can create a custom pattern by duplicating and editing an existing pattern type.

1. Select an existing region or create a boundary.

2. In Properties, click (Edit Type).

3. In the Type Properties dialog box, click **Duplicate** and name the new pattern.

4. Select a *Fill Pattern*, *Background*, *Line Weight*, and *Color*, as shown in Figure 16–22.

Graphics		☆
Fill Pattern	Concrete [Drafting]	⋯
Background	Opaque	
Line Weight	1	
Color	■ Black	

Figure 16–22

5. Click **OK**.

• You can select from two types of Fill Patterns: **Drafting**, as shown in Figure 16–23, and **Model**. Drafting fill patterns scale to the view scale factor. Model fill patterns display full scale on the model and are not impacted by the view scale factor.

Figure 16–23

Adding Detail Tags

*The **Detail Item Tag.rfa** tag is located in the Annotations folder in the Library.*

Besides adding text to a detail, you can tag detail components using (Tag By Category). The tag name is set in the Type Parameters for that component, as shown in Figure 16–24. This means that if you have more than one copy of the component in your drawing, you do not have to rename it each time you place its tag.

Nominal
Cut
Lumber
2x6

Type Parameters

Parameter	Value
Dimensions	⊗
Width	0' 1 1/2"
Depth	0' 5 1/2"
Identity Data	⊗
Keynote	06110.F4
Type Comments	
Assembly Description	
Assembly Code	
Type Mark	Nominal Cut Lumber 2x6
OmniClass Number	

Figure 16–24

Hint: Multiple Dimension Options

If you are creating details that show one element with multiple dimension values, as shown in Figure 16–25, you can easily modify the dimension text.

Figure 16–25

Select the dimension and then the dimension text. The Dimension Text dialog box opens. You can replace the text, as shown in Figure 16–26, or add text fields above or below, as well as a prefix or suffix.

Figure 16–26

Practice 16a

Create a Detail Based on a Section Callout

Practice Objectives

- Create a detail based on a section.
- Add filled regions, detail components, and annotations.

Estimated time for completion: 15 minutes

In this practice you will create a detail based on a callout of a wall section. You will add repeating detail components, break lines, and detail lines, create filled regions, and add annotation to complete the detail, as shown in Figure 16–27.

Figure 16–27

Task 1 - Create a callout of a wall section.

1. Open the file **Modern-Hotel-Detailing.rvt**.

2. Open the **Floor Plans: Floor 1** view.

3. Double click on the wall section head shown in Figure 16–28. This guarantees that you open the right section.

Display the view defined by this section

Figure 16–28

4. Zoom in to the top of the wall showing the parapet and the roof.

5. In the *View* tab>Create panel, click (Callout).

6. In the Type Selector, select **Detail View: Detail**.

7. Create a callout as shown in Figure 16–29. Open the callout.

Parapet
107' - 0"

Roof
102' - 0"

Views : Section : Section 1 - Callout 1

Figure 16–29

8. In the View Control Bar, set the following parameters:

   - *Scale*: **1"=1'-0"**

   - *Detail Level*: (Fine)

9. Hide the levels, grids, and section markers (if displayed).

10. Turn off the Crop Region.

11. In the Project Browser, in the *Detail Views (Detail)* node, rename the view to **Parapet Detail**.

12. Save the project.

Task 2 - Add repeating detail components and break lines.

---

1. In the *Annotate* tab>Detail panel, expand ⬚ (Component) and then click ⬚ (Repeating Detail Component).

2. In the Type Selector, verify that the type is set to **Repeating Detail: Brick**.

3. Draw the brick line from the top of the parapet cap down, as shown in Figure 16–30.

Drawing from the top down insures that "mortar" is between the cap and the brick. This is how the detail elements were created.

Figure 16–30

4. In the Type Selector, select **Repeating Detail: CMU**. Draw over the other side of the wall.

The Autodesk Revit software lists the last tool you used at the top of the drop-down list.

5. In the *Annotate* tab>Detail panel, expand ⊟ (Repeating Detail Component) and click ⬚ (Detail Component).

6. In the *Modify | Place Detail Component* tab>Mode panel, click ⬇ (Load Family).

7. In the Load Family dialog box, navigate to the *Detail Items> Div 01-General* folder, select **Break Line.rfa**, and then click **Open**.

8. Add break lines to the bottom and right side of the detail. Press <Spacebar> to rotate the Break Line as required and use the controls to modify the size and depth, as shown in Figure 16–31

Figure 16–31

9. Save the project.

Task 3 - Add a filled region for the concrete cap.

1. In the Quick Access Toolbar, ensure that ≣ (Thin Lines) is off and that you can see the various line weights in the detail.

2. Zoom in to the concrete cap.

3. In the *Annotate* tab>Detail panel, expand ⬚ (Region) and then select ⬚ (Filled Region).

4. In the *Modify | Create Filled Region Boundary* tab>Line Style panel, select **Wide Lines**

5. In the Draw panel, click ⚲ (Pick Lines).

6. In the Options Bar, select **Lock**.

7. Select the edges of the cap, as shown in Figure 16–32.

Figure 16–32

8. In the Type Selector, select **Filled Region Concrete**.

9. Click ✔ (Finish Edit Mode).

10. Save the project.

Task 4 - Draw flashing using detail lines.

---

1. In the *Annotate* tab>Detail panel, click ⎰ (Detail Line).

2. In the *Modify | Place Detail Lines* tab>Line Style panel, verify that **Wide Lines** is still selected.

3. Draw flashing similar to that shown in Figure 16–33.

Figure 16–33

4. Using Detail Lines, add a cant strip under the flashing.

5. Save the project

Task 5 - Annotate the detail.

1. In the Quick Access Toolbar or on the *Annotate* tab>Text panel, click **A** (Text).

2. In the *Modify | Place Text* tab>Format panel, select A (Two-Segments).

3. Add the text and leaders shown in Figure 16–34. Use Alignments to place the leader points and text.

Figure 16–34

4. Save the project.

At this point you have a hybrid between detail items and model items. You can continue to add detail items to replace the roofing. You can also add structural elements if you have time.

16.4 Keynoting and Keynote Legends

Keynotes are special kinds of tags that apply specific numbering to various elements in a detail. They can be used on all model and detail elements, as well as materials.Using keynotes requires less room on a drawing than standard text notes, as shown in Figure 16–35. The full explanation of the note is shown in a corresponding *keynote legend* placed elsewhere in the drawing.

By default, the Autodesk Revit software uses the CSI master format system of keynote designations.

Figure 16–35

- Keynote tags are found in the Library in the *Annotations* folder and must be loaded into a project before you can apply them.

There are three types of keynote tags:

- **Element:** Used to tag elements, such as a door, wall, or detail components.

- **Material:** Used for the material assigned to a component or applied onto a surface.

- **User:** A keynote that must first be developed in a keynote table.

- Keynotes are stored in a keynote table (a text file), as shown in Figure 16–36. Any updates made to the keynote table are reflected in the project after it is closed and then re-opened.

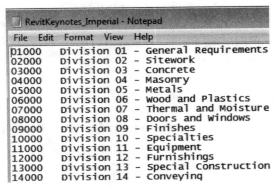

Figure 16–36

How To: Place a Keynote

1. In the *Annotate* tab>Tag panel, expand ⌐1 (Keynote) and click ⌐1 (Element), ⌐1 (Material), or ⌐1 (User).
2. Move the cursor over the element you want to keynote and select it.
3. If an element has keynote information assigned to it, the keynote is automatically applied. If it is not assigned, the Keynotes dialog box opens, as shown in Figure 16–37.

Figure 16–37

The keynote remembers the leader settings from the last time it was used.

4. Select the keynote you need from the list of divisions and click **OK**.

- The options for keynotes are the same as for other tags, including orientation and leaders, as shown in Figure 16–38.

Figure 16–38

Hint: Setting the Keynote Numbering Method

Keynotes can be listed in a drawing by the full keynote number or by sheet, as shown in Figure 16–39. Only one method can be used at a time in a project, but you can change between the two methods at any time in the project.

In the *Annotate* tab>Tag panel, expand (Keynote) and click (Keynote Settings).

Figure 16–39

In the Keynoting Settings dialog box, you can set the *Keynote Table* and *Path Type* used for keynote information, as shown in Figure 16–40.

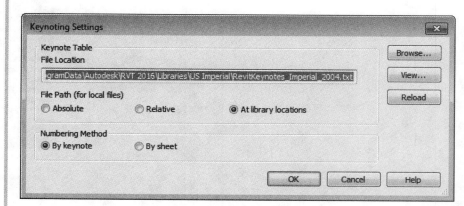

Figure 16–40

Keynote Legends

A keynote legend is different from a standard legend.

A keynote legend is a table containing the information stored in the keynote that is placed on a sheet, as shown in Figure 16–41. In the Autodesk Revit software, it is created in a similar way to schedules.

Keynote Legend	
Key Value	**Keynote Text**

04050	Basic Masonry Materials and Methods
05050	Basic Metal Materials and Methods
05100	Structural Metal Framing
08110.G1	2 3/4" Single Rabbet HM Door Frame
08210	Wood Doors
10150	Compartments and Cubicals
12400	Furnishings and Accessories

Figure 16–41

How To: Create a Keynote Legend

1. In the *View* tab>Create panel, expand (Legends) and click (Keynote Legend).
2. Type a name in the New Keynote Legend dialog box and click **OK**.
3. The Keynote Legend Properties dialog box typically only displays two scheduled fields, which are already set up for you, as shown in Figure 16–42.

Figure 16–42

4. In the other tabs, set up the format of the table as required.
5. Click **OK** to create the keynote legend.
6. When you are ready to place a keynote legend, drag it from the Project Browser onto the sheet. You can manipulate it in the same way, similar to modifying other schedules.

• As you add keynotes to the project, they are added to the keynote legend, as shown in Figure 16–43.

Keynote Legend			Keynote Legend	
Key Value	Keynote Text		Key Value	Keynote Text
04 21 00.A	Standard Brick – 3/8" Joint		04 21 00.A	Standard Brick – 3/8" Joint
04 21 00.A	Roman Brick – 3/8" Joint		04 21 00.A	Roman Brick – 3/8" Joint
04 21 00.A	Triple Brick – 1/2" Joint		04 21 00.A	Triple Brick – 1/2" Joint
05 12 00.A	L9x4x0.625		05 12 00.A	L9x4x0.625
			06 01 10.A	1x8R
			09 30 13.A	Ceramic Tile

Figure 16–43

Practice 16b | Create Additional Details

Practice Objective

- Create and annotate details.

In this practice you will create a window sill detail and a structural detail, and then annotate them. The following tasks are designed to be completed without detailed steps. Refer to the earlier topics and practice for assistance, as required. You can also use keynotes instead of text notes if required.

Estimated time of completion: 30 minutes

- Use the **Modern-Hotel-Detailing.rvt** project as the base file for these tasks.

Task 1 - Create a window sill detail.

In this task you will create a window sill detail, as shown in Figure 16–44.

Figure 16–44

- Use detail components from the Library, detail lines, patterning, text, and dimensions to create the window sill.

Task 2 - Add structural detail.

In this task you will create a structural detail, as shown in Figure 16–45.

Figure 16–45

- Create a new drafting view and draw the structural detail using the various sketching tools and structural detail components.

- Use the **Invisible lines** line type when you draw the lines for the fill boundary. The curved lines are made with splines.

- Create the Earth pattern type by duplicating an existing type and assigning a new drafting pattern to it.

Practice 16c

Create a Detail Based on a CAD File

Practice Objectives

- Import a CAD file.
- Explode the CAD file and change all of the elements to Autodesk Revit specific elements.
- Save the new detail view and import it into a project.

Estimated time for completion: 10 minutes

In this practice you will create a detail in a drafting view based on an existing detail created in the AutoCAD software, as shown in Figure 16–46. You will explode the imported file and change the text types and line styles of the elements to Autodesk Revit types. You will then create leaders for text and add patterning using filled regions. Finally, you will save the detail and import it into a project to create a clean Autodesk Revit detail without any CAD-based elements.

Figure 16–46

Task 1 - Create a detail based on an AutoCAD drawing.

1. Start a new project based on the default architectural template.

2. In the *View* tab>Create panel, click (Drafting View).

---

3. In the New Drafting View dialog box, set the name and scale to the following:

- Name: **Parapet Detail**
- Scale: **1 1/2" = 1'-0"**

4. In the *Insert* tab>Import panel, click (Import CAD).

5. In the Import CAD Formats dialog box, select the AutoCAD drawing **Roof-Detail.dwg** from your practice folder. Change the *Colors* to **Black and White** and keep the other default options, as shown in Figure 16–47.

Figure 16–47

6. Click **Open** to place the detail.

7. Zoom in and select the detail. It is all one element, as shown in Figure 16–48.

Figure 16–48

8. In the *Modify | Roof-Detail.dwg* tab>Import Instance panel, expand ▤ (Explode) and click ▥ (Full Explode). You are now able to edit individual sections of the imported detail.

9. Select all of the text, as shown in Figure 16–49.

Figure 16–49

10. In the Type Selector, select **Text: 3/32" Arial**.

11. Click (Modify) and select all of the individual elements. (Hint: use a crossing window.)

12. In the *Modify | Multi-Select* tab>Selection panel, click (Filter).

13. In the Filter dialog box, click **Check None** and then select **Lines (Heavy)** as shown in Figure 16–50. Click **OK.**

These lines are referenced to AutoCAD layers names rather than Autodesk Revit Line Type names.

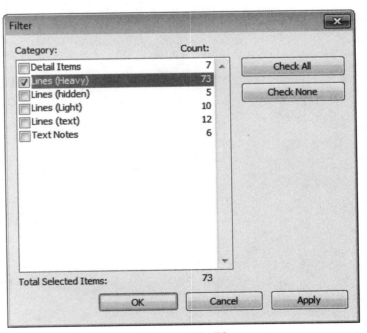

Figure 16–50

14. In the *Modify | Lines* tab>Line Style panel, change the *Line Style* to **Medium Lines**.

15. Return to the **Modify** command to finish.

16. Repeat the process with the other line types changing *Lines (hidden)* to **Hidden Lines** and *Lines (Light)* to **Thin Lines**.

Task 2 - Modify text and leaders.

1. Select everything again and use the **Filter** command to select **Lines (text)**. Delete these lines as they are not used.

2. Select one of the arrowheads that remain in the drawing. Right-click and select **Select All Instances>Visible in View**. Delete the elements.

3. Select a text element. In the *Modify | Text Notes* tab>Format panel, click **A⁺** (Add Right Side Straight Leader). Modify the leader to point to the correct element, as shown in the example in Figure 16–51.

Figure 16–51

4. Repeat the process of adding leaders to the text, pointing to the appropriate parts of the detail, as shown in Figure 16–52.

Figure 16–52

Task 3 - Add filled regions.

Use the <Invisible lines> type because the boundary does not need to display.

1. In the *Annotate* tab>Detail panel, click ![Region icon] (Region).

2. In the *Modify | Create Filled Region Boundary* tab>Line Style panel, set the line style to **<Invisible lines>**.

3. In the Draw panel, click ![Rectangle icon] (Rectangle) and add a box around each of the four rectangular brick sections, as shown in Figure 16–53. You can do all four areas in one sketch.

Figure 16–53

4. In the Type Selector, set the *pattern type* to **Diagonal Up** and click in empty space to clear the selection.

5. Click ![Finish Edit Mode icon] (Finish Edit Mode).

This area was hatched in the AutoCAD drawing. The hatching was automatically converted to a filled region when the drawing was imported into the project, but was not assigned an Autodesk Revit based pattern.

6. Select the large region between the areas that you just hatched, as shown in Figure 16–54.

Figure 16–54

7. In Properties, click (Edit Type).

8. In the Type Properties dialog box, click **Duplicate** and name the new pattern **Concrete**.

9. In the *Value* field for the *Fill Pattern* parameter, click (Browse).

10. In the Fill Patterns dialog box, in *Pattern Type* area, select **Drafting** and then select the pattern **Concrete**.

11. Click **OK** twice to create the Filled Region type and apply it to the selected boundary.

12. The detail view now consists of only Autodesk Revit elements and is safe to use in another project.

Task 4 - Create a View and Import it in to a Project.

1. In the Application Menu, expand (Save As), expand (Library), and select **View**.

2. In the Save Views dialog box, verify that **Drafting View: Parapet Detail** is selected, as shown in Figure 16–55 and click **OK**.

Figure 16–55

3. In the Save As dialog box, navigate to your practice folder and click **Save**.

4. Close the project and do not save it.

5. Open **Modern-Hotel-Detailing.rvt**.

6. In the *Insert* tab>Import panel, expand (Insert from File) and click (Insert Views from File).

7. In the Open dialog box, navigate to your practice folder and open **Parapet-Detail.rvt**.

8. In the Insert Views dialog box only this view is available. Click **OK**.

9. Accept any warnings that might display about duplicate types. They do not impact the project.

10. Save the project.

Chapter Review Questions

1. Which of the following are ways in which you can create a detail? (Select all that apply.)

    (a). Make a callout of a section and draw over it.

    (b). Draw all of the elements from scratch.

    (c). Import a CAD detail and modify or draw over it.

    d. Insert an existing drafting view from another file.

2. In which type of view (access shown in Figure 16–56) can you NOT add detail lines?

    Figure 16–56

    (a.) Plans

    b. Elevations

    (c). 3D views

    d. Legends

3. How are detail components different from building components?

    a. There is no difference.

    b. Detail components are made of 2D lines and annotation only.

    (c). Detail components are made of building elements, but only display in detail views.

    d. Detail components are made of 2D and 3D elements.

4. When you draw detail lines they are...

    a. Always the same width.

    b. Vary in width according to the view.

    c. Display in all views associated with the detail.

    d. Display only in the view in which they were created.

5. Which command do you use to add a pattern (such as concrete or earth as shown in Figure 16–57) to part of a detail?

Figure 16–57

a. Region
b. Filled Region
c. Masking Region
d. Pattern Region

Command Summary

Button	Command	Location
CAD Import Tools		
	Delete Layers	• **Ribbon:** *Modify	<imported filename>* tab>Import Instance panel
	Full Explode	• **Ribbon:** *Modify	<imported filename>* tab>Import Instance panel> expand Explode
	Import CAD	• **Ribbon:** *Insert* tab>Import panel
	Partial Explode	• **Ribbon:** *Modify	<imported filename>* tab>Import Instance panel> expand Explode
Detail Tools		
	Detail Component	• **Ribbon:** *Annotate* tab>Detail panel> expand Component
	Detail Line	• **Ribbon:** *Annotate* tab>Detail panel
	Insulation	• **Ribbon:** *Annotate* tab>Detail panel
	Region	• **Ribbon:** *Annotate* tab>Detail panel
	Repeating Detail Component	• **Ribbon:** *Annotate* tab>Detail panel> expand Component
View Tools		
	Bring Forward	• **Ribbon:** *Modify	Detail Items* tab> Arrange panel
	Bring to Front	• **Ribbon:** *Modify	Detail Items* tab> Arrange panel
	Drafting View	• **Ribbon:** *View* tab>Create panel
	Insert from File: Insert Views from File	• **Ribbon:** *Insert* tab>Import panel> expand Insert from File
	Send Backward	• **Ribbon:** *Modify	Detail Items* tab> Arrange panel
	Send to Back	• **Ribbon:** *Modify	Detail Items* tab> Arrange panel

Introduction to Worksets

Worksharing is a workflow used in the Autodesk® Revit® software when multiple people are working on a single project model. The model is broken up into worksets. Individuals open and work on in local files that are synchronized to a central file upon saving.

Learning Objectives in this Appendix

- Review worksharing principles.
- Open a local file to make changes to your part of a project.
- Synchronize with the central file, which contains all of the changes from local projects.

A.1 Introduction to Worksets

When a project becomes too big for one person, it needs to be subdivided so that a team of people can work on it. Since Autodesk Revit projects include the entire building model in one file, the file needs to be separated into logical components, as shown in Figure A–1, without losing the connection to the whole. This process is called *worksharing* and the main components are worksets.

Figure A–1

When worksets are established in a project, there is one **central file** and as many **local files** as required for each person on the team to have a file, as shown in Figure A–2.

*The **central file** is created by the BIM Manager, Project Manager, or Project Lead, and is stored on a server, enabling multiple users to access it. A **local file** is a copy of the central file that is stored on your computer.*

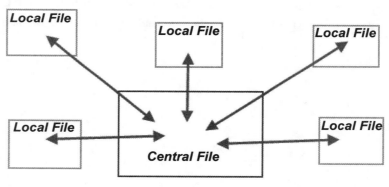

Figure A–2

- All local files are saved back to the central file, and updates to the central file are sent out to the local files. This way, all changes remain in one file, while the project, model, views, and sheets are automatically updated.

How To: Create a Local File

1. In the Application Menu or Quick Access Toolbar click

    (Open). You must use this method to be able to create a local file from the central file.
2. In the Open dialog box, navigate to the central file server location, and select the central file. Do not work in this file. Select **Create New Local**, as shown in Figure A–3.
3. Verify that this option is selected and click **Open**.

Figure A–3

User Names can be assigned in Options.

4. A copy of the project is created. It is named the same as the central file, but with your *User Name* added to the end.

*   You can save the file using the default name, or use

    (Save As) and name the file according to your office's standard. It should include *Local* in the name to indicate that it is saved on your local computer, or that you are the only one working with that version of the file.

*   Delete any old local files to ensure that you are working on the latest version.

How To: Work in a Workset-Related File

1. Open your local file.
2. In the Status Bar, expand the *Active Workset* drop-down list and select a workset, as shown in Figure A–4. By setting the active workset, other people can work in the project but cannot edit elements that you add to the workset.

Figure A–4

3. Work on the project as required.

Saving Workset-Related Files

When you are using a workset-related file, you need to save the file locally and centrally.

- Save the local file frequently (every 15-30 minutes). In the Quick Access Toolbar, click ▣ (Save) to save the local file just as you would any other project.

- Synchronize the local file with the central file periodically (every hour or two) or after you have made major changes to the project.

Hint: Set up Notifications to Save and Synchronize

You can set up reminders to save and synchronize files to the central file in the Options dialog box, on the *General* pane, as shown in Figure A–5.

Figure A–5

Synchronizing to the Central File

There are two methods for synchronizing to the central file. They are located in the Quick Access Toolbar or the *Collaborate* tab> Synchronize panel.

Click 🗇 (Synchronize Now) to update the central file and then the local file with any changes to the central file since the last synchronization. This does not prompt you for any thing. It automatically relinquishes elements borrowed from a workset used by another person, but retains worksets used by the current person.

Click 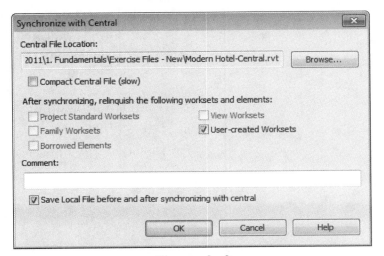 (Synchronize and Modify Settings) to open the Synchronize with Central dialog box, as shown in Figure A–6, where you can set the location of the central file, add comments, save the file locally before and after synchronization, and set the options for relinquishing worksets and elements.

Figure A–6

- Ensure that **Save Local file before and after synchronizing with central** is checked before clicking **OK**. Changes from the central file might have been copied into your file.

- When you close a local file without saving to the central file, you are prompted with options, as shown in Figure A–7.

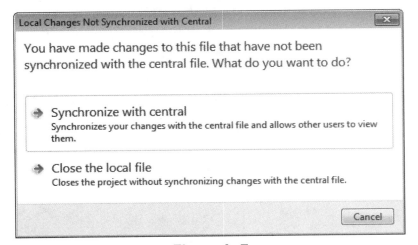

Figure A–7

Command Summary

Button	Command	Location
	Save	• **Quick Access Toolbar** • **Application Menu:** Save • **Shortcut:** <Ctrl>+<S>
	Synchronize and Modify Settings	• **Quick Access Toolbar** • **Ribbon:** *Collaborate* tab> Synchronize panel>expand Synchronize with Central
	Synchronize Now	• **Quick Access Toolbar** • **Ribbon:** *Collaborate* tab> Synchronize panel>expand Synchronize with Central

Additional Tools

There are many other tools available in the Autodesk® Revit® software that you can use when creating and using models. This appendix provides details about several tools and commands that are related to those covered in this training guide.

Learning Objectives in this Appendix

- Save and use selection sets of multiple building elements.
- Add wall sweeps and reveals as well as roof fascias, gutters, and floor slab edges.
- Create a Curtain Wall type with an equally spaced grid pattern.
- Clarify views using Split Face, Edit Wall Joints, Paint, Linework and cut profiles.
- Add dormers to roofs.
- Use guide grids to help place views on sheets.
- Add revision clouds, tags, and information.
- Annotate dependent views with matchlines and view references.
- Import and export schedules.
- Create basic building component schedules.
- Create repeating detail types.

B.1 Reusing Selection Sets

When multiple elements types are selected you can save the selection set so that it can be reused. For example, a structural column and an architectural column need to move together. Instead of picking each element, create a selection set that you can quickly access as shown in Figure B–1. You can also edit selection sets to add or remove elements from the set.

Figure B–1

- Selection sets are a filter of specific elements rather than types of elements.

How To: Save Selection Sets

1. Select the elements that you want to include in the selection set.
2. In the *Modify | Multi-Select* tab>Selection panel, click ⬚ (Save).
3. In the Save Selection dialog box, type a name for the set as shown in Figure B–2, and click **OK**.

Figure B–2

How To: Retrieve Selection Sets

1. Select any other elements you might want to use. In the *Modify | Multi-Select* tab>Selection panel, click 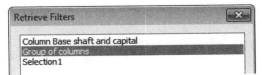 (Load). Alternatively, without any other selection, in the *Manage* tab> Selection panel, click (Load).

2. In the Retrieve Filters dialog box (shown in Figure B–3), select the set that you want to use and click **OK**.

Figure B–3

3. The elements are selected and you can continue to select other elements or use the selection.

How To: Edit Selection Sets

1. If elements are selected, in the *Modify | Multi-Select* tab> Selection panel, click (Edit). Alternatively, without any selection, in the *Manage* tab>Selection panel, click (Edit).

2. In the Filters dialog box (shown in Figure B–4), select the set that you want to edit and click **Edit...**.

Some filters in this dialog box are not selection sets but apply to categories of elements, such as the Interior filter shown in Figure B–4.

Figure B–4

- If you want to modify the name of the Filter, click **Rename...**.

3. The selection set elements remain black while the rest of the elements are grayed out. The *Edit Selection Set* contextual tab displays as well, as shown in Figure B–5.

Figure B–5

4. Use (Add to Selection) to select additional elements for the set and (Remove from Selection) to delete elements from the set.

5. When you have finished editing, click (Finish Selection).

• In the Filters dialog box, click **OK** to finish.

B.2 Wall Sweeps and Reveals

The Autodesk Revit software includes a series of commands that enable you to modify walls, roofs, and floors by sweeping a profile along an element. For example, you can quickly add a gutter along the full length of a roof, or a curb at the edge of a floor used as a balcony, as shown in Figure B–6. The element modified by the sweep is called the host. Therefore, all of these operations are known as host sweeps.

Figure B–6

- The software comes with a few standard profiles for the sweeps. You can also create your own custom profiles.

- Open a 3D view if you are working with walls. You can be in a plan or elevation view for working with roof and floor sweeps.

- There are specific commands to create wall sweeps and reveals, roof fascias and gutters, and floor slab edges. These are located by expanding the associated command in the *Architecture* tab>Build panel, as shown in Figure B–7. For walls and floors, they are also located in the *Structure* tab> Structure.

Figure B–7

- Wall Sweeps and Wall Reveals can only be applied in elevation, section, or 3D views.

How To: Use the Wall Sweep Command

The process of creating reveals, gutters, and floor slab edges is similar.

1. Open an elevation or 3D view.

2. In the *Architecture* tab>Build panel, expand (Wall) and click (Wall Sweep).

3. In Properties, select a Wall Sweep type. (The Wall Sweep type needs to be set up before you start the command.)

4. In the *Modify | Place Wall Sweep* tab>Placement panel, click either (Horizontal) or (Vertical). (This is only for walls.)

5. Move the cursor over the element where you want to add the sweep and click to place it.

6. If you are doing horizontal sweeps, continue selecting elements. The sweep is placed at the same height as the first element.

7. To change sweep styles or the height, in the Placement panel, click (Restart Wall Sweep), or return to the **Modify** command.to finish.

To specify a precise location for the sweep element, select it after you have created it and modify the dimensions as required.

How To: Set Up Sweep Profiles

1. In the *Insert* tab>Load from Library panel, click (Load Family).

2. In the Load Family dialog box, select the profile you want to use (in the *Profiles* folder) or select a custom profile.

3. Start the related host sweep command. For example, if you are working with a gutter, click (Roof: Gutter).

4. In Properties, select a Sweep type and click (Edit Type).

5. In the Type Properties dialog box, click **Duplicate...**.

6. Enter a new name for the type.

7. In the Type Properties dialog box, under *Construction*, select the *Profile*. You can also apply *Constraints*, *Materials and Finishes*, and *Identity Data*, as shown in Figure B–8.

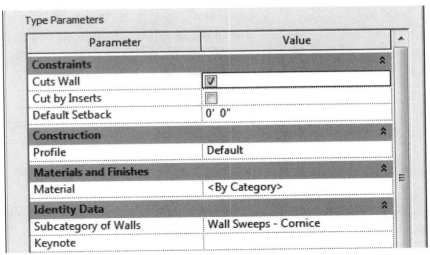

Figure B–8

8. Click **OK** to close the dialog box. The new type is set to be current.

Constraints

Constraints give you more control over how the sweep works.

Cuts Wall	If selected, cuts the geometry out of the host wall where it overlaps. Turning this off might increase the performance if the project contains a large amount of sweeps.
Cut by Inserts	If selected, when doors or windows are inserted into a wall with a wall sweep, the insert cuts the sweep.
Default Setback	Specify the distance that the sweep is set back from interacting wall inserts.

B.3 Creating Curtain Wall Types with Automatic Grids

If you have a curtain wall with a fixed distance or a fixed number of grids in the vertical or horizontal direction, you can create a curtain wall type containing this information, as shown in Figure B–9. The automatic grid lines can also be set to an angle.

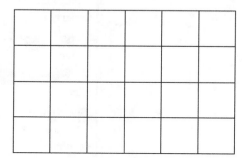

Figure B–9

How To: Create a Curtain Wall with Automatic Grids

1. In the *Architecture* tab>Build panel, click ⬜ (Wall).
2. In the Type Selector, select a curtain wall similar to the one you want to create.
3. In Properties, click ▦ (Edit Type).
4. In the Type Properties dialog box, click **Duplicate...** to create a copy of the existing family type.
5. In the Name dialog box, give the curtain wall a name that describes its purpose, as shown in Figure B–10. The new name automatically includes the family name, such as **Curtain Wall**. Therefore, you do not have to include the family name.

Figure B–10

6. In the Type Properties dialog box, enter information for the *Construction*, *Vertical* and *Horizontal Grid Pattern*, and *Vertical* and *Horizontal Mullions* parameters, as shown in Figure B–11.

Type Parameters apply to all instances of that type inserted into the Autodesk Revit software. This is true for all families (e.g., walls, doors, windows, etc.). Changing a Type Parameter changes all instances of that type in the project.

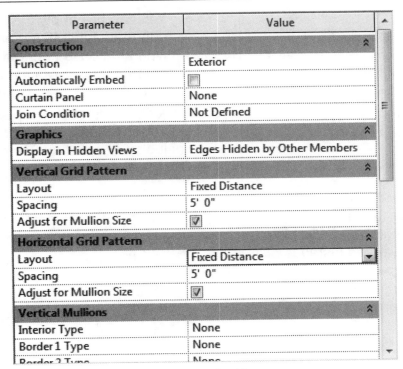

Figure B–11

- Enable the *Automatically Embed* parameter if you want to use the curtain wall as a storefront.

- Set the *Curtain Panel* to the primary type you plan to use. You can modify the panels once they are in the project.

- The Grid Patterns can be set to the following:

Fixed Distance	Grids are placed a specified distance apart. Specify the size in the **Spacing** option.
Fixed Number	Grids are divided across a wall based on a specified number. The *Number* of grid lines is specified in the Instance Parameters.
Maximum Spacing	Grids are spaced evenly with the greatest distance between them specified in the **Spacing** option.
None	No grids are specified.

- The **Adjust for Mullion Size** parameter ensures that panels inserted between grid lines are equal in size. This is very important if you use a different size of mullion on the borders from the ones on the interior separations.

- Mullions can be specified in the Type Parameters for Interior and Border mullions. The vertical **Border 1** type is applied to the left of the curtain wall and **Border 2** is applied to the right. The horizontal **Border 1** type is at the bottom and **Border 2** is at the top.

The options in
Properties are Instance
Parameters applied to
the selected instance of
the type inserted into
the Autodesk Revit
software.

- You can pre-apply the mullions to the grid in the type or add them later. If you are planning to use the curtain wall type as a base to create a more complex curtain wall, do not add mullions in the type because doing so makes it difficult to select the grid lines to modify them.

7. Click **OK** to close the Type Properties dialog box.
8. In Properties, set the *Vertical* and *Horizontal Grid Pattern* (including *Number* for Fixed Number, *Justification*, *Angle*, and *Offset*), as shown in Figure B–12.

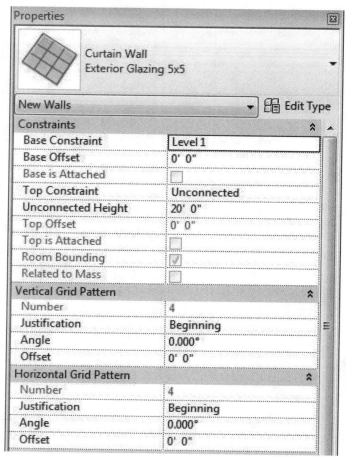

Figure B–12

B.4 Enhancing Views

When you start detailing views (such as elevations and sections), several tools can help clarify what you are trying to show. **Split Face** divides an elevation face into smaller separate faces. You can then use **Paint** to apply different materials to the faces, as shown in Figure B–13. **Linework** enables you to change the lineweight or line style of lines in a view to emphasize various components. In plan views and sections, you can use **Cut Profile** to enhance the views.

Figure B–13

- The changes made with **Split Face** and **Paint** are displayed in elevations and 3D views.

- Changes made using **Linework** are view-specific, applying only in the view in which they are made.

Hint: Changing the Host of an Element

You can change the wall that a window or door is associated with by re-hosting the element. Select the window or door and in the *Modify contextual* tab>Host panel, click 🚪 (Pick New Host). Then select the new wall where you want the door or window to be located.

- This also works with other hosted and workplane-based elements.

Splitting Faces

You can split a face into separate surfaces so you can apply different materials to each part. A sketch defines the split, which must be a closed shape completely inside the face, or an open shape that touches the face edges, as shown in Figure B–14. Windows are cut out of faces automatically.

Figure B–14

How to:

*If you have **Select elements by face** toggled on you can click directly on the face.*

How To: Create a Split Face

1. Switch to an elevation view (a 3D view works as well).

2. In the *Modify* tab>Geometry panel, click (Split Face).
3. Select the edge of the face that you want to modify. Use <Tab> as required to toggle through the available faces.
4. In the *Modify | Split Face>Create Boundary* tab>Draw panel, use the sketch tools to create a sketch as required to define the split.

5. Click (Finish Edit Mode).

• To save time, use a wall style that includes the primary material you want to use on the split face. For example, if you are working with brick, set the wall to a type that has a brick face. This way, you can work with the brick courses when you are creating the split face.

- When using a material, such as brick, you can snap to the pattern and even lock the split lines to the pattern as shown in Figure B–15.

Figure B–15

- You can double-click on the edge of the split face lines to switch to Edit Boundary mode. If you double-click on the face (with **Select elements by face** toggled on) it switches to Edit Profile mode, which impacts the entire wall, not just the split face boundary.

Editing Wall Joins

Before you start working with split faces, ensure the walls are mitered, as shown in Figure B–16. By default, the walls are butted to each other. This creates a problem when you select faces. Use **Edit Wall Joins** to modify the configuration of the intersections. Do not use this command if you have complex wall joins; instead, modify the length of the wall in relation to the adjoining walls.

Figure B–16

How To: Modify the Configuration of a Wall Join

Only one join can be selected for this process.

1. In the *Modify* tab>Geometry panel, click ⬐ (Wall Joins).
2. Click on the wall join that you want to edit. There is a square box around the join.
3. In the Options Bar, the configuration options display, as shown in Figure B–17. Select the required option.

Figure B–17

- You can select from three configurations: **Butt**, **Miter**, and **Square off**, as shown in Figure B–18. Click **Previous** and **Next** to toggle the butt or squared-off corner configurations through the various intersection options.

Figure B–18

4. The **Wall Joins** command remains active until you select another command.

How To: Modify Display Options of Wall Joins

Enhanced in **2016**

1. In the *Modify* tab>Geometry panel, click ![icon] (Wall Joins).
2. Click on the wall join that you want to edit.

- To modify multiple joins at the same time, draw a window around several wall intersections (as shown in Figure B–19), or hold <Ctrl> and pick additional intersections. A square box displays around each join.

Figure B–19

- The *Display* controls whether or not wall joins are displayed. The options are **Use View Settings** (set up in View Properties), **Clean Join**, and **Don't Clean Join**, as shown in Figure B–20.

Figure B–20

3. If you select the end of a wall that is not joined to another wall, you can change the option to **Allow Join** in the Options Bar, as shown in Figure B–21. Reselect the wall join to make the configurations available.

Figure B–21

Applying Materials

Once you have a face split into sections, you can apply different materials to each part. For example, you might want a soldier course under each window on a brick wall. First, you would create the split face and then apply the new material using **Paint**, as shown in Figure B–22.

Figure B–22

How To: Apply Material with Paint

1. In the *Modify* tab>Geometry panel, click (Paint) or type **PT**.
2. In the Material Browser, select a material. You can run a search or filter the list using specific types of materials, as shown in Figure B–23.

The browser remains open as you are applying the paint.

Figure B–23

3. Move the cursor over the face you want to paint. It should highlight. Click on the face to apply the material.
4. Continue selecting materials and painting other faces as required.
5. In the Material Browser, click **Done** to finish the command.

- Some material patterns display as shaded when you zoom out. Zoom in to display the pattern. Other material patterns only display when you are in the ⬛ (Realistic) Visual Style.

- To change the material applied to a face, in the *Modify* tab> Geometry panel, expand 🎨 (Paint) and click 🎨 (Remove Paint). Select the face(s) from which you want to remove the material.

Adjusting Linework

To emphasize a particular line or change the look of a line in elevations and other views, modify the lines with the **Linework** command. Changes made to lines with the **Linework** command are view-specific, applying only to the view in which you make them, as shown in Figure B–24.

- The **Linework** command can be used on project edges of model elements, cut edges of model elements, edges in imported CAD files, and edges in linked Autodesk Revit models.

Figure B–24

How To: Adjust Linework

1. In the *Modify* tab>View panel, click ⬇ (Linework) or type the shortcut **LW**.
2. In the *Modify | Linework* tab>Line Style panel, select the line style you want to use from the list.
3. Move the cursor and highlight the line you want to change. You can use <Tab> to toggle through the lines as required.
4. Click on the line to change it to the new line style.
5. Click on other lines as required or return to the **Modify** command to finish.

- If the line is too long or short, you can modify the length using the controls at the end of the line.

How To: Create Line Styles

1. In the *Manage* tab>Settings panel, expand (Additional Settings) and click (Line Styles).
2. In the Line Styles dialog box, as shown in Figure B–25, in the *Modify Subcategories* area, click **New**.

Line Styles

Category	Line Weight Projection	Line Color	Line Pattern
Lines	1	RGB 000-166-000	Solid
<Area Boundary>	6	RGB 128-000-255	Solid
<Beyond>	1	Black	Solid
<Centerline>	1	Black	Center 1/4"
<Demolished>	1	Black	Demolished 3/16"
<Hidden>	1	Black	Hidden 1/8"
<Overhead>	1	Black	Overhead 1/16"
<Room Separation>	1	Black	Solid
<Sketch>	3	RGB 225-000-255	Solid
<Space Separation>	1	Black	
Axis of Rotation	6	Blue	Center 1/4"
Hidden Lines	1	RGB 000-166-000	Dash
Insulation Batting Lines	1	Black	Solid
Lines	1	RGB 000-166-000	Solid
Medium Lines	3	Black	Solid
Thin Lines	1	Black	Solid
Wide Lines	5	Black	Solid

Select All   Select None   Invert

☐ Show categories from all disciplines

Modify Subcategories

New   Delete   Rename

OK   Cancel   Apply   Help

Figure B–25

3. In the New Subcategory dialog box, type a name for the new style, as shown in Figure B–26, and click **OK**.

*The **Subcategory of:** option is automatically set to **Lines**.*

New Subcategory

Name:

Property Line

Subcategory of:

Lines

OK   Cancel

Figure B–26

4. In the Line Styles dialog box, assign the required line weight, color, and pattern to the new style.

Editing Plan and Section Profiles

*If you are working on a compound face (such as a wall with several layers of information), change the Detail Level to **Medium** or **Fine** to display the fill patterns.*

In plan and section details, you might need to modify portions of the cut to show the specific intersection of two faces, as shown in Figure B–27. This can be done using **Cut Profile**. The cut profile changes the shape of the elements at their cut plane, but does not modify their 3D information. The cut is only displayed in the view in which it is drawn.

Figure B–27

- You can modify the cut of walls, floors, and roofs.

How To: Use Cut Profile

1. In the *View* tab>Graphics panel, click 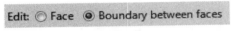 (Cut Profile).
2. In the Options Bar, select to edit the **Face** or the **Boundary between faces**, as shown in Figure B–28.

Edit: ○ Face ● Boundary between faces

Figure B–28

3. Select the face or boundary that you want to edit.
4. In the *Modify | Create Cut Profile Sketch* tab>Draw panel, use the sketch tools to sketch a new profile, as shown in Figure B–29.

Figure B–29

5. Click ✔ (Finish Edit Mode).

- If a warning box opens, verify that the lines start and end on the same boundary line and that they do not make a closed loop or cross over each other.

B.5 Creating Dormers

You can add two types of dormers to a project. One type of dormer cuts through the roof, as shown in Figure B–30. This dormer type has walls supporting a separate roof. You create the supporting walls and dormer roof, and then cut a hole in the roof.

Figure B–30

The other type of dormers are part of the roof, as shown in Figure B–31. This is created by sketching the roof, modifying it, and adding slope arrows to define the additional peak.

Figure B–31

- The dormer must be added to a plane that defines a slope.

How To: Add a Dormer with Supporting Walls to a Roof

1. Draw the main roof. When it is placed correctly, create a secondary dormer roof and supporting walls, as shown in Figure B–32.

Figure B–32

2. Move the new dormer (walls and roof) into position as required.

3. In the *Modify* tab>Geometry panel, use ⬦ (Join Geometry and ▭ (Join/Unjoin Roof) to connect the dormer walls/roof to the existing roof.

4. In the *Architecture* tab>Opening panel, click ⬦ (Dormer Opening).

5. In a roof plan view, select the main roof (the one to be cut).

6. In the *Modify | Edit Sketch* tab>Pick panel, click ⬠ (Pick Roof/Wall Edges) and select the opening to be cut.

- The dormer opening sketch does not need to be closed.

- Clean up the roofs and roof edges as required using tools such as **Join**, **Attach Top/Base**, etc.

How To: Add A Dormer Using Slope Arrows to a Roof

1. Draw a roof. When it is placed, select the roof. In the *Modify | Roofs* tab>Mode panel, click ▭ (Edit Footprint) to edit the roof sketch.

2. In the *Modify | Roofs>Edit Footprint* tab>Modify panel, click ⊹ (Split Element) to split the edge of the roof between the two points where you want the dormer to be located. Do not delete the inner segment. You can use dynamic dimensions to help locate the points to split.

3. In the Selection panel, click (Modify) and select the new segment between the split points. In the Options Bar, clear the **Defines Slope** option for this segment.

4. In the Draw panel, click ▱ (Slope Arrow).
5. Draw a slope arrow from one end of the segment to the midpoint. Then draw a second slope arrow from the other end to the midpoint, as shown in Figure B–33.

Figure B–33

6. Select the slope arrows. In Properties, specify the **Height at the Tail** or **Slope** option and type the required properties.

7. In the Mode panel, click ✓ (Finish Edit Mode).
8. View the roof in a 3D view to verify the results, as shown in Figure B–34.

Figure B–34

B.6 Working with Guide Grids on Sheets

You can use a guide grid to help you place views on a sheet, as shown in Figure B–35. Guide grids can be set up per sheet. You can also create different types with various grid spacings.

When moving a view to a guide grid, only orthogonal datum elements (levels and grids) and reference planes snap to the guide grid.

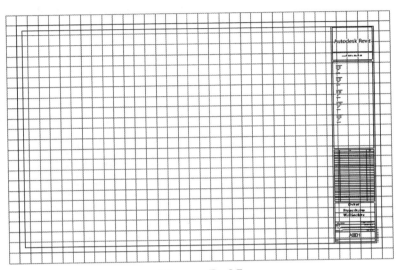

Figure B–35

• You can move guide grids and resize them using controls.

How To: Add A Guide Grid

1. When a sheet is open, in the *View* tab>Sheet Composition panel, click ⠿ (Guide Grid).
2. In the Assign Guide Grid dialog box, select from existing guide grids (as shown in Figure B–36), or create a new one and give it a name.

Figure B–36

3. The guide grid displays using the specified sizing.

How To: Modify Guide Grid Sizing

1. If you create a new guide grid you need to update it to the correct size in Properties. Select the edge of the guide grid.
2. In Properties, set the *Guide Spacing*, as shown in Figure B–37.

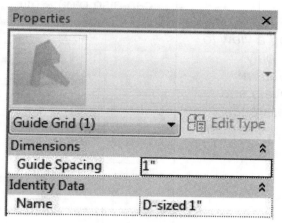

Figure B–37

B.7 Revision Tracking

When a set of drawings has been put into production, you need to show where changes are made. Typically, these are shown on sheets using a revision cloud. Each cloud is then tagged and the number is referenced elsewhere on the sheet with the description and date, as shown in Figure B–38. The Autodesk Revit software has created a process where the numbering and description are automatically applied to the title blocks when you associate a revision cloud with the information.

Figure B–38

The information is displayed in a revision table. This table can be created before or after you start adding revision clouds to the project. Once the table is created, you can modify the parameter of the cloud to match the corresponding information.

- More than one revision cloud can be associated with a revision number.

- The title blocks that come with the Autodesk Revit software already have a revision schedule inserted into the title area. It is recommended that you also add a revision schedule to your company title block.

How To: Add Revision Clouds

1. In the *Annotate* tab>Detail panel, click (Revision Cloud).
2. In the *Modify | Create Revision Cloud Sketch* tab>Draw panel, use the draw tools to create the cloud.
3. Click (Finish Edit Mode).

If the revision table has not be set up, you can do this at a later date.

4. In the Options Bar or Properties, expand the Revision drop-down list and select from the Revision list, as shown in Figure B–39.

Figure B–39

- Revision clouds can be added before or after you create a revision table that assigns the number and value.

- The *Revision Number* and *Date* are automatically assigned according to the specifications in the revision table.

- You can create an open cloud (e.g., as a tree line), as shown in Figure B–40.

Figure B–40

- You can double-click on the edge of revision cloud to switch to Edit Sketch mode and modify the size or location of the revision cloud arcs.

How To: Tag Revision Clouds

1. In the *Annotate* tab>Tag panel, click [icon] (Tag By Category).
2. Select the revision cloud to tag. A tooltip containing the revision number and revision from the cloud properties displays when you hover the cursor over the revision cloud, as shown in Figure B–41.

Figure B–41

- If the revision cloud tag is not loaded, load **Revision Tag.rfa** from the *Annotations* folder in the Library.

How To: Create a Revision Table

1. Open an existing project or a template,

2. In the *View* tab>Sheet Composition panel, click [icon] (Sheet Issues/Revisions), or in the *Manage* tab>Settings panel, expand [icon] (Additional Settings) and click [icon] (Sheet Issues/Revisions).

3. In the Sheet Issues/Revisions dialog box, set the type of *Numbering* you want to use.

4. Click **Add** to add a new revision.

5. Specify the *Numbering*, *Date*, and *Description* for the revision, as shown in Figure B–42. Do not modify the *Issued*, *Issued by*, or *Issued to* columns.

- When a revision is issued, you cannot modify the information. Therefore, you should wait to issue revisions until just before printing the sheets.

Figure B–42

6. Click **OK** when you have finished adding revisions.

Revision Options

- If the numbering method is set to **Per Project**, then the numbering sequence is used throughout the project. In many cases, companies prefer to use the **Per Sheet** method where the numbers are sequenced per sheet.

Enhanced in **2016**

- You can select one or more revisions and click **Delete** to remove the rows, if required.

- If you need to reorganize the revisions, select a row and click **Move Up** and **Move Down** or use **Merge Up** and **Merge Down** to combine the revisions into one.

- The *Numbering* options include: **Numeric**, **Alphanumeric**, and **None**. To set how they display, in the *Numbering options* area, click **Numeric...** or **Alphanumeric...** to bring up the Customize Numbering Options dialog box, shown for the Alphanumeric tab in Figure B–43.

Figure B–43

- The starting number for a *Numeric* sequence can start at 0 or any positive number.

- The *Alphanumeric* sequence can consist of one or more characters.

- You can add a prefix or suffix to the numbering values.

- The *Arc length* option sets the length of the arcs that form the revision cloud. It is an annotation element and is scaled according to the view scale.

Issuing Revisions

When you have completed the revisions and are ready to submit new documents to the field, you should first lock the revision for the record. This is called issuing the revision. An issued revision is noted in the tooltip of a revision cloud, as shown in Figure B–44.

Revision Clouds : Revision Cloud: 1 - Move door (Issued)

Figure B–44

How To: Issue Revisions

1. In the Sheet Issues/Revisions dialog box, in the row for the revision that you are issuing, type a name in the *Issued to* and *Issued by* fields, as required.
2. In the same row, select the **Issued** option.
3. Continue issuing any other revisions, as required.
4. Click **OK** to finish.

- Once the **Issued** option is selected, you cannot modify that revision in the Revisions dialog box or by moving the revision cloud(s). The tooltip on the cloud(s) note that it is **Issued**.

- You can unlock the revision by clearing the **Issued** option. Unlocking enables you to modify the revision after it has been locked.

B.8 Annotating Dependent Views

The **Duplicate as a Dependent** command creates a copy of the view and links it to the selected view. Changes made to the original view are also made in the dependent view and vice-versa. Use dependent views when the building model is so large you need to split the building up on separate sheets, with views that are all at the same scale. Having one overall view with dependent views makes viewing changes, such as to the scale or detail level, easier.

Dependent views display in the Project Browser under the top-level view, as shown in Figure B–45.

Figure B–45

How To: Duplicate Dependent Views

1. Select the view you want to use as the top-level view.
2. Right-click and select **Duplicate View>Duplicate as a Dependent**.
3. Rename the dependent views as required.

- If you want to separate a dependent view from the original view, right-click on the dependent view and select **Convert to independent view**.

Annotating Views

Annotation Crop Region and Matchlines can be used in any type of view.

When you work with a dependent view, you can use several tools to clarify and annotate the view, including **Matchlines** and **View References**, as shown in Figure B–46.

Figure B–46

How To: Add Matchlines

Matchlines are drawn in the primary view to specify where dependent views separate. They display in all related views, as shown in Figure B–47, and extend through all levels of the project by default.

Figure B–47

1. In the *View* tab>Sheet Composition panel, click

    🗐 (Matchline).

2. In the Draw panel, click ✒ (Line) and draw the location of the matchline.

3. In the Matchline panel, click ✔ (Finish Edit Mode) when you are finished.

•   To modify an existing matchline by selecting it and clicking

    🖉 (Edit Sketch) in the *Modify | Matchline* tab>Mode panel.

•   In the *Manage* tab>Settings panel, click 🗄 (Object Styles) to open the Object Styles dialog box. In the *Annotation Objects* tab, you can make changes to Matchline properties including color, linetype, and line weight.

How To: Add View References

Once you have dependent views and a matchline in place, you might want to add view references on either side of the matchline.

1. In the *View* tab>Sheet Composition panel or *Annotate* tab> Tag panel, click 🗝 (View Reference).

2. In the *Modify | View Reference* tab> View Reference panel specify the *View Type* and *Target View*, as shown in Figure B–48.

Figure B–48

3. Place the tag on the side of the matchline that corresponds to the target view.
4. Select another target view from the list and place the tag on the other side of the matchline.
5. The tags display as empty dashes until the views are placed onto sheets. They then update to include the detail and sheet number, as shown in Figure B–49.

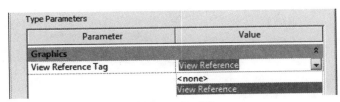

Figure B–49

- Double-click on the view reference to open the associated view.

- If only a label named **REF** displays when you place a view reference, it means you need to load and update the tag. The **View Reference.rfa** tag is located in the *Annotations* folder. Once you have the tag loaded, in the Type Selector, select one of the view references and, in Properties, click ⊞ (Edit Type). Select the **View Reference** tag in the drop-down list, as shown in Figure B–50, and click **OK** to close the dialog box. The new tag displays.

Type Parameters	
Parameter	Value
Graphics	
View Reference Tag	View Reference
	<none>
	View Reference

Figure B–50

B.9 Importing and Exporting Schedules

Schedules are views and can be copied into your project from other projects. Only the formatting information is copied; the information about individually scheduled items is not included. That information is automatically added by the project the schedule is copied into. You can also export the schedule information to be used in spreadsheets.

How To: Import Schedules

1. In the *Insert* tab>Import panel, expand ⬇ (Insert from File) and click ⬇ (Insert Views from File).
2. In the Open dialog box, locate the project file containing the schedule you want to use.
3. Select the schedules you want to import, as shown in Figure B–51.

If the referenced project contains many types of views, change Views: to Show schedules and reports only.

Figure B–51

4. Click **OK**.

How To: Export Schedule Information

1. Switch to the schedule view that you want to export.

2. In the Application Menu, click (Export)> (Reports)> (Schedule).

3. Select a location and name for the text file in the Export Schedule dialog box and click **Save**.

4. In the Export Schedule dialog box, set the options in the *Schedule appearance* and *Output options* areas that best suit your spreadsheet software, as shown in Figure B–52.

Figure B–52

5. Click **OK**. A new text file is created that you can open in a spreadsheet, as shown in Figure B–53.

Figure B–53

B.10 Creating Building Component Schedules

A Building Component schedule is a table view of the type and instance parameters of a specific element. You can specify the parameters (fields) you want to include in the schedule. All of the parameters found in the type of element you are scheduling are available to use. For example, a door schedule (as shown in Figure B–54) can include instance parameters that are automatically filled in (such as the **Height** and **Width**) and type parameters that might need to have the information assigned in the schedule or element type (such as the **Fire Rating** and **Frame**).

A	**B**	**C**	**D**	**E**	**F**	**G**	**H**
Mark	Height	Width	Fire Rating	Frame Type	Frame Material	Finish	Function
2	7' - 0"	10' - 0"	A	A	Steel	Brushed	Exterior
3	6' - 8"	3' - 0"	B	B	Wood	Paint	Interior
4	6' - 8"	3' - 0"	B	B	Wood	Paint	Interior
5	6' - 8"	3' - 0"	B	B	Wood	Paint	Interior
6	6' - 8"	3' - 0"	B	B	Wood	Paint	Interior

<Door Schedule>

Figure B–54

How To: Create a Building Component Schedule

1. In the *View* tab>Create panel, expand ▦ (Schedules) and click ▦ (Schedule/Quantities) or in the Project Browser, right-click on the Schedule/Quantities node and select **New Schedule/Quantities**.
2. In the New Schedule dialog box, select the type of schedule you want to create (e.g., Doors) from the *Category* list, as shown in Figure B–55.

In the Filter list drop-down list, you can specify the discipline(s) to show only the categories that you want to display.

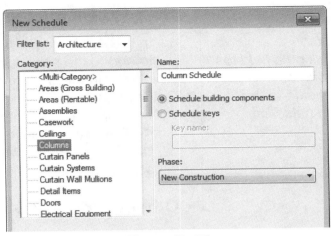

Figure B–55

3. Type a new *Name*, if the default does not suit.
4. Select **Schedule building components.**
5. Specify the *Phase* as required.
6. Click **OK**.
7. Fill out the information in the Schedule Properties dialog box. This includes the information in the *Fields*, *Filter*, *Sorting/Grouping*, *Formatting*, and *Appearance* tabs.
8. Once you have entering the schedule properties, click **OK**. A schedule report is created in its own view.

Schedule Properties – Fields Tab

In the *Fields* tab, you can select from a list of available fields and organize them in the order in which you want them to display in the schedule, as shown in Figure B–56.

Figure B–56

You can also double-click on a field to move it from the Available fields to the Scheduled fields list.

How To: Fill out the Fields Tab

1. In the *Available fields* list, select one or more fields you want to add to the schedule and click **Add -->**. The field(s) are placed in the *Scheduled fields (in order)* list.
2. Continue adding fields as required. If you add one you did not want to use, select it in the *Scheduled fields* list and click **<-- Remove** to move it back to the *Available fields* list.
3. Use **Move Up** and **Move Down** to change the order of the scheduled fields.

Other Fields Tab Options

Select available fields from	Enables you to select additional category fields for the specified schedule. The available list of additional fields depends on the original category of the schedule. Typically, they include room information.
Include elements in linked files	Includes elements that are in files linked to the current project, so that their elements can be included in the schedule.
Add Parameter...	Adds a new field according to your specification. New fields can be placed by instance or by type.
Calculated Value...	Enables you to create a field that uses a formula based on other fields.
Edit...	Enables you to edit custom fields. This is grayed out if you select a standard field.
Delete...	Deletes selected custom fields. This is grayed out if you select a standard field.

Schedule Properties – Filter Tab

In the *Filter* tab, you can set up filters so that only elements meeting specific criteria are included in the schedule. For example, you might only want to show information for one level, as shown in Figure B–57. You can create filters for up to eight values. All values must be satisfied for the elements to display.

Figure B–57

• The parameter you want to use as a filter must be included in the schedule. You can hide the parameter once you have completed the schedule, if required.

Filter by	Specifies the field to filter. Not all fields are available to be filtered.
Condition	Specifies the condition that must be met. This includes options such as **equal**, **not equal**, **greater than**, and **less than**.
Value	Specifies the value of the element to be filtered. You can select from a drop-down list of appropriate values. For example, if you set *Filter By* to **Level**, it displays the list of levels in the project.

Schedule Properties – Sorting/Grouping Tab

In the *Sorting/Grouping* tab, you can set how you want the information to be sorted, as shown in Figure B–58. For example, you can sort by **Mark** (number) and then **Type**.

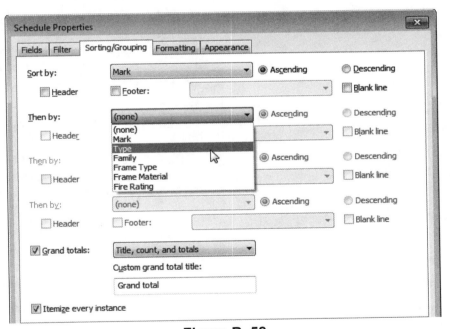

Figure B–58

Sort by	Enables you to select the field(s) you want to sort by. You can select up to four levels of sorting.
Ascending/ Descending	Sorts fields in **Ascending** or **Descending** order.
Header/ Footer	Enables you to group similar information and separate it by a **Header** with a title and/or a **Footer** with quantity information.

Blank line	Adds a blank line between groups.
Grand totals	Selects which totals to display for the entire schedule. You can specify a name to display in the schedule for the Grand total.
Itemize every instance	If selected, displays each instance of the element in the schedule. If not selected, displays only one instance of each type, as shown in Figure B–59.

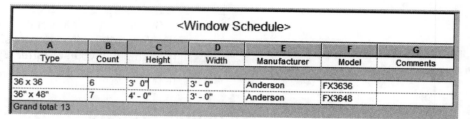

<Window Schedule>

A	B	C	D	E	F	G
Type	Count	Height	Width	Manufacturer	Model	Comments
36 x 36	6	3' 0"	3' - 0"	Anderson	FX3636	
36" x 48"	7	4' - 0"	3' - 0"	Anderson	FX3648	
Grand total: 13						

Figure B–59

Schedule Properties – Formatting Tab

In the *Formatting* tab, you can control how the headers of each field display, as shown in Figure B–60.

Figure B–60

Fields	Enables you to select the field for which you want to modify the formatting.
Heading	Enables you to change the heading of the field if you want it to be different from the field name. For example, you might want to replace **Mark** (a generic name) with the more specific **Door Number** in a door schedule.

Heading orientation	Enables you to set the heading on sheets to **Horizontal** or **Vertical**. This does not impact the schedule view.
Alignment	Aligns the text in rows under the heading to be **Left**, **Right**, or **Center**.
Field Format...	Sets the units format for the length, area, volume, angle, or number field. By default, this is set to use the project settings.
Conditional Format...	Sets up the schedule to display visual feedback based on the conditions listed.
Hidden field	Enables you to hide a field. For example, you might want to use a field for sorting purposes, but not have it display in the schedule. You can also modify this option in the schedule view later.
Show conditional format on sheets	Select if you want the color code set up in the Conditional Format dialog box to display on sheets.
Calculate totals	Displays the subtotals of numerical columns in a group.

Schedule Properties – Appearance Tab

In the *Appearance* tab, you can set the text style and grid options for a schedule, as shown in Figure B–61.

Figure B–61

Grid lines	Displays lines between each instance listed and around the outside of the schedule. Select the style of lines from the drop-down list; this controls all lines for the schedule, unless modified.
Grid in headers/footers/spacers	Extends the vertical grid lines between the columns.
Outline	Specify a different line type for the outline of the schedule.
Blank row before data	Select this option if you want a blank row to be displayed before the data begins in the schedule.
Show Title/Show Headers	Select these options to include the text in the schedule.
Title text/Header text/Body Text	Select the text style for the title, header, and body text.

Schedule Properties

Schedule views have properties including the *View Name*, *Phases* and methods of returning to the Schedule Properties dialog box as shown in Figure B–62. In the *Other* area, select the button next to the tab that you want to open in the Schedule Properties dialog box. In the dialog box, you can switch from tab to tab and make any required changes to the overall schedule.

Figure B–62

B.11 Creating a Repeating Detail

Repeating detail components are very useful when working on complex details, such as those that include a brick wall. You can also create a repeating detail using any detail component, such as the glass block shown in Figure B–63.

Figure B–63

How To: Create a Repeating Detail

1. Load the detail component you want to use.

2. In the *Annotate* tab>Detail panel, expand ▢ (Component) and click ▤ (Repeating Detail Component).

3. In Properties, click ▣ (Edit Type).
4. In the Type Properties dialog box, click **Duplicate...**. Enter a name.
5. Set the *Detail* parameter. This is the component name.
6. Fill out the rest of the parameters, as shown in Figure B–64.

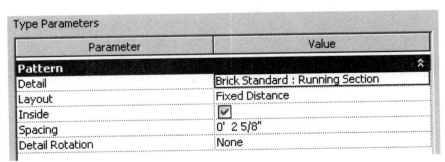

Type Parameters	
Parameter	Value
Pattern	≫
Detail	Brick Standard : Running Section
Layout	Fixed Distance
Inside	☑
Spacing	0' 2 5/8"
Detail Rotation	None

Figure B–64

7. Set the *Layout* to **Fill Available Space**, **Fixed Distance**, **Fixed Number**, or **Maximum Spacing**. Select the **Inside** option if you want all components to be within the specified distance or line. Leaving this option clear causes the first component to start before the first point.
8. Set the *Spacing* between components if you are using **Fixed Distance** or **Maximum Spacing**.
9. Set the *Detail Rotation* as required, and close the dialog box.

Command Summary

Button	Command	Location
Annotations		
	Matchline	• **Ribbon:** *View* tab>Sheet Composition panel
	View Reference	• **Ribbon:** *View* tab>Sheet Composition panel or *Annotate* tab> Tag panel
Curtain Walls		
	Edit Type	• **Properties** (with a Curtain Wall type selected)
Details		
	Edit Type	• **Properties** (with a Repeating Detail element selected)
Dormers		
	Dormer	• **Ribbon:** *Architecture* tab>Opening panel
Revisions		
	Revision Cloud	• **Ribbon:** *Annotate* tab>Detail panel
	Sheet Issues/ Revisions	• **Ribbon:** *Manage* tab>Settings panel> expand Additional Settings
Schedules		
	Insert Views from File	• **Ribbon:** *Insert* tab> expand **Insert from File**
n/a	**Schedule (Export)**	• Application Menu: expand Export>Reports>Schedule
	Schedule/ Quantities	• **Ribbon:** *View* tab>Create panel> expand Schedules • **Project Browser:** right-click on Schedule/Quantities node> New Schedule/Quantities...
Selection Sets		
	Edit Selection	• **Ribbon:** *Modify | Multi-Select* tab>Selection panel
	Load Selection	• **Ribbon:** *Modify | Multi-Select* tab>Selection panel
	Save Selection	• **Ribbon:** *Modify | Multi-Select* tab>Selection panel

Sweeps and Reveals

	Floor: Slab Edge	• **Ribbon:** *Architecture* tab>Build panel or *Structure* tab>Structure panel> expand Floor
	Roof: Fascia	• **Ribbon:** *Architecture* tab>Build panel> expand Roof
	Roof: Gutter	• **Ribbon:** *Architecture* tab>Build panel> expand Roof
	Wall: Reveal	• **Ribbon:** *Architecture* tab>Build panel or *Structure* tab>Structure panel> expand Wall
	Wall: Sweep	• **Ribbon:** *Architecture* tab>Build panel or *Structure* tab>Structure panel> expand Wall

Views

	Cut Profile	• **Ribbon:** *View* tab>Graphics panel
	Insert Views from File	• **Ribbon:** *Insert* tab>Import panel> expand Insert from File
	Join Geometry	• **Ribbon:** *Modify* tab>Geometry panel>expand Join
	Line Styles	• **Ribbon:** *Manage* tab>Settings panel> expand Additional Settings
	Linework	• **Ribbon:** *Modify* tab>View panel • **Shortcut:** LW
	Paint	• **Ribbon:** *Modify* tab>Geometry panel
	Pick New Host	• **Ribbon:** *Modify	varies* tab>Host panel
	Split Face	• **Ribbon:** *Modify* tab>Geometry panel
	Unjoin Geometry	• **Ribbon:** *Modify* tab>Geometry panel>expand Join
	Wall Joins	• **Ribbon:** *Modify* tab>Geometry panel

A p p e n d i x

C

Autodesk Revit Certification Exam Objectives

The following table will help you to locate the exam objectives within the chapters of the Revit training guides to help you prepare for the Autodesk Revit Certified Professional (Pro.) and User exams.

User	Pro.	Exam Objective	Training Guide	Chapter & Section(s)
User Interface				
✓		Change the view scale	• Fundamentals	• 1.2
✓		Identify file types	• Fundamentals	• 1.3
✓		Identify primary parts of the User Interface (UI)	• Fundamentals	• 1.2
✓	✓	Use the Project Browser	• Fundamentals	• 1.2
Collaboration				
	✓	Copy and monitor elements in a linked file	• Collaboration Tools	• 2.3
	✓	Import DWG and image files	• Fundamentals	• 3.4
			• Collaboration Tools	• 3.1, 3.3
	✓	Use worksharing	• Collaboration Tools	• 4.1, 4.3

User	Pro.	Exam Objective	Training Guide	Chapter & Section(s)
Documentation				
✓		Create a title sheet	• Fundamentals	• 13.1
	✓	Create and modify filled regions	• Fundamentals	• 16.3
	✓	Place detail components and repeating details	• Fundamentals	• 16.2
	✓	Set the colors used in a color scheme legend	• Conceptual Design and Visualization	• 2.3
✓	✓	Tag elements (doors, windows, etc.) by category	• Fundamentals	• 15.1
	✓	Use dimension strings	• Fundamentals	• 14.1
	✓	Work with phases	• Collaboration Tools	• 1.1
Elements				
	✓	Change elements within a curtain wall	• Fundamentals	• 6.2, 6.3, 6.4
	✓	Create a new family type	• Fundamentals	• 5.3
			• BIM Management	• 4.5
	✓	Create a stacked wall	• BIM Management	• 3.3
✓		Create and modify walls	• Fundamentals	• 4.1, 4.2
	✓	Create compound walls	• BIM Management	• 3.1
	✓	Differentiate system and component families	• BIM Management	• 3.1 / • 4.1
✓		Edit doors	• Fundamentals	• 5.1
✓		Edit windows	• Fundamentals	• 5.1
✓		Trim objects	• Fundamentals	• 2.4
	✓	Work with family parameters	• BIM Management	• 4.2
Families				
	✓	Assess review warnings in Revit	• Fundamentals	• 12.1
	✓	Use Family creation procedures	• BIM Management	• 4.1 to 4.7
✓	✓	Work with families	• Fundamentals	• 8.1, 8.2
Modeling				
✓		Add dimensions	• Fundamentals	• 14.1
✓		Add model text to a plan	• Fundamentals	• 14.2

User	Pro.	Exam Objective	Training Guide	Chapter & Section(s)
	✓	Attach walls to a roof or ceiling	• Fundamentals	• 11.2
	✓	Change a generic floor/ceiling/roof to a specific type	• Fundamentals	• 9.1 • 10.1 • 11.2
	✓	Create a building pad	• Site and Structure	• 1.2
✓		Create a roof and modify roof properties	• Fundamentals	• 11.2, 11.4
✓	✓	Create a stair with a landing	• Fundamentals	• 12.1
	✓	Create elements such as floors, ceiling, or roofs	• Fundamentals	• 9.1 • 10.1 • 11.2, 11.4
✓	✓	Define floor for a mass	• Conceptual Design and Visualization	• 1.8
	✓	Edit a model element's material	• Fundamentals	• 5.3 • B.4
	✓	Edit room-aware families	• BIM Management	• 4.4
	✓	Generate a toposurface	• Site and Structure	• 1.1
✓	✓	Model railings	• Fundamentals	• 12.3
✓		Use grids	• Fundamentals	• 3.2

Views

User	Pro.	Exam Objective	Training Guide	Chapter & Section(s)
	✓	Control visibility	• Fundamentals	• 7.1
	✓	Create a duplicate view for a plan, section, elevation, drafting view, etc.	• Fundamentals	• 7.2
✓		Create a schedule and add schedule tags	• Fundamentals	• 15.1, 15.3 • B.10
	✓	Create and manage legends	• Fundamentals	• 14.4
✓		Create section views	• Fundamentals	• 7.4
	✓	Define element properties in a schedule	• Fundamentals	• 15.3
	✓	Manage view position on sheets	• Fundamentals	• 13.2
	✓	Organize and sort items in a schedule	• Fundamentals • BIM Management	• B.10 • 2.2
✓	✓	Use levels	• Fundamentals	• 3.1

Index

#
3D Views **1-26**

A
Align command **2-37**
Application Menu **1-8**
Array command
    Linear **2-26**
    Radial **2-27**
Autodesk Seek **8-4**

B
Break Lines **16-9**
Building Information Modeling (BIM) **1-2**

C
Camera command **1-27**
Cascade **1-16**
Ceilings
    Components **10-6**
    Create **10-3**
    Grids **10-2**
    Sketch **10-4**
Central File **A-2**
Clipboard
    Copy to **5-5**
    Cut to **5-5**
Column command **3-12**
Columns **3-12**
Components
    Adding **8-2**
    Loading **5-12, 8-3**
    Modifying **8-6**
Copy command **2-22**
Copy To Clipboard **5-5**
Create
    Building Component Schedules **B-36**
    Ceilings **10-3**
    Curtain Grids **6-6**
    Curtain Wall Panels **6-15**
    Custom Stairs **12-31**
    Floor Slab Edges **B-6**

Floors **9-2**
Gutters **B-6**
Levels **3-2**
Local Files **A-3**
Multi-Segment Grid **3-11**
Plan Views **3-6**
Ramps **12-34**
Reflected Ceiling Plan Views **3-6**
Repeating Details **B-43**
Revision Table **B-27**
Schedule/Quantities **B-36**
Stairs (Custom) **12-31**
Structural Grids **3-10**
Sweep Profiles **B-6**
Text Types **14-17**
Wall Reveals **B-6**
Wall Sweep **B-6**
Curtain Grids
    Add/Remove Segments **6-8**
    Automatic **B-8**
    Create **6-6**
    Curtain Walls **6-6**
    Modifying **6-7**
Curtain Wall Panels **6-13**
    Create **6-15**
Curtain Walls **6-2**
    Adding Mullions **6-17**
    Curtain Grids **6-6**
    Placing Doors in **6-15**
Cut Profile command **B-19**
Cut to Clipboard **5-5**

D
Default 3D View command **1-26**
Dependent Views **B-31**
Detail Components **16-8**
Detail Lines **14-19**
Details
    Annotating **16-12**
    Import **16-7**
    Tagging **16-15**

Dimensions
    Aligned **14-4**
    Angular **14-4**
    Arc Length **14-4**
    Constraints **14-7**
    Diameter **14-4**
    Dimension command **14-2**
    Feet and inches **2-6**
    Linear **14-4**
    Modifying **14-5**
    Radial **14-4**
Drafting Views
    Creating **16-2**
    Referencing **16-4**
    Saving **16-5**
Draw Order **16-10**
Draw tools **2-2**

E

Edit Crop **7-22**
Edit Wall Joins **B-13**
Editing the Top Rail or Handrail **12-24**
Elevations **7-28**
Export Schedules **B-35**

F

Families **5-12**
    Loading **5-12**
File Types **1-18**
Filled Regions
    Add **16-13**
    Patterning **16-12**
Filter command **2-14**
Floor Slab Edges **B-6**
Floors
    Create **9-2**
    Modify **9-4**
    Shape Editing **9-18**
    Slope Arrows **9-17**

G

Geometry
    Join **9-6**
    Unjoin **9-6**
Grids
    Modifying **3-11**
    Multi-Segment **3-11**
    Structural **3-10**
Gutters **B-6**

I

Images
    Add to a Sheet **13-9**
Import
    CAD Files **3-17**
    Details **16-7**
    Schedules **B-34**

Import CAD command **3-16**
Insert
    Views from File **B-34**
Instance Properties **1-12**
Insulation **16-11**
Interface **1-6**

J

Join Geometry **9-6**

K

Keynotes **16-24**
    Legends **16-27**
    Placing **16-25**

L

Legend **14-27**
    Components **14-28**
    Create **14-28**
Levels
    Create **3-2**
    Modify **3-4**
Line Styles
    Creating **B-18**
Linework command **B-17**
Link CAD command **3-17**
Load Families **5-12**
Local Files **A-2**
    Create **A-3**

M

Match Type command **4-9**
Matchlines **B-32**
Materials **B-15**
Measure
    Along An Element **5-16**
    Between Two References **5-16**
Move command **2-22**
Mullions **6-17**
    Modify **6-18**
Multi-Segment Grid **3-11**

N

New command **1-21**
Nudge **2-11**, **2-21**

O

Offset command **2-42**
Openings
    Shaft Opening **9-16**
Options Bar **1-11**
Overriding Graphics **7-4**

P

Paint command **B-16**
Paste
    Aligned to Current View **5-5**
    Aligned to Picked Level **5-5**

Aligned to Same Place **5-5**
Aligned to Selected Levels **5-5**
Aligned to Selected Views **5-5**
From Clipboard **5-5**
Pick New Host command **8-6**
Pick tools **2-5**
Pinned Elements **2-23**
Plan Views
Create **3-6**
Print command **13-16**
Project Browser **1-14**
Purge Unused **8-7**

Q
Quick Access Toolbar **1-7**

R
Railings **12-24**
Add by Selecting a Host **12-21**
Add by Sketching **12-20**
Editing the Path of **12-22**
Modify **12-20**
Modifying Joins **12-23**
Tags **15-9**
Ramps **12-34**
Reflected Ceiling Plan Views **3-6**
Rehost **B-11**
Rendering **1-31**
Repeating Details **B-43**
Reset Crop **7-22**
Revision Clouds
Tagging **B-27**
Revision Table **B-27**
Revision Tracking **B-25**
Revisions **B-30**
Ribbon **1-9**
Roofs
Attach Walls **11-5**
By Extrusion **11-16**
By Footprint **11-3**
Dormers **B-21**
Joining **11-18**
Roof Plan View **11-6**
Slope Arrow **B-22**
Rooms **15-14**
Separation Lines **15-15**
Tags **15-14, 15-15, 15-16**
Rotate command **2-23**

S
Schedule Properties
Appearance Tab **B-41**
Fields Tab **B-37**
Filter Tab **B-38**
Formatting Tab **B-40**
Sorting/Grouping Tab **B-39**

Schedule/Quantities **B-36**
Schedules
Building Component Schedule **B-36**
Export **B-35**
Import **B-34**
Modifying Cells **15-25**
On Sheets **15-26**
Working with **15-24**
Sections **7-29**
Selecting elements **2-12**
Selection Options
Drag elements **2-13**
Select elements by face **2-13**
Select links **2-13**
Select pinned elements **2-13**
Select underlay elements **2-13**
Selection Sets **B-36**
Shape Editing **9-18**
Sheets
Add **13-2**
Guide Grids **B-23**
Modifying Views **13-7**
Placing Views **13-5**
Size Crop **7-22**
Slope Arrow **B-22**
Spelling **14-16**
Split command **2-39**
Split Face command **B-12**
Stairs
Adding Supports **12-9**
Convert Component to Sketches **12-12**
Create Assembled Stairs **12-2**
Create Center-Ends Spiral Runs **12-6**
Create Custom **12-31**
Create Full-Step Spiral Run **12-6**
Create Runs **12-3**
Create Straight Runs **12-4**
Create Winder Runs **12-7**
Edit Sketched **12-33**
Modify Assembled Stairs **12-10**
Tags **15-9**
Status Bar **1-7**
Storefronts **6-4**
Structural Grids **3-10**
Sweep Profiles **B-6**
Sweeping a Profile **B-5**
Switch Windows **1-16**
Symbols **14-20**

T
Tags
Adding **15-3**
By Category **15-2**
Room **15-15**
Stair and Railings **15-9**

Text
    Adding **14-13**
    Create Types **14-17**
    Model **14-16**
    Paragraph Formats **14-15**
Thin lines **7-34**
Tile **1-16**
Transfer Project Standards **5-14**
Tread and Riser Numbers **15-9**
Trim command **2-40**
Type Properties **1-12**

U
Unjoin Geometry **9-6**

V
View References **B-32**
ViewCube **1-29**
Views
    3D **1-26**
    Camera **1-27**
    Dependant **B-31**
    Duplicate View **7-14**
    Duplication Types **7-13**
    Insert from File **B-34**
    Perspective **1-27**
    Roof Plan **11-6**
    View Range **7-8**
Visibility/Graphics Overrides **3-19**, **7-5**
Visual Styles **1-30**

W
Wall Openings **4-7**
Wall Reveals **B-6**
Wall Sweep **B-6**
Walls
    Attach Roofs **11-5**
    Modify **4-2**
Workplane Viewer **11-13**
Worksets **A-2**
    Saving Files **A-4**

Z
Zoom commands **1-24**